W9-BNT-536

THE CARY LEGACY

DR. CHARLES ALLEN CARY

FATHER OF VETERINARY MEDICINE
AT AUBURN AND IN THE SOUTH

THE CARY LEGACY

DR. CHARLES ALLEN CARY
FATHER OF VETERINARY MEDICINE AT AUBURN AND IN THE SOUTH

SAM HENDRIX

THE DONNELL GROUP
Montgomery, Alabama

THE
DONNELL
GROUP
The Donnell Group
3514 Lansdowne Drive
Montgomery, AL 36111
(334) 303-2355
www.thedonnellgroup.com

The Cary Legacy: Dr. Charles Allen Cary, Father of Veterinary Medicine at Auburn and in the South
Copyright 2018 © by Sam Hendrix

Photography courtesy of Auburn University Special Collections & Archives, the Colleges of Veterinary Medicine and Human Sciences, AU Photo Services, Tajuan Sellars, and the Cary Family Collection.

The publisher assumes no liabilities for the written or photographic contents of this book.

Cover photos by Scott Brown. Painting by Mrs. Clyde J. Moore, printed with permission.

Jacket design by Jodi Teel.

Printing: Wells Printing, Montgomery, Alabama

Library of Congress Control Number: 2018949793
ISBN 9780998590424

First Edition
10 9 8 7 6 5 4 3 2 1

*For all the friends Mary Ellen & I
have made during our years in Auburn
and
In memory of two Tigers:
Doris Kelso from Mizzou, later of UNA;
and Kaye Lovvorn of Auburn.
Each trained many cubs.*

*Great problems develop great men to solve them
in all branches of human effort.*

—L. A. Merillat and D. M. Campbell

CONTENTS

FOREWORD

Veterinary medicine at Auburn—*inspired* to advance animal and human health in the face of widespread disease and poverty in the post-reconstruction South, *sustained* by the fortitude to emerge from World War 1, the Great Depression, and the transition from horsepower to mechanized power and *propelled* by the optimism of its leadership that education, science, and innovation would prevail—these forces shaped Auburn Veterinary Medicine in the early twentieth century, orchestrated by the college's founding dean, Dr. Charles Allen Cary.

In 1892, the stage was set for veterinary medicine at Auburn. Dr. William LeRoy Broun, president of the Agricultural and Mechanical College of Alabama, met Dr. Charles Allen Cary of South Dakota State College and courted him in so compelling a way that Dr. Cary eventually elected to spend the remainder of his academic career—forty-two years—in Auburn. An academic assignment that began with studies in Germany in the laboratory of Nobel Laureate Robert Koch, and three months of lectures in veterinary science at Auburn, soon evolved into a professorial appointment in the Department of Physiology and Veterinary Science. Dr. Cary's mission was to mount an aggressive effort to control diseases that inflicted misery on humanity in the South. Those diseases included Texas tick fever, tuberculosis, brucellosis, hog cholera, and rabies. As an early practitioner of One Health, Dr. Cary understood that human lives depended on the success of his work to block the transmission of certain infectious diseases from animals to people, and to enhance the production of wholesome meat and milk. Dr. Cary conceived of summer institutes and the practice of Saturday free clinics as methods to deliver critically needed veterinary services and knowledge to the public. This foundation, fifteen years in the making, culminated in the formation of an independent School of Veterinary Medicine in 1907, with Dr. Cary at its helm. In the same year, Dr. Cary founded the Alabama Veterinary Medical Association and was appointed Alabama's first State Veterinarian by the Alabama Legislature. At Auburn, Dean Cary led the first veterinary college in the entire southern United States below the Mason-Dixon Line, from Maryland to Oregon, until his death in 1935. Today, Auburn and Colorado State University share the distinction of having the seventh-oldest veterinary colleges in the United States.

What is Dr. Cary's legacy for Auburn's College of Veterinary Medicine today? One need not look further than "The Auburn Creed," written by George Petrie fifty years after Dr. Cary's arrival in Auburn as a faculty member:

I believe that this is a practical world and that I can count only on what I earn. Therefore, I believe in work, hard work.

I believe in education, which gives me the knowledge to work wisely and trains my mind and my hands to work skillfully.

I believe in honesty and truthfulness, without which I cannot win the respect and confidence of my fellow men.

I believe in a sound mind, in a sound body and a spirit that is not afraid, and in clean sports that develop these qualities.

I believe in obedience to law because it protects the rights of all.

I believe in the human touch, which cultivates sympathy with my fellow men and mutual helpfulness, and brings happiness for all.

I believe in my country, because it is a land of freedom and because it is my own home, and that I can best serve that country by "doing justly, loving mercy, and walking humbly with my God."

And because Auburn men and women believe in these things, I believe in Auburn and love it.

Charles Allen Cary and his peers modeled the qualities that inspired George Petrie to write "The Auburn Creed." Its tenets—practicality, perseverance, education, technical proficiency, honesty, truthfulness, obedience to law, collegiality, patriotism, humility, and reverence—are the distillation of what it means to be an Auburn veterinarian—then, now, and tomorrow.

I wish to thank Sam Hendrix for his deep dedication to defining and preserving the details of Charles Allen Cary's life and his life's mission, the Auburn University College of Veterinary Medicine, which we love, respect, and serve today.

Calvin M. Johnson, DVM, PhD
Dean
June 1, 2018

AUTHOR'S NOTE

The plan for this book was brought to light on a Saturday morning in December 2015, when Mary Ellen and I wandered through the Cary House on North College Street. It was our first stop on the Auburn Preservation League's annual Christmas Tour of Homes, and upstairs, we ran into Sid James Nakhjavan, executive director of the Cary Center and its AU College of Human Sciences programming. Sid and I were long-time Office of Development colleagues, and we hadn't crossed paths since my retirement thirty months earlier. "What have you been doing?" led to "We've been thinking about having a book written about Dr. and Mrs. Cary. Would you be interested?"

I had wondered why no biography had been written on Dr. Charles Allen Cary, who founded the veterinary college at Auburn in the late nineteenth century and who made his mark on many levels professionally and in the Auburn community. With time to tackle such a project, and with two years' labor on a history of our church congregation having been published a month earlier, I was game—and blindly ambitious enough—to leap into this project.

Dr. Cary was, the record shows, a workaholic. He was a high-achiever who got things done. Big things. He remains a figure larger than life in the eyes of Auburn veterinary graduates. Mrs. Emma Cary, too, instigated progress in the Auburn community that still resounds, but this volume focuses on Dr. Cary.

The work Dr. Cary performed touched many and varied subjects, and he proved an astounding multi-tasker. For this reason, I compartmentalized this book with chapters focused on particular aspects of his work rather than a chronological narrative. Separate chapters address, for example, his launching Auburn's veterinary science program, serving as state veterinarian, and fighting tick fever, tuberculosis, and hog cholera. I am sure he had plenty of days when he did all of that before lunch. Given his work ethic and the multitude of activities he maintained, I am not sure he slept much, never mind took a lunch break. Also, I hope the chapters on President Broun and late nineteenth-century Auburn offer a broader look at that era and the village in which Dr. and Mrs. Cary made their home.

As chapter one concludes, I opine that Dr. Cary represented the most important of the incredible, visionary hires President Broun made during his tenure at Auburn. A case may be argued for several of the legendary faculty members Dr. Broun recruited: Dr. George Petrie, Dr. John Wilmore, Dr. Emerson Miller, Dr. John F. Duggar among them.

Each of those, and a few others, had stellar, influential careers at Auburn. They were great teachers, important to their times, and each begat legions of Auburn graduates who have advanced their respective disciplines. Collectively, the team President Broun assembled built the foundation on which today's Auburn excels.

What sets Dr. Cary apart, from my perspective, is this resonating truth: there are untold thousands of individuals, entire families, who are alive and well, prospering and making a difference in society today who, without the work and persistence of Charles Allen Cary, would not be here. Without the development and implementation of meat and milk inspection protocols—which Dr. Cary designed and championed at the turn of the century in the face of the uninformed, the short-sighted, and the politically expedient—many people in all walks of our lives never would have been born. Their grandparents and great-grandparents survived childhood because of the advent of public health policies brought about by the knowledge and, as importantly, by the resolve and courage shown by Charles Allen Cary and his compatriots.

These Carys—both Charles and Emma—remain heroic figures, and it simply would be wrong for those who have come after them in Auburn, in Alabama, and in our part of the country not to remember them.

Twenty years after long-time veterinary medicine Associate Dean Dr. H. C. Morgan died, I found among many items in the estate sale at his home a document he had compiled related to some of the stellar figures in the first century of the Alabama Veterinary Medical Association. Dr. Morgan wrote of Dr. Cary:

> Dr. Cary must be considered the true father of veterinary medicine in the southern United States. When he came south there were no veterinary schools, no state associations and only a few graduate veterinarians. Few men have made such an impact on a state and region and all who are associated with veterinary medicine in the south have benefited from his visions and hard work. It is therefore incumbent on us to [e]nsure that future generations of Auburn veterinarians recognize, respect and appreciate his contributions.

TIMELINE

CHARLES ALLEN AND EMMA HECK CARY

November 28, 1861 • Charles Allen Cary born in Millersburg, Iowa.

December 7, 1867 • Emma Lucile Heck born in Nauvoo, Illinois.

1879/1880 • Charles Allen Cary teaches high school

1881/1882 • Charles Allen Cary enrolls at Iowa Agricultural College.

1885 • Charles Allen Cary graduates with B.S. in agricultural sciences.

May 27, 1886 • Emma Heck graduates from Nauvoo High School.

May 1887 • Charles Allen Cary receives DVM from Iowa Agricultural College.

May/June 1887 • Dr. Cary begins work at private practice in Keokuk, Iowa.

1887/1888 • Dr. Cary meets Emma Heck.

1889 • Dr. Cary named professor of veterinary sciences at South Dakota A&M College.

Winter 1890 • Dr. Cary studies with Dr. Paul Paquin at University of Missouri, Columbia.

September 16, 1890 • Dr. Cary joins United States Veterinary Medical Association.

November 27, 1890 • Charles Allen Cary and Emma Heck marry at Presbyterian Church, Nauvoo, Illinois.

1891-1892 • Dr. Cary serves as South Dakota's resident secretary of USVMA.

1891 • Dr. Cary meets President William LeRoy Broun of Alabama Agricultural and Mechanical College; accepts offer to launch veterinary science program in Auburn.

November 16, 1891 • President Broun confirms in writing Dr. Cary's appointment for January-March 1892 at Auburn.

January-March 1892 • Dr. Cary serves three months as lecturer in veterinary science at Auburn.

April 11, 1892 • Dr. and Mrs. Cary welcome their first child, son Elwyn.

May 9, 1892 • President Broun informs Dr. Cary by letter that he will recommend the Board of Trustees name Dr. Cary to the chair of veterinary science at Auburn.

Summer/Fall 1892 • Dr. Cary and family in Germany for study under Dr. Robert Koch and associates.

June 17, 1892 • President Broun writes to inform Dr. Cary he has been elected professor of veterinary science and physiology, to report January 1, 1893.

July 16, 1892 • Dr. Cary writes to President Broun, accepting the position.

1892-1893 • Dr. Cary appointed to USVMA Committee on Animal Food.

1893-1913 • Dr. Cary serves as Alabama's resident secretary to AVMA.

1893 • Dr. Cary begins many years' work in directing and coordinating Farmers' Institutes in Alabama.

1893 • Dr. and Mrs. Cary take part in the Conversation Club, organized for citizens of Auburn to meet and discuss art, literature, and events of the day.

1893-1894 • Dr. Cary serves on USVMA Committee on Intelligence and Education.

1893 • Cary family makes its first Auburn home along present-day Mell Street, where Duncan Hall now sits. Their second home would be on Gay Street, in the block between Thach and Miller Avenues.

September 3, 1893 • Dr. and Mrs. Cary welcome their second child, daughter Phoebe.

September 7, 1893 • API Trustees approve $2,000 to construct first veterinary building at API along Magnolia Avenue.

1895 • Dr. Cary receives first of four appointments to AVMA Committee on Diseases. Chairs committee during 1899-1900.

1895 • Dr. Cary authors Experiment Station *Bulletin 67, Bovine Tuberculosis.*

1896 • Dr. Cary authors ordinance providing for meat and milk inspection by veterinarians in City of Montgomery, first city in the South to adopt such protocols.

1896 • Dr. Cary appointed an elder in Auburn Presbyterian Church; also served many years as superintendent of Sunday School.

1896 • Dr. Cary given approval and funds by trustees to construct small veterinary hospital facility adjacent to veterinary building.

1897 • Dr. Cary hires W.J. Nixon as assistant in veterinary medicine.

1897 • Dr. Cary buys, for $1,625, four acres with house along North Main Street, later North College.

1898-1899 • Dr. Cary chairs AVMA Executive Committee and serves as secretary of the AVMA.

1898 • Dr. Cary authors Experiment Station *Bulletin 97, Dairy and Milk Inspection.*

December 28, 1899 • Death of Dr. Cary's mother, Lucy Ellen O'Hara Cary.

February 3, 1900 • Death of Emma Heck's father, Ernest Heck.

1903 • Dr. Cary invites Dr. George Washington Carver to address Alabama Live Stock Association convention in Birmingham.

June 16, 1904 • Dr. and Mrs. Cary welcome their third child, Alice.

1904 • Dr. Cary hires local man, Luke "Dr. Luke" Sales, as handyman in the school.

1904 • Dr. Cary initiates Summer School for Farmers, which runs for several years.

1906 • Dr. Cary hires Dr. Ward Giltner as assistant in veterinary medicine.

1906 • Federal government begins funding USDA plan to eradicate cattle ticks in Southern states.

December 1906 • Dr. Cary attends tick eradication meeting in Nashville.

March 12, 1907 • Alabama Legislature approves bill forming State Live Stock Sanitary Board and naming Dr. Cary as state veterinarian.

May 2, 1907 • Death of Dr. Cary's father, William E. Cary.

1907 • Work begins in Alabama on eradicating the cattle tick.

July 1907 • Dr. Cary authors Experiment Station *Bulletin 141, Tick Eradication.*

1907 • Dr. Cary begins appointment to the board of Auburn Bank.

1907 • Dr. Cary organizes student chapter of AVMA.

1907 • API trustees approve School of Veterinary Medicine and its Doctor of Veterinary Medicine degree curriculum. Dr. Cary appointed founding dean.

December 20, 1907 • Dr. Cary calls meeting of Alabama veterinarians, leading to reorganization of the Alabama Veterinary Medical Association. He is elected secretary, an office he holds the rest of his life.

1907-1908 • Dr. Cary serves as one of five vice presidents of AVMA.

January 30, 1908 • Dr. Cary submits his first *Report of the State Veterinarian.*

1908 • Dr. Cary hires Dr. I.S. McAdory as assistant in veterinary medicine.

1909 • School of Veterinary Medicine awards first DVM degrees at API.

1910 • Death of Emma Heck's mother, Margaretha Kessler Heck.

1910 • Dr. Cary builds Cary Castle next to his own home to house veterinary students. During construction, Dr. Cary falls off roof and breaks leg; requests fracture be set by his assistant, Dr. McAdory.

December 1912 • Dr. Cary leads contingent of Southern veterinarians to Washington, DC, to meet with congressional leaders about tick eradication. He was appointed to chair a committee to report back to Congress, and the group met in DC again in January 1913.

1912 • Dr. Cary reports Alabama hog farmers lost $1 million due to hog cholera.

February 1913 • Dr. Cary authors Experiment Station *Bulletin 171, Dipping Vats and Dips*.

1913-1915 • Dr. Cary serves consecutive terms as secretary of AVMA.

August 1914 • Emma Cary leads effort to establish Auburn Equal Suffrage Association. She serves as group's secretary/treasurer.

January 1915 • Dr. Cary appointed by combined Montgomery Cattlemen's Club, Southern Cattlemen's Association, Alabama Live Stock Association and Blackbelt Live Stock Association to chair committee and draft proposed legislation toward a "State Campaign for the Eradication of the Cattle Tick."

1915 • Dr. Cary and Auburn receive $25,000 from state to construct hog cholera serum plant at Auburn.

1915 • Dr. Cary appointed to Alabama State Board of Veterinary Medicine, later the Board of Veterinary Medical Examiners.

1915-1916 • Dr. Cary chairs AVMA's Committee on the Reorganization of the Association.

January 15, 1916 • Dr. Cary and Auburn host dedication ceremony for hog cholera serum plant.

1918 • Dr. Cary nominated for president of AVMA, but is second in voting.

February 1919 • Alabama Legislature approves state-wide tick eradication law.

1919 • Dr. Cary hires Dr. Everett S. Winters to manage hog cholera serum plant.

1919-1920 • Dr. Cary serves one term as president of the AVMA.

March 27, 1919 • Organizational meeting of Auburn Woman's Club. Emma Cary elected chair of Department of Civics and Health.

October 12, 1920 • Emma Cary and other women begin registering to vote.

1921-1923 • Emma Cary elected to two terms as president of Auburn Woman's Club.

1922-1924 • Dr. Cary named to AVMA Special Committee on Revision of the Constitution and By-laws.

1922 • API opens its Physiology Building on campus.

February 1924 • State veterinary meeting at Auburn first offers continuing education for practitioners, which Dr. Cary referred to as a "Short Course."

1926 • Dr. Cary buys his first car: a Model A, which he drives primarily in first gear.

1927-1928 • Dr. Cary serves as president of the US Live Stock Sanitary Association.

1928 • Dr. Cary begins six-year appointment to AVMA Committee on International Veterinary Congress.

1929 • Alabama declared free of the cattle tick.

February 1935 • Dr. Cary hosts his final meeting of the Alabama VMA in Auburn.

April 24, 1935 • Dr. Charles Allen Cary pronounced dead of heart failure at home, age 73.

April 27, 1935 • Dr. Cary's funeral held in Langdon Hall.

May 1935 • Emma Cary gives API many of Dr. Cary's books, providing basis for Cary Veterinary Library.

February 21, 1936 • Alabama VMA presents plaque memorializing Dr. Cary.

February 27, 1946 • Cary Hall dedicated on campus.

October 15, 1954 • Emma Heck Cary dies at home, age 88.

October 17, 1954 • Mrs. Cary's funeral held at Cary home.

June 9, 1976 • Halliday-Cary-Pick House named to Alabama Register of Landmarks and Heritage.

October 19, 1978 • Halliday-Cary-Pick House named to National Register of Historic Places.

November 1992 • Auburn College of Veterinary Medicine hosts Cary Centennial program.

2011 • Frances Dillard, granddaughter-in-law of Dr. and Mrs. Cary, and her family give Halliday-Cary-Pick House to Auburn University. College of Human Sciences bases its Cary Center for the Advancement of Philanthropy and Nonprofit Studies at Cary House.

2015 • Cary Frances Clark, great-great-granddaughter of Dr. and Mrs. Cary, graduates from AU College of Veterinary Medicine.

CHAPTER ONE

THE MAN WHO FOUND DR. CARY

Twenty-seven years after Union troops marched violently across the Deep South—Civil War destroying lives, livestock, and livelihoods—another outsider appeared in the haggard land. A fiery redhead from the Midwest, he traveled by train to East Alabama, landing on a bleak winter day. Determined to overturn certain status quo, his enemies were formidable: ignorance, disease, and despair. Armed not with a rifle, but with advanced medical and scientific training—plus a keen vision of what was possible and a work ethic that belied his nominal stature—Charles Allen Cary set up camp.

Over four decades, he became one of the most significant individuals ever affiliated with Auburn University and one of the most influential people in Alabama's first two centuries.

How did a thirty-year-old veterinarian, working then in South Dakota, find his way to Auburn, Alabama?

The story told—believed—for decades by folks affiliated with Auburn's College of Veterinary Medicine held that one day, or night, in 1891, Dr. Cary and another man found themselves on the same train, though exactly where and how their paths converged was never explained. Two intelligent, ambitious men, thirty-four years apart in age, met. One found or created some reason to speak to the other. A conversation began. An introduction. An acknowledgement of some item, a question related to an accent, or to the other's attire. Something kick-started a dialogue that would determine the fortunes of many people.

As their conversation concluded, the legend held, Dr. Cary accepted an offer from Alabama Agricultural and Mechanical College President Dr. William LeRoy Broun to relocate to Auburn and launch the veterinary science department.

The story sounds compelling, and there may be elements of truth in it. But the reality behind Dr. Cary's coming to Auburn is less mysterious than a serendipitous meeting on a train somewhere in America.

The truth, however, also provides a good tale. Another young veterinarian figures into it, and another fledgling post-war school: Mississippi Agricultural and Mechanical College, the future Mississippi State University. This institution's first president, former Confederate Lieutenant General Stephen Dill Lee, was cut from the same cloth as William LeRoy Broun. Lee "was determined not only to establish agriculture as the main foundation stone, but also to entice northern capital to help create an agribusiness concept, long before that term came into use."[1]

President Lee "envisioned a future south where scientific agricultural principles and mechanization went hand in hand." In general, Lee worked toward agricultural diversification in the college's teaching program. He launched an experiment farm. He appointed a professor of agriculture. He promoted the state's dairy industry by bringing a herd to campus and hiring someone to oversee it. A next, natural step in 1891, he figured, was to begin a program in veterinary science. A few years earlier, in 1885, Lee had petitioned the Mississippi legislature to fund a position he could use to attract to Starkville a graduate veterinarian to train students and address farm animals' health. Two years later, some funding came, though not enough to attract a qualified veterinarian. Later, the experiment station contributed funds, and applicants were promised the opportunity to engage in private practice to supplement the meager salary. A Canadian, Dr. Tait Butler, accepted President Lee's offer, and by 1891, veterinary science had come to Starkville and Mississippi A&M. Tait Butler was twenty-nine.

Dr. Butler (1862-1939), an 1885 graduate of the Ontario Veterinary College in Toronto, faced mountainous obstacles in addressing animal health issues in the Reconstruction-era South and he desired a partner in his efforts, if not in Starkville, then *somewhere* not far away. He had heard of the new mechanical and agricultural programs at the Alabama Agricultural and Mechanical College, so—he claimed years later—he wrote to President Broun, asking if Broun might like to bring on board a veterinary science professor at Auburn. It just so happened, Dr. Butler acknowledged, he knew this fellow up in South Dakota who might be open to a change of scenery.

On May 18, 1935, Butler wrote to one of Broun's successors, President Luther Noble Duncan of the Alabama Polytechnic Institute (API), in regard to the late Dr. Cary's successor as dean of veterinary medicine. Writing from Memphis, where he then edited *Progressive Farmer* magazine, Butler told of his role in Dr. Cary's coming to Auburn:

> You may be interested to know that I was largely responsible for Dr. Cary coming to Alabama. In the late fall of 1891 I wrote Dr. [LeRoy Broun], President, asking him if he wished to employ a veterinarian at Auburn and he at once replied that he did and if I knew of a suitable man to please put him in touch with him. I immediately wrote Dr. [Broun] a strong recommendation of Dr. Cary and the next I heard he had been employed. He visited me in Mississippi A&M College on his way to Auburn January 1, 1892.[2]

As Butler surmised back in 1891, President Broun already had been thinking along these lines. Building on the work of former President Isaac Taylor Tichenor, President Broun in the mid-1880s had launched the Agricultural Experiment Station and had begun staffing it with specialists in areas of crop science and animal husbandry. The president had attended the national conventions of the American Association of Agricultural Colleges and Experiment Stations in 1889 in Washington, DC, and in 1890 in Champaign, Illinois. He would have heard of other campuses' successes in bringing on board specialists trained in veterinary science. Tait Butler's 1891 recommendation of C. A. Cary proved a perfect fit at the right time for Broun and Auburn.

The sequence of events connecting Butler's initial letter to President Broun and Dr. Cary's arrival in Auburn some months later is left to speculation. There surely was an interview, if only by correspondence. Perhaps that was where the train meeting came in. Whatever events took place, a most unique individual was soon on his way to East Alabama.

Tait Butler did not stay in Starkville for long. He married a local girl, and they had a son while there, but the Butlers would live in North Carolina, Kansas, Iowa, and Tennessee, among other places, as Dr.

Butler gained national prominence, not only for his work as a state veterinarian and as president of the AVMA, but for a thirty-year stint during which he edited *Progressive Farmer* magazine. He and Dr. Cary would collaborate any number of times during the decades to come.

By 1891, Dr. Charles Allen Cary was four years into his career as a veterinarian, one of a small number in the United States to have attained that certification. An 1887 graduate of the Iowa Agricultural College—today's Iowa State University—Dr. Cary had begun his professional work in Iowa and had relocated after a couple of years to Brookings, South Dakota, where he was a professor of veterinary science and the assistant state veterinarian. He was thirty years old, a newly married man. Dr. Cary and Miss Emma Heck had exchanged vows on Thanksgiving Day 1890 in her hometown of Nauvoo, Illinois.

On a day in 1891—whether in person or by correspondence, whether in Auburn or somewhere each man reached by train that day—Charles Allen Cary met William LeRoy Broun, a stocky, bearded, well-dressed man with a large head. A noted Auburn man, years later, would describe it as "the most fantastic feature of his whole person . . . the ugliest head I ever saw, and yet one of the most striking."[3] Alert eyes suggested to all who met Broun that he was a force. His broad vocabulary and his obvious understanding of many issues confirmed his intelligence, his far-reaching experience, and advanced educational attainment. A contemporary faculty member at Auburn would describe Broun as "a leader, a man born to be a captain."[4] When Charles Allen Cary first laid eyes on him and heard what President Broun had to offer, Dr. Cary was intrigued.

This volume focuses on Dr. Cary and his achievements in veterinary science, in public health, in education, and in organized veterinary medicine in the twentieth century. But what of Dr. Broun, who convinced the Carys to bring their vast talents to the rural South still struggling with Reconstruction? To understand the Auburn Dr. and Mrs. Cary would call home, one should first be familiar with President Broun, his background, and his goals for the land-grant college in his charge. President Broun's leadership, specifically his faculty appointments, set the stage for Auburn's survival in the hard times to come, as well as its broad impact years later.

William LeRoy Broun was born on October 1, 1827, in Middleburg, Loudoun County, Virginia, forty-five miles west of Washington, DC.

He was educated in private schools and at the University of Virginia, graduating with a bachelor's in 1849 and a master's degree in 1850. While there, he studied under outstanding scholars, none more important nor more influential than Geologist William Barton Rogers, who in 1861 would establish the Massachusetts Institute of Technology. Broun's successor as president at Auburn, Dr. Charles C. Thach, years later, would write that, through Dr. Rogers' "advice and influence, Dr. Broun was largely guided in shaping the early policies of the institution at Auburn."[5]

After college, Broun taught for a year at a private school in Virginia, for two years at a small college in Mississippi (1852-54), and for two years as a professor of mathematics at the University of Georgia (1854-56). He then taught at a private school until the outbreak of the Civil War, at which time he joined the Confederacy and rose to the rank of lieutenant colonel in the Ordnance Department. This period proved a key time in his life as he conducted numerous experiments and furthered knowledge with his work.

Broun eventually was made head of the Confederacy's Ordnance Department and superintendent of armories and then commandant of the Richmond Arsenal, a role he maintained until General Lee's surrender at Appomattox.[6]

One of Broun's faculty members at the Alabama Agricultural and Mechanical College, later API, Professor P. H. Mell, would contribute to a publication called the *Confederate Veteran* in May 1902 this overview of Dr. Broun's role in the war:

> He entered the service of the Confederate government as an artillery officer, and spent one year in the field with the Army of Virginia. He was then ordered to Richmond and made superintendent of armories, with the rank of major, and was detailed to examine into the resources and facilities at the command of the South for the manufacture of arms and ammunition. He visited many places, particularly in North Carolina and Georgia, to determine the practicability of making sulphuric acid and other chemicals required for making powder and percussion caps. In 1862 he was stationed at Holly Springs, Miss., in charge of a factory designed for the manufacture of small arms, but the defeat of General A. S. Johnston's army at Shiloh, Tenn., compelled him to remove the machinery to Meridian, Miss., and shortly afterward he was attached to the ordnance department and ordered to Richmond, where he remained until its evacuation.... He suggested and conducted the first civil service

examination ever held in this country. This was brought about by the
numerous applications for service in the ordnance department, because
of an enactment of the Confederate Congress authorizing the appointment of fifty new ordnance officers. This examination was held in 1862.
Colonel Broun was the president of the board of examiners . . . . He was
appointed commander of the Richmond arsenal in 1863, where the
greater part of the ordnance stores were manufactured. It is said that but
for the valuable work performed in this connection by Colonel Broun the
Confederate struggle would have ended long before it did."[7]

Years later, writing a few weeks after Dr. Broun's death to Thomas
Broun, William LeRoy Broun's older brother, colleague and Professor
C. L. C. Minor of Baltimore said of Broun's Civil War contributions,
"You know, he kept our army fit to meet the best equipped army the
world had ever seen, though on our side everything had to be made
from the egg. From mining iron and coal to growing peas on rented
land and making lubricating oil for his machinery—he did it all." And,
"After Jackson and Lee no man that served under President Davis was
a more necessary part of all that was accomplished than Colonel
LeRoy Broun."[8]

After the war, Broun returned to Athens and taught natural philoso-
phy and physics at the University of Georgia and served from 1872 to
1875 as president of the Georgia Agricultural and Mechanical College,
a branch of the university. Relocating to Nashville in 1875, Dr. Broun
taught mathematics at Vanderbilt University until 1882 and then
moved to Auburn, where he served as the second president of the Alabama Agricultural and Mechanical College for the 1882-83 year. He
succeeded the college's first president, the afore-mentioned Tichenor,
who served a decade before resigning in 1882.

President Broun, following a dispute with Auburn trustees, moved
to Austin, Texas, where he taught mathematics at the University of
Texas during the 1883-84 school year. Over several months, trustees
changed their collective minds and asked Dr. Broun to return as president in 1884. He accepted and served the Alabama Agricultural and
Mechanical College as president until his death. It was written of
Broun: "Under his supervision, API became a pioneer and model for
all Southern technical schools. To him chiefly is due the development
of industrial and technical training in the South. His was the most constructive, the most influential of the work done since the War of
Secession in Southern education."[9]

William LeRoy Broun's parents—his father was a merchant and postmaster at Middleburg—died when William was a boy: his mother in 1838 at age thirty-five, his father the following year at fifty-eight. William, an orphan at eleven, assumed grown-up duties. Before breakfast, he would drive the family's cows a mile-and-a-half to the farm and return for them in the late afternoon. He attended morning and afternoon school sessions until five o'clock. Rather than playing with friends after school, young William tended cows. He worked for his brother, Edwin, in Edwin's store for a year, continuing the back-and-forth pattern of work and school. His duties at the store included calling on customers to collect debts. Always interested in learning, he talked Edwin into buying him the eight volumes of *Rollin's Ancient History*, authored by eighteenth-century French scholar Charles Rollin. Broun described this collection as "the driest thing on earth. From a sense of duty, I read the whole thing through."[10]

At age twenty, Broun borrowed $1,000 and enrolled at the University of Virginia. In two years, he graduated in all six UVA schools and received the Master of Arts degree. He spent an extra year in Charlottesville studying higher mathematics and German before launching his teaching career.[11]

Broun married on November 1, 1859, and the UVA faculty thought enough of him to give the new couple four large dinner parties.[12] This marriage was the culmination of a courtship begun in 1850 and years in the making.

Broun was twenty-two in 1850 and teaching in a private school in or near Charlottesville when he attended a party hosted by friends in Richmond, seventy miles away. That night, he met a beauty named Sarah Jane Fleming. She was fourteen. It was the young lady's first party, and she apparently made quite the impression.

"Her beautiful face and sweet expression induced me to ask for an introduction and to accompany her to the supper room," Broun would later write. Eight years later, when Broun was at White Sulphur Springs, Virginia, he met Sarah Jane again. She was twenty-two by this time and went by "Sallie." She had matured into "a charming young lady with a pleasant company of friends." Several of those friends would serve the next year as bridesmaids at Sallie's wedding in Chantilly, Hanover County, Virginia, to the young scholar William LeRoy Broun.[13]

The Brouns had seven children between 1861 and 1873: first came William LeRoy, Jr., or "Roy," then twin daughters, then two more daughters, a son, and finally a daughter named Katherine or "Kate."

They lived for a time after the war on a plantation where Broun tried cotton farming, but soon the University of Georgia asked Broun to return to Athens and lead UGA's Agricultural and Mechanical College. He and Sallie remained in Athens into 1875 when another offer arrived, this one from Chancellor Landon C. Garland of the new Vanderbilt University in Nashville, asking Broun to join its faculty as a professor of mathematics. To Nashville they went.

A colleague, Dr. Humphreys, in a letter after Broun's death, detailed that both he and Broun were recruited to Vanderbilt University in 1875 and to the University of Texas in 1883, each time on the occasion of the institution getting off the ground "when it is of so great importance that no errors should be committed, but the best possible foundation should be laid for subsequent years to build upon . . . ." In another letter, Dr. Humphreys noted that in their days before going to Texas, Broun, a man named Joynes, and Humphreys "drew up the whole course of study and formulated the details of administration for Vanderbilt University."[14] Those details included the graduation requirements.[15]

Because of his noteworthy work at Vanderbilt, Broun gained a sterling reputation among educators in the South. As a result, he was invited to deliver the commencement speech at Alabama Agricultural and Mechanical College for its 1880 graduation event. He turned heads with his brilliant overview of what the Auburn institution was and, with commitment to its role as a land-grant college, could become.[16]

The Alabama Agricultural and Mechanical College's president at the time, Dr. Tichenor, had been appointed to ease the transition from a classics-based curriculum into a program offering instruction in agriculture, science, and other practical disciplines. Tichenor's decade-long tenure was marked by constant struggles with extremely modest state support to the degree that the original four degree courses had been diminished to two: agriculture and chemistry as one course, and mechanics and engineering as the other. Times were so tough that President Tichenor himself was the lone instructor in agriculture and director of agricultural experiments during the first five years of the institution's land-grant status.[17]

President Tichenor finally had enough, resigning in 1882 at age fifty-seven to move to Atlanta to head the Southern Baptist Home Missionary Board. In considering Tichenor's successor, the Board of Trustees remembered the man who had delivered the A&M College's commencement speech in 1880: the mathematics professor from Vanderbilt University, Dr. Broun. The trustees remembered the thorough, inspiring address Broun had delivered, in which he lauded the institution's technical course of study. Trustees likewise appreciated Broun's favoring courses in the classics and liberal arts. In his 1880 address, Broun called to mind names familiar to those with a broad education: Thomas Carlyle, John Ruskin, John Milton, Thomas Hobbes. Broun impressed the trustees with references to scientific educational advancements with which he was familiar in Philadelphia, Boston, Moscow, and the University of Edinburgh. In this remarkable oration, Dr. Broun had proven himself on the same page with the trustees by suggesting the state re-name the institution the "Alabama Polytechnic Institute," which would happen nineteen years later during his presidency. He even made clear his support for higher education for women, which also would begin at Auburn under his administration. Trustees had Broun's speech and his vision of a strong, innovative, comprehensive land-grant institution in mind when they contacted Broun and offered him the job. Notice of his election is found in the Board of Trustees meeting minutes of June 28, 1882.

During Broun's first year at the helm, disagreements arose between the president and the trustees over how much of the president's vision the governing board would enact and how broadly they would expand the curriculum. Frustrated, Broun considered an offer from the University of Texas to move to Austin and serve as that institution's faculty chair. He at first declined the offer, thinking he would be able to work out his administrative problems at Auburn. But when Texas officials responded by increasing their offer to $4,000 per year, Broun reconsidered, discussed the situation with Sallie, and changed his mind. He sent a telegram to officials at Texas, accepting their offer. Minutes from the AAMC trustees' meeting of June 28, 1883, show Broun had resigned.

Needing a new president, Alabama Agricultural and Mechanical College trustees quickly hired Colonel David French Boyd from Louisiana as President Broun's successor. Colonel Boyd's appointment appeared in the same June 28, 1883, trustee minutes as the announcement of Dr. Broun's resignation. However, the Boyd presidency was short-lived. While Colonel Boyd was able to persuade the trustees to initiate many of Dr. Broun's recommended strategies for the land-grant institution, apparently he—or the trustees—found he was an inadequate fit for the job. Less than a year after he arrived, Boyd accepted an offer to return to Baton Rouge; and the Auburn trustees, in June 1884, elected Dr. Broun once again as their president.[18]

Dr. Broun spent his remaining eighteen years building the land-grant college.

A Birmingham newspaper article from 1891 suggested, with perhaps some hyperbole, that Auburn was a place where, despite having suffered the deaths of his wife and one of his daughters during this time, President Broun felt at home. This account also described the community Dr. Cary found when he determined to move his wife to Auburn not long afterwards. The article, which no modern-day chamber of commerce director could top, read:

> They are doing a great work at the Agricultural and Mechanical College at Auburn. There are over 280 names on the catalogue, and the college was never so prosperous and never so useful. The technological department is especially interesting, the students displaying remarkable skill in wood and iron work. The engine and dynamo which supply the electric light were made by the boys, and the visitor is shown numberless evidences of their skill in other directions. To the visitor, Auburn's chief charm lies in its sociability. The entire village, including the temporary inhabitants, in brass-buttoned uniforms, seems to be made up of one large family. Everybody keeps "open house" all the year round, and the very gates to the front yard are kept ajar to save the trouble of the constant opening and shutting to which they would be subjected. The students are thus kept constantly under home influences, and the result is most happy. And the wanderer from the outside world is made to feel welcome to the tree-embowered homes of "sweet Auburn," and there he would fain linger awhile and praise the gods for the good things set before him. There is more of human kindness, of human fellowship, of human sympathy, of human refinement and intelligence within that quaint and happy college town of Alabama than in almost any other community which one calls to mind. There is less of humbug, less of sham, less of veneering, less of unholy pretense there. Those shady streets echo more laughter, and those lovely homes give one more light than one finds in communities that cry aloud their vulgar pinchbeck wares of assumed greatness. It is a pity that every man who has a son at Auburn doesn't go there and "bide a wee."
>
> President Broun, of the Auburn College, is a grand man. It is safe to say there is no nobler educator in the South. Alabama has not had an abler in a generation, if it ever had. He is a man whose soul is in his

work, and added to his great learning is his rare administrative ability. Dr. Broun is like a father to those hundreds of boys, and there is not one among them who does not love and reverence him. He is doing a greater work than is in the power of any politician, and how enviable his position! Sturdily and bravely he goes on his way, and the world is the better because he is a part of it.[19]

The writer noted Dr. Broun's administrative ability, and he would prove that in spades the next year when he attracted Dr. Cary to Auburn.

William LeRoy Broun died at his home in Auburn on January 23, 1902. His successor, President Thach, in writing about President Broun in 1904, offered abundant laudatory comments, but one sentence may stand as the ultimate tribute to this educated man and educator: "There was not a chair in the college that he was not able to fill."[20]

After returning to Auburn, President Broun completely retooled the institution's basic courses of study. He established courses in engineering, shopwork, botany, zoology, chemistry, and pharmacy. He created separate departments of civil engineering, electrical and mechanical engineering, and physics. This reorganization elevated Auburn to the top among the Morrill Act land-grant colleges of the South.

Funds collected by the state from taxing fertilizer beginning in 1883 and guidelines included in the federal government's Hatch Act of 1887 enabled Dr. Broun to acquire land for an Experiment Station and to further prepare the institution for the thorough system of agricultural research he had long envisioned. But as History Professor and future Auburn University President Ralph Brown Draughon would later declare, President Broun's "greatest genius lay in his ability to select and bring to the faculty a remarkable group of young men, many of whom were destined to shape the institution and guide it for fifty years after his death."[21]

Under President Broun, campus grounds expanded, and vital new equipment was secured for laboratories. Fraternities had been formed in 1878, but they were not recognized by the school until 1883 when Broun, a member of Sigma Alpha Epsilon during his years at the University of Virginia, gave approval. An old photo printed in the first *Glomerata* yearbook, in 1897, shows President Broun surrounded by his fellow SAE brothers and a few other members of the faculty at Auburn.[22]

Auburn first admitted women into its academic programs under

President Broun in 1892, his daughter Kate being one of the first three coeds to graduate in 1894 and the first woman to earn a master's degree from the institution in 1895. Broun's Auburn began fielding an intercollegiate football team in 1892. Pragmatic to a fault, Broun refused to authorize any college funds to support the team's needs, reserving college finances exclusively for academic and research purposes. The Auburn Alumni Association formed under his watch in 1893.[23] He also championed the institutional name change to Alabama Polytechnic Institute, approved by the Legislature in 1899.

More than simply a brilliant administrator, President Broun apparently took a first-hand interest in the students. He presented Saturday morning lectures which President Thach later described as "lectures which were terse, often epigrammatic lay sermons, models of pointed wisdom and sound counsel that will long live in the lives of thousands of Auburn men."[24] Dr. Broun also was capable of sending home the occasional student whose behavior failed to meet expectations, as a small number of letters to these misbehaving students' parents in the Auburn University Archives attest.

At the time of his death in 1902, the API faculty had grown to nineteen professors and ten assistants. The student body registered 403 men and nine women.[25]

As practical and as "Ag & Mechanic"-minded as he was, William LeRoy Broun also never forgot his educational roots in the classics and in the liberal arts. He pursued and promoted a broad education for all students. With this mindset, he personally recruited to Auburn the following individuals, listed in no particular order, each of them a testament to the vision this man brought to his work, these names collectively standing as proof that William LeRoy Broun is the man who should most be credited for building the institution that evolved into today's Auburn University:

Dr. George Petrie, who arrived in September 1887 at age twenty-one, fresh out of the University of Virginia's Master of Arts degree program, began his Auburn appointment as an adjunct professor of modern languages at a salary of $750 per year. He was well-suited for this role as his undergraduate and graduate curricula at Charlottesville had included Latin, Greek, French, and German.[26] Dr. Petrie's time on the Auburn faculty would total fifty-four years, interrupted briefly during the late 1880s while he earned his PhD at Johns Hopkins—the first Alabamian to earn a PhD and the first Auburn faculty member to possess an earned doctorate—and ending with his retirement in fall 1942.[27] During that time, he was one of Auburn's most important and popular professors, teaching history and a variety of subjects and lecturing weekly for years on current events for an open audience in Langdon Hall. Dr. Petrie would serve as Auburn's chief academic dean and as dean of the Graduate School. Dr. Petrie supervised the building of Auburn's first tennis court in 1888. He persuaded President Broun to allow him to set up the college's first gymnasium in the otherwise unused attic of the Main Building. He coordinated Auburn's first-ever summer academic term in 1892. He organized and coached Auburn's first football game, a 10-0 win over Georgia in Atlanta's Piedmont Park in February 1892. He even selected the school colors as burnt orange and navy blue. Dr. Petrie also, in the year after his retirement, authored a one-page statement about Auburn and its spirit that he called "The Auburn Creed."

Dr. Petrie, serving through several administrations and with a perspective built both from his intellect and from his profession, seemed to gravitate toward an unofficial role of institutional spokesman. In that capacity, he reflected in the *Plainsman* of May 2, 1929, on the tenure of President Broun:

> Dr. William Leroy Broun was the creative spirit who shaped the destiny of this college while it was still in the plastic stage. He had rare foresight and sound judgment along with his constructive talent. More clearly than other leaders of his day he saw that all practical education to be of real value must be combined with sound scholarship and high scientific training. Under his guidance Auburn became the pioneer for all this section in Electrical Engineering, in Biology, in the emphasis on laboratory work, in co-education, and in the development of graduate courses on a high plane.[28]

Another impressive recruit among President Broun's faculty, Nathaniel Thomas Lupton, was a former president of the University of Alabama (1871-74) and one of President Broun's colleagues at Vanderbilt after his time in Tuscaloosa. Professor Lupton, who had earlier studied in Germany under the famous Dr. Robert Bunsen, came to Auburn in 1885 to teach chemistry and, while at the college, served as state chemist. Shortly after his arrival, he launched an important social/intellectual effort, the Conversation Club, which enabled faculty members, their spouses, and others from the community to meet and discuss literature, art, music, and other pursuits. When Dr. Lupton died in the summer of 1893, newspapers called him "the most eminent scientist and teacher in the South . . ."[29]

Bennett Battle Ross was an 1881 A&M College graduate who also earned a master's degree at Auburn in 1886. He studied part of a year in Germany, taught at A&M College 1884-87, then at LSU until 1893 when President Broun invited him to join the API faculty as professor of general and agricultural chemistry, chemist of the Agricultural Experiment Station, and Alabama's state chemist. He succeeded Professor Lupton as the chief chemistry instructor at Auburn and would serve the institution for thirty-seven years, including a stint as acting president and as dean of agriculture. Dean Ross was described as "the most popular professor at Auburn," and his funeral was attended by one thousand or so grieving API cadets in their gray uniforms. It was for Dean Ross that Ross Hall on campus was named.

John Jenkins Wilmore, mechanical engineer, joined the faculty at President Broun's request in 1888 and, in addition to teaching many years' worth of engineers, built the steam engine which generated electricity for lights in Langdon Hall and the Main Building. He would serve the college for more than fifty years, including as one of three top administrators at the institute during 1932-1935, the darkest days of the Great Depression. He served as dean of engineering from 1907 until 1943. Wilmore Laboratories at AU honors his memory.

Charles H. Barnwell, professor of modern languages and history from 1889 to 1892, came to Auburn at President Broun's invitation when Professor Petrie left to pursue his doctorate at Johns Hopkins. Professor Barnwell played fullback and punter on the first Auburn football team. He left for a position at the University of Alabama where he would eventually serve as academic dean and professor of English, earning recognition as "one of the strongest educators in the South."[30]

Arthur St. Charles Dunstan came to Auburn as a student in the mid-1880s, and after impressing Broun and Dr. Foster McKissick, was hired by the president in 1889 for a faculty position. He would be the second professor—after McKissick—to teach electrical engineering, and he would serve on the faculty for more than fifty years, many of those as department head. He also would lend his skills to bringing electric light to O. D. Smith Hall along Main Street in 1908, the City of Auburn's first electric lights. Dunstan would repeat this process in numerous communities in the years to come.

Bolling H. Crenshaw arrived in 1889 to teach mathematics. He would later head the math program and, in 1932, would join Professors Wilmore and Luther Noble Duncan to form the Administrative Committee leading the institution upon the resignation of President

Bradford Knapp. These three steered the school through three years of the Depression and, for their efforts, would receive honorary doctor of laws degrees from Alabama Governor B. M. Miller in 1934 for their role in shepherding API through the terrible economic time.

Henry Clay Armstrong, Jr., 1887 civil engineering graduate of Alabama Agricultural and Mechanical College, joined the faculty in 1889. Armstrong Jr. pursued graduate study in political science at Johns Hopkins University, then returned to Auburn as an instructor in English and history before working several months in 1890 as administrative assistant to US Rep. William C. Oates (D-Ala.), a future governor of Alabama. Armstrong held the post of college librarian at AAMC in 1891-92, then lived abroad from 1893 to 1898, serving as the American consul in Grenoble, France, and later relocating to Madrid, Spain, to serve as Secretary of the American Legation. After serving in the Spanish-American War, Armstrong Jr. lived in Pensacola, where he founded and oversaw a classical school for almost forty years and found time to serve as mayor.

Dr. Anthony Foster McKissick, a rugged 225-pound man, held the distinction of serving as the first professor of electrical engineering in the South. President Broun hired him from the University of South Carolina in 1891. McKissick, a Cornell University graduate, had played intramural football while teaching at South Carolina and, before rules were in place to prohibit such actions, served as the center on Dr. Petrie's first Auburn football team, providing, as one of his teammates would describe, an "awe inspiring, almost terrifying . . . countenance."[31] McKissick would teach at Auburn for a decade, and in a contribution that may even outweigh his football playing, he installed a dynamo, a generator, in Langdon Hall which he used to power up lights in his engineering laboratory and, eventually, to other campus buildings. This included a three-thousand-foot power line connecting to the Agricultural Experiment Station building where Professor McKissick helped provide the first electricity for an agricultural use in Alabama. He also was "one of the first in America to experiment with X-rays."[32]

Dr. Emerson R. Miller came to Auburn in 1895 as adjunct professor of pharmacy, essentially launching Auburn's School of Pharmacy. A University of Michigan graduate, Miller also trained at Marburg University in Germany and earned his PhD at the University of Minnesota. He took a break during his time at Auburn to head the Experiment Station in Cuba during 1913-14. At the dedication of Miller Hall in 1953, the first building dedicated to pharmacy education in the state, Dr. Miller was remembered as "a scholar with exceptional training and an outstanding chemist and educator." He was a frequent contributor to the *Journal of the American Pharmaceutical Association*.

Franklin S. Earle came to Auburn in 1896, hired by President Broun from the Mississippi Agriculture Experiment Station. Earle, appointed associate professor of biology and horticulture, co-authored an important early book, *A Preliminary List of Alabama Fungi*. Professor Earle would teach the first forestry courses at Auburn and serve as the first head of an entomology department in 1901. He left Auburn in 1901 for a position on the faculty of Columbia University in New York City. He also served as an assistant curator of mycological collections at the New York Botanical Garden. In 1904, he was appointed director of the Agricultural Experiment Station at Santiago de las Vegas, Cuba. His work in Cuba, as a business consultant, as president of the Cuba Fruit Exchange, and later as a US Department of Agriculture investigator, focused on sugarcane both from an agricultural and a business perspective.

Dr. John F. Duggar accepted President Broun's invitation to join the faculty in 1895 with the title of assistant professor of agriculture. Dr. Duggar would later head the Experiment Station and would become world-famous for his research productivity, including pioneering work in cotton and legume experiments. Dr. Duggar established what Auburn people know today as the "Old Rotation" cotton experiment field adjacent to the Davis Arboretum. He and associates contributed an exhibition on their cotton research findings at the World's Fair in Paris in 1900 and received a silver medal as one of the best exhibits there.

Clifford Leroy Hare, 1891 graduate of the A&M College, was a member of Auburn's first football team and earned a master's degree from the school in 1892. He joined the Auburn faculty in 1895 as instructor in the chemistry laboratory. He served as first president of the Southern Athletic Conference, predecessor to the Southeastern Conference, in 1932, and as chair of API's faculty athletic committee for years. He was named dean of the School of Chemistry and Pharmacy in 1932. Hare also took active interest in local affairs, serving as a director of the Bank of Auburn 1914-1948, as a member of the Auburn City Council 1917-1920, and as interim mayor for a brief period before 1920. Auburn's Jordan-Hare Stadium is named for him.

George N. Mitcham attended Alabama Agricultural & Mechanical College and played on the football team 1896-1898, earning praise as "one of the gamest warriors that ever wore the orange and blue."[33] Had he done nothing else at Auburn, he cemented his place in college lore for his role in an 1898 football game. The University of Georgia led 17-0 headed to the fourth quarter, and lineman Mitcham changed positions, lining up at running back for the Tigers. He became Superman of a sort, scoring bruising touchdowns on three consecutive drives and kicking all the extra points to bring AAMC back for an 18-17 win. He had joined the faculty as professor of civil engineering and drawing in 1897, later teaching mathematics. He designed and directed construction of the first major sewage line in Auburn in 1908. This sewer line connected the new dining hall—O. D. Smith Hall—and other campus buildings to pipes bringing water from "an excellent spring of water with a capacity of about one hundred twenty thousand gallons per day" which had been purchased by the college, according to minutes from the Auburn Board of Trustees meeting on May 22, 1908. The spring was two miles from campus, and as a part of this enterprise, a tower holding 75,000 gallons was constructed nearby. Water was pumped by an electrical-driven centrifuge pump, installed at the pump house adjacent to the spring basin. Professor Mitcham was the consulting engineer in charge of this operation, assisted by colleagues from the Departments of Electrical and Mechanical Engineering.

Michael Thomas Fullan arrived in 1898 as assistant in mechanic arts and would later serve as head of the Department of Machine, Design, and Drawing. In that role, he would hold membership on the Joint Committee on Physics of the National Education Association. A music enthusiast, he formed and directed the first Auburn band. He—along with Professor Wilmore—also lent mechanical expertise to Orville and Wilbur Wright when the brothers came to Auburn for several weeks in 1910, helping the famed aviation pioneers with technical aspects of an airplane project they were tackling.[34]

Dr. George F. Atkinson came to Auburn in 1889 to occupy the South's first chair in biology. During his three years on Broun's faculty, he made significant discoveries regarding plant diseases caused by parasitic insects and fungi. Dr. Atkinson was made chair of the Entomological Section of the American Scientific Association for the Advancement of Science in 1892. He helped George Petrie coach the first football team, but he also played on that team. He left Auburn to head the botany program at Cornell.

James Powell Cocke Southall joined the faculty in 1901 as associate professor of physics, recruited personally by President Broun to take his place as the college's physics instructor. Southall would author a few important science texts, including *Mirrors, Prisms and Lenses: A Text-Book for Geometrical Optics.* This book became a classic work for inventors, engineers, engineering students, and aficionados of physics and optical studies.

A few years before President Broun hired Southall, he brought on board a recent AAMC/API engineering honors graduate to teach the first-year physics classes and physics laboratory. Walter Merritt Riggs, Class of 1893, was a South Carolina native who returned home after a year or two of service to President Broun, but he made his mark on Auburn and later on his home state's land-grant college, Clemson. Riggs had played on the first Auburn football team and was still involved as a manager in the mid-1890s. When the head coaching position came open, Riggs was the one-man search committee appointed to find the next Tiger coach. He found John Heisman on a tomato farm in Texas, convinced him to come to Auburn, and, over the next five seasons, Heisman brought energy and success to the API squad. Riggs left Auburn in 1896 to join the engineering faculty at Clemson and serve as its first football coach. He later recruited Coach Heisman to Clemson, and Riggs—freed from his coaching duties— went on to become president of Clemson University from 1910 to 1924.[35]

Another successful hire during the Broun years brought James Stanley Newman, son of an educated Virginia farmer and a graduate of the University of Virginia. He was recruited from the Georgia Department of Agriculture to fill the dual role of Experiment Station director and professor of agriculture. Newman stayed eight years at Auburn, pioneering an approach by which results learned through experiments conducted on the College Farm were transferred to the classroom, where agriculture was taught as an applied science. He also served as president of the Alabama Agricultural Society when that organization re-started after the Civil War.[36] When he left Auburn, it was to chair the agriculture program and direct the South Carolina Experiment Station at Clemson.[37]

Paul Shields Haley was named an assistant professor of civil engineering and drawing in 1901, the year after he was graduated from API. Haley would later be named to the Board of Trustees and would serve for more than fifty years in that role. Haley Center, which opened in 1969, was named for him.

President Broun expressed a clear vision of what Auburn—as an institution focused on excellence in the agricultural and mechanic arts, but not excluding traditional, classical subjects—could become. His vision attracted these distinguished men to faculty positions in the middle of dirt-poor East Alabama. Their achievements on campus, in town, and beyond became a testament to the wisdom Broun held in judging character and talent and in formulating a multi-faceted team that would help the Agricultural & Mechanical College reach its president's lofty ambitions.

One name remains from the illustrious roster, arguably the most important hire of Broun's life: the young veterinarian whose existence he first learned about in a letter from Dr. Tait Butler in 1891. Of all the masterful moves the Virginian made in building the institution that would become Auburn University, no action would prove more significant to Auburn and to the State of Alabama of the early twentieth century than the day Charles Allen Cary agreed to join President Broun's faculty.

CHAPTER TWO

MIDWESTERNERS

Charles Allen Cary was born in Millersburg, Iowa, on November 28, 1861, a son of William and Lucy Ellen O'hara Cary, a couple who also apparently spent a good amount of time in Louisiana. A profile on Dr. Cary in the December 1915 *American Journal of Veterinary Medicine* indicated that in working early on "as a country school teacher, he caught the knack of governing youth, early learned to govern and guide men and to evoke the best in them." This teaching stint came either before his college and veterinary school training, or perhaps during the summer or Christmas breaks his college terms afforded.[1] He came from a long, distinguished line of ancestors named Cary or similar spelling, stretching back to England, Wales, and France. (His family history is detailed in Chapter 3.)

Dr. Cary's wife, Emma Lucile Heck, was born on December 7, 1867, the first of three children born to Ernest Heck and his wife, Margaretha Kessler Heck, both of German heritage.[2] Emma made her entrance at the family home in Nauvoo, Illinois, a small community on the Mississippi River near Fort Madison, Iowa, almost the extreme west central point of Illinois. Nauvoo is the next river town north from a larger community called Keokuk, Iowa. The distance between Nauvoo and Keokuk is around fifteen miles, proximity that has significant bearing on how the Cary-Heck world eventually turned. Nauvoo remains known for its connection with early Mormons, though the Hecks were Presbyterian.

Emma was a sharp young woman and matriculated in local schools. She topped her Nauvoo High School graduating class of six girls, and at the commencement, held on the evening of Thursday, May 27, 1886, at Nauvoo's City Hall, she delivered for the audience her essay on "The Force of Inclination and Belief."

The circumstances of exactly where and when Emma Heck first encountered Charles Allen Cary, six years older than she, have been lost to history. But their acquaintance and subsequent life together undoubtedly was assisted by the short distance between Nauvoo and Keokuk. After his graduation from Iowa Agricultural College in spring 1887, Dr. Cary, at age twenty-six, entered the practice of veterinary medicine and surgery at Keokuk, in Iowa's southeastern corner. He stayed with this work in Keokuk into 1889, when he was selected professor of veterinary sciences at South Dakota Agricultural and Mechanical College in Brookings.

During the young bachelor's almost two years in Keokuk, it is reasonable to envision him and twenty-year-old Emma Heck meeting at church, at a county fair, or at Ernest Heck's farm if he had sent for a veterinarian to treat a cow, a horse, or a hog. Perhaps someone who knew one had met the other and considered they might make a good pairing. However the Charles-Emma introduction took place, sparks of some degree flew. Subsequent opportunities brought these young people together, when the veterinarian would call on his intended. Their marriage did not take place until Dr. Cary had moved to South Dakota, so it may have been a case of "absence making the hearts grow fonder."

Two weeks before her twenty-third birthday, Emma married the handsome, auburn-haired veterinarian. Their wedding took place at the First Presbyterian Church of Nauvoo at high noon on Thanksgiving Day, November 27, 1890—the day before Dr. Cary's twenty-ninth birthday. To arrive for his wedding, the groom traveled five hundred miles to the southeast—by train, one presumes—to Nauvoo from Brookings, the east central South Dakota prairie town of around fifteen hundred residents and the first home for Dr. and Mrs. Cary.

Dr. Cary, likely unknown to most of Nauvoo at this time, was lauded in a newspaper article the day of the wedding as "a young man of sterling worth and integrity, of excellent habits and business qualifications."[3] Miss Heck, her family well known in town, was described in the same article as "a young lady of culture and amiable social qualities . . . held in high esteem by all of her large circle of friends and acquaintances. She is a graduate of our high school and disciplined in other departments of education which grace the womanly society of our day."

The newspaper congratulated Dr. Cary on showing "admirable taste in selecting one of Nauvoo's young ladies for a wife. He has surrendered to the bewitching smiles of one of our best young ladies, and we predict that he will never regret the day he captivated."

The wedding ceremony was conducted by Minister J. B. Worrall of Keokuk, and the newlyweds took a honeymoon to New Orleans, perhaps traveling for a couple of days on a romantic Anchor Line steamboat down the Mississippi. Once settled in New Orleans, the dashing husband surely endeared himself to his cultured wife by taking her to various sites around the "Crescent City," including the opera. They would be opera fans all their married lives, taking in performances in New Orleans, Chicago, and New York when opportunity arose. Possibly, part of their honeymoon doubled as family reunion time. Emma Heck Cary had relatives who owned property in or near New Orleans; perhaps there was time for meeting family there. The couple also had planned to travel to Florida, and may have done so, but that portion of the honeymoon itinerary remains unconfirmed.

After a few days' visit with the Hecks and others upon their return to Nauvoo, on a Thursday evening, likely two weeks after their wedding, Emma and Charles were hosted in a farewell party at the bride's family home. The paper called the gathering "a brilliant social event of extreme elegance and superlative pleasure . . . a farewell surprise." The night included charades and other games, music, and dancing into the "wee small hour." About thirty people attended. The professor and his wife left the next morning for their first home in Brookings.

According to Dr. and Mrs. Cary's papers from their final family home in Auburn, one other event of note involving the newlyweds occurred before they ventured to South Dakota. A photocopy of a church bulletin called "The Westminster," from Keokuk, Iowa, dated January 1891, revealed a brief article titled "A Wedding With a Sequel." This article recounted the story of Minister Worrall's return to Nauvoo about two weeks after the wedding:

> The wedding of Prof. Chas. A. Cary and Miss Emma Heck was announced in our last issue as having occurred on Thanksgiving day, at Nauvoo, the ceremony performed by the pastor of this church. About

two weeks ago, he was called to go and preach there, and receive into membership on profession of Christ these two who had so lately started to walk life's journey as husband and wife, and for a second time they stood up in the same church together so soon to take together the solemn covenant of faith and to dedicate their lives to the service of the Master. A very large audience was present and it was an occasion of deep and tender interest. What a blessed thing it would be if every young couple would start their married life in this way. Surely the blessing of God would be upon such marriages.

Apparently, the Cary honeymoon included serious spiritual discussion, prompting their church response upon return. This church event likely took place on either December 7 or 14, depending on how long Emma and Charles were away or how long they stayed in Nauvoo before venturing on to Brookings. Church would be important during their married lives.

The newlyweds received a number of interesting, even curious, letters from friends and relatives wishing them well in their marriage, several of which were preserved in the family collection. Dr. Cary's mother wrote on November 27, 1890, the day of the wedding:

> Dear Son and Daughter . . . I'm sorry to say that I could not attend your wedding, but did not get your card in time. If I had gotten it one day sooner, I would have come. Please pay us a visit at the old home this winter at Millersburg. Your mother, Mrs. Lucy E. Cary

Dr. Cary received what modern readers may consider an unconventional, even eccentric letter from his aunt, dated November 26, 1890:

> Charles Cary, Dear Nephew, I am supposing this will reach you after the ceremony so I will wish you and the Dear lady you have chosen for a wife (dear to you at least) may live happily and wisely, for a reasonable number of years, leaving the world better for your having lived in it, so when the time of a ripe old age makes it your time to depart, may it be your happy lot to inherit eternal blessedness. Come and visit us on your way west. If convenient, let us know and we will meet you at the train. Yours truly, Mrs. M.E. _____ [illegible], Marengo, Illinois.

With the Carys marrying on Thanksgiving 1890 and honeymooning into December, one might expect the New Year would have found them setting up house in Brookings and Dr. Cary picking back up his work schedule. But, apparently, his duties were not required at South Dakota Agricultural until the latter part of February 1891. After spending a short time in Brookings to give the new Mrs. Cary a look at the Northern prairie, the couple made their way south for an extended honeymoon. Much of this excursion was spent in Louisiana, where apparently Dr. Cary's father was living and operating a weekly newspaper, the *Jennings Reporter*. It is not clear from family papers the extent to which Dr. Cary's parents split time between Iowa and Louisiana. Dr. Cary kept a diary of this trip, which was included in family papers preserved for more than a century and which survives as one of the few first-person accounts of Dr. Cary's personal life. Highlights from these several weeks' travel, with his spellings, favored expressions, and personal notes, include:

Tuesday, Jan 6, 1891

Crossed the Miss R in skiff ladened with 12 persons and 2 trunks. Ice was very heavy and moving slowly. Took 1 hr to cross from Nauvoo to Montrose. Stopped at Keokuk from 4:30 pm to 9:30 with the Hornes. Played _____ to about 9:45. We took sleeper for St. Louis. Arrived there at 6:30 a.m. on Wednesday the 7th. Spent the day at Aunt Celia's (Mrs. [illegible]) and went to the Olympic to hear Joe Jefferson and Florence in "The Rivals." It was very good. To be appreciated they must be heard. Fire at St Louis on our way from Olympia Theatre to Mosier Hotel. Remained at Hotel Mosier Wednesday night.

Thursday, Jan 8, 1891

At 7 a.m. we took train to East St. Louis and after breakfasting boarded the M&O for Jackson, Tenn. At Cairo, Ill., the passenger train was ferried over the Ohio River—a novel experience to us. In Kentucky we saw the Mistle Toe in many of the larger trees. At Jackson Tenn we arrived at 9:30 p.m. Thursday. It rained and snowed the greater part of the day and also rained that evening or night. We remained at the Armour House that night and took the 10:30 a.m. train for Mobile Friday. The green shrubs and trees increased gradually all the way.

Arrived at Mobile Saturday morning at 5:30 a.m. Quartered at Hotel Royal 6 hrs then at the Getz (?) House for room (corner Royal and Government Sts opposite Court House). Went down to dock on Mobile River. Saw large river stmrs and Cotton Ocean Steamers from Liverpool and Glasgow. Went on board the Dalton and viewed Mobile Bay in the distance. Spent evening at room writing letters and listening to organ grinder, cow carts and Woad! Woad!

Sunday, Jan 11, 1891

Breakfast at Delmonico's Restaurant at 10 a.m. Attended services at Government St. Presbyterian Church. Heard Rev. A. L. Phillips of Tuskaloosa [sic] Ala preach on Mission work among the colored people of the South. Good many hard facts on ignorant colored ministers.

At 1 p.m. we took "Dummy Motor" to Spring Hill a place about 5 min from Mobile. Visited Forest Park and wandered about in pine groves among the live oaks and many evergreen plants and trees. It was a lovely sunny day and we enjoyed it very much. Also saw a Catholic college on the banks of the red clay ravine. A beautiful brick red clay banked ravine which wound its way among the pines and cedars. The banks were very picturesque from the time of the clay and the way they (the banks) were moulded by washing rain (erosion).

Sunday evening we attended services at Christ's Church Episcopal and listened to a good sermon by Rev. J.L. Tucker on Divine Grace and Faith.

We visited the Palentino, a Liverpool Iron Steam and Sail Ship (cotton). It was a huge ship and carries about 6000 bales of cotton.

Monday, Jan 12, 1891

Rose—late—too late to relate.

Went to Magnolia Cemetery. Saw many very beautiful and grand monuments. The Confederate Cemetery where about 1200 Confederates are buried among which is the grave of Gen. Braxton Bragg at the south western corner beneath a neat marble slab surrounded by a modest mound. In the center of the Gray graves is a pedestal about 80 ft. high on the summit of which is a soldier in gray bowing upon his musket. The small slabs over the confederate dead are a grey cement.

About 80 yd SW of the Grays is the National Cemetery where about 920 Union boys lie in honored graves. The glorious flag floats above their peaceful remains like a constant sentinel. The cemetery is neatly kept and all the northern states have honored dead among the graves of the Blue.

Mobile Ala. Tuesday, Jan 13, 1891

Rose too late to go sketching before breakfast. Went to Photo-Galleries. Bought 2 photos. Took 1 o'clock Dummy to Spring Hill and there Dearest sketched in oil the Brick Banked Ravine while I caught sand and brick and clay. The sketch is beautiful and shall be preserved many—

many years. Saw some "poor white trash" driving little poor pony horses to rickety wagons and carts. Had been hauling wood to market. Also saw more little cow carts, etc.

Wednesday, Jan 14, 1891

Took breakfast at Delmonico's then went to L and N train to go to New Orleans. Train 3 hrs late. While waiting Dearest spent the time sketching a sail vessel anchored in Mobile River. Took sleeper at 2:15 p.m. for New Orleans.

Passed Bay St. Louis, Bolixi [sic] & other winter resorts and saw the Gulf. Much swampy land. Arrived at Crescent City at 7:20 and after a little trouble found room at Vauntebank Hotel. Dempsy & Fitzsimmons fight filled the hotels, etc.

New Orleans, Thursday, Jan 15, 1891

Found new room. Visited wharf and went on board large river steamer. Visited cemetery. Saw Albert Sidney Johnson's grave. He fell at Shiloh. Many very beautiful vaults. Nearly all above the ground. Went to opera to hear Tom Keene in Richard III. It was good. But Shakespeare was ___ 6 acts Keene instead of 5 Shakespeare. Oranges 10 ct per doz.

New Orleans Jan 16, 1891

Visited U.S. Mint. Saw the Bullion in large bars through bars. Smelting furnace where 90% of Silver is mixed alloyed with 10% of copper in clay crucibles. It is then molded into bars ½ in thick (6 in long). Then they (the bars) are pressed until they are . . . the thickness of $1 silver. Then the sticks are cut into circular "dollars" milled on the ridge around border is raised. Then they are weighed by about 30 to 40 ladies who file off the edge if too heavy and return them to smelting room if too light. They are next polished by heating and passing through acid and hot water, etc. Now they are stamped at the rate of 90 per minute by a die etc. New Orleans mint make nothing but $1 silver pieces. Have 8 die machines but were working only two on the day we saw the mint. The mints are allowed to make 100000 per month. Phila is the "Fed" U.S. Mint where the[y] make all kinds—all denominations of gold, silver, etc.

New Orleans, Jan 16, 1891

In afternoon we took St. Charles Avenue car for Carrolton and saw the residential st of N.O. St Charles Av is broad with a grassy center and very fine drives on either side. Many tropical plants adorn the yards or lawns.

Saw live oaks covered with Spanish Moss.

In evening we heard Rhea at Academy of Music in "Josephine," an historical play. She has strong voice, heavy physique and French twang. Mr. Harris was remarkable Napoleon. In all the play was very good. The costumes and stage scenery was likewise excellent.

Saturday Morning, Jan 17, 1891

Left N.O. by Southern Pacific Ferry to Algiers and then through Southern La across swamp and bayous through the creole district. Cotton. Sugar cane. Heard . . . French creole. Negroes were separated from whites by curtains in car. The deciduous trees in the swamps were covered with Sp Moss also many of the live oaks. Moss will not grow Hard Pine trees.

Left N.O. at 7:45 arrived at Jennings at 4 p.m. After cleansing at Kistner Hotel we saw my folks at Reporter Office.

Jennings Sunday Jan 18, 1891

Attended services at Congregational Church. Heard Rev. Mills of Meade, Kansas. Took dinner at brother Wilford's and went over to Sulphur Springs to which is about 8 miles over the Bayou where a Southerner before the war held slaves, had a plantation, a sanitarium at Sulphur Springs and a rendezvous for hunters etc. Saw rice fields. Saw mills and Arcadian Creole shanties with low hovel like roofs. Saw Creoles which were wanting in beauty. At last the traditional idea of Creole beauty. Went to M.E. church in evening. Heard Quaker lady evangelist preach.

Jan 18, 1891

Jennings La

Rose at 7:45 a.m. At house all morning quietly perusing papers etc. In afternoon took a walk about the city viewing sights such as gardens, arcadian Creole woman (fat) on horseback (a little thin bay pony ½ as large as the woman). Listened to southern stories about big crops of figs and about butter not melting in "July sun," about Southern intimidations, e.g., Col. H. telling about stealing ballot box—permitting negroes to vote then exchanging the ballot box for another and all the votes counted and Democratic. Again, about 1884 at New Iberia the Negroes and Whites had a war at falls on election day. Papers reported 15 negroes killed. In fact, according to one of the southerners (who participated in the fight and said he was ashamed of it ever after) said if there were 15 there were 215 killed and the buzzards fed upon them for days.

Jan 20, 1891
Jennings La
Started for Lake Arthur at 9:25. Arrived . . . 11 a.m. Crossed lake in skiff to ship yards where river boats and gulf ships are made. Mr. Haberger, a German, owns the old ship yard. Lived there 18 years. The ship yard on a peninsula.

Went to . . . Orange grove on S banks of lake. Ate our dinner in orange grove and out and ate oranges from there. Saw buds green and ripe oranges on same trees. Then we passed by land to another orange grove.

Orange grove #2 yielded 69000 oranges sold at Galveston for $900 at 1½ cents each. We paid 50 cts per doz at Grove.

In going we passed a little Arcadian school house at the grove and we saw negress washing on bank of lake with plank board and mallet. They beat the clothes on the board which is just above the water then they boil the clothes in iron kettle. We passed from boat landing by canoe to Shell Beach—a very pretty landing at mouth of Mermeutau River. At Shell Beach we found an old saw mill—60 years old, made of cypress. Had a steam boat engine and made cypress lumber chiefly. Here we got a molding board of cypress of Mr. Dechamps who owns a store . . . .

The saw mill is made of hewn timber—before the day of saw mills and it is very strong and well built. The cypress lumber is sold, in Galveston at $40 per M. From Shell Beach we went by canoe in Lake to Lake Arthur. At Lake Arthur Mr. Lee of De Moines Iowa built a large hotel of to $10,000 house for pleasure seekers. The lake is 4 or 5 miles long by 1-2 broad. Surrounded by cypress and gums and live oaks.

Jennings La Jan 21, 1891
Rained nearly all day. Dearest and I printed letter head all morning and visited at brothers and sisters and played Parchisey (?) and I won 2 only of 3 playing with Laura and Dearest. Read A. Ward to Dearest.

Jennings La Thursday Jan 22, 1891
Worked in Printing Office folding papers etc.

Jan 23 1891 Friday Jennings La
Father and I drove 20 miles north to China to see the claims which he had taken where the French count and countess lived. Picked some cotton on the way. Rained all P.M. Arrived at Jennings at 9:30 P.M.

Dearest was at Laura's and Wilfred's writing letters etc—homesick.

Jennings Jan 24, 1891

9 am Dearest, father and I drove out to Esterly to see my 160 A land. After much trouble in getting over bridges, bayous etc we reached it. We drove 6 or 8 miles out of the direct south to get over the bayou and in crossing a run we drove into water that ran into the buggy bed. Arrived home about 11 p.m.

Sunday Jan 25, 1891

Went to church morning and evening. Rev. Shelland preached in the morning and Rev Mrs. Rogers the Quakeress in the evening. At Laura's and Wilfred's for dinner.

Monday Jan 26, 1891

Took 12:1 train from Jennings for New Orleans. At N.O. 7:25. Lodged at Victor House #92 Royal St and ate at Fabachere Restaurant. Went to Academy of Music to hear Roland Reed in "Lend Me Your Wife."

New Orleans Tuesday Jan 27, 1891

In morning took car out to Audubon Park to see Green House and U.S. Experiment Station.

Station work with sugar cane chiefly and makes chemical analyses etc. The Audubon Park Green House is grand indeed one of the very largest in the U.S.

Took 6:20 pm L&N to Mobile. Lodged in Mr. Gertz (?) House.

Mobile Jan 28, 1891

Took st car . . . to Base Ball Park and Shell Road. At an old nursery plantation we secured 6 Magnolia and 2 Japonica flowers . . . Saw two old war forts on the Bay. At 9:20 pm we took M and O for St. Louis

Jan 29 on M & O

Going to St. Louis. Arrived at St. Louis Jan 30 at 7:30 a.m. Took Keokuk and N Road for home at 9:20 a.m. Arrived at Nauvoo 6:30 P.M. Jan 30, 1891 . . . .

Arrived at Brookings February 17, 1891.

Thus ends the small window into the first few months of married life for Dr. and Mrs. Cary.

CHAPTER THREE

FOREBEARS

Charles Allen Cary grew up in Millersburg, Iowa, then and now a smaller-than-small community of fewer than 200 people in east-central Iowa, toward the southeast of the state. The plan for the town of Millersburg—a relatively new settlement when the Cary family arrived—had been laid out formally in 1852, with the village named for Reuben Miller, who headed the founding family.

Charles Allen Cary's family background is much more fully documented than that of his wife. The Cary family's collection of papers and other items includes a photocopy of a 105-page book by Henry Grosvenor Cary, which dates to 1906, though the photocopy includes prefaces for both 1894 and 1898 editions of this work. This compilation recounts in relatively brief manner more than eight centuries of Cary family history. Henry Grosvenor Cary wrote in his preface, "This record is made possible by the existence of a 'Pedigree of the Cary Family' which was drawn up by the Royal College of Heralds by command of Queen Anne Boleyn," which would seem sufficiently authoritative.[1]

Dr. Cary's father, Ohioan William E. Cary (1833-1907), and Lucy Ellen O'Hara (1838-1899) had four sons in addition to Charles: Eldridge born in 1857, Frank born in 1859, Wilford born in 1866, and Walter born in 1873.

Charles Allen's grandfather Cary was born in New Jersey, with previous great-grandfathers born in Maine and Massachusetts. It appears his great-grandfather eight generations back—John Cary, born in 1614 in Somersetshire, England—brought the family line over from Europe. Charles Allen Cary was aware of this family history: he wrote on a biographical form at API in 1907, "The first Cary who came to America landed at the Mass. Bay Colony in 1634. A marker is near there now, erected by his descendants in 1904 or 5. His name was John Cary and he was an Englishman by birth." That great-grandfather died in Plymouth, Massachusetts, on November 7, 1681. The marker in Massachusetts reads:

> Near this spot was the home of John Cary, born in Somersetshire, England. He became in 1651 an original proprietor and honored settler on this river. He was Clerk of the Plantation. When the town of Bridgewater was incorporated in 1656, he was elected constable, the first and only officer of that year. He was the Town Clerk until his death in 1681. Tradition says that he was the first teacher of Latin in Plymouth Colony. The tablet is erected by his descendants in memory of their historic and noble ancestor.

Charles Allen Cary's family from John Cary dates to England in the seventeenth century through the mists of time, perhaps to the village of Castle Cary, Somerset, England. Castle Cary is twenty-five miles south of Bath, and the location takes its name from the River Cary nearby. According to Henry Grosvenor Cary's account, ancestors were headquartered at St. Giles-in-the-Heath, in Devon in extreme southwest England. This location in Devon sits about 130 miles west of the Castle Cary/River Cary site. It is unclear which location was the earliest home of anyone named Cary. But there may have been family members in both places—at Castle Cary and at Devon—by the eleventh or twelfth centuries. Interestingly, according to Henry Grosvenor Cary, William the Conqueror's *Domesday Book* of 1086, which surveyed the estates of the realm, spelled the surname "Kari" for those in Devonshire and "Cari" for those in Somersetshire.

Spelling during the Middle Ages was inconsistent. While we speak of "Cary," it becomes apparent in reading Henry Grosvenor Cary's book that family members could have chosen any of the name's versions used at various times: Carey, Carye, Carei, Cari, de Cari, Carew, Kary, Kory, Kari, or de Kari. Other spellings may have existed, as well.

Also, the family namesake's small river was known as the Kari, or Kari-brook, or the River Cary, which runs—or ran during the Middle Ages—near the settlement of Cary and its castle.

That castle—called Cary Castle, as opposed to the town's name of Castle Cary—was reportedly one of the largest in twelfth-century England. Cary Castle was, on at least two occasions in the twelfth century, used for defense purposes by forces opposed to the king. It was reportedly besieged twice by King Stephen, a grandson of William the Conqueror. First, in 1138, the king's army used fire and catapulted stones to break the will of those inside, leading to their surrender. The castle came under attack again in 1153 with siege so fiercely launched that the structure was nearly demolished.

Cary Castle was abandoned when someone built one of those trendy—and far better insulated—manor houses next door. Local historians today believe many of the old castle's stones were removed and repurposed in building other structures in the town. An 1890 excavation yielded foundation evidence of a square keep measuring seventy-eight feet on each side, with walls fifteen feet thick.

A few generations later, John Cary—a knight—and wife Jane (she was his second wife; his first, Agnes, died with no children) had a son named John, born in 1350 in Holway, another western outpost. Henry G. Cary reported of him in that 1906 book, with some quotations from an earlier writer:

> This Sir John was a very noted man . . . . "On the fifth of November, 1387, he was by the King Richard II, made Chief Baron of the Exchequer, and advanced to be a Judge of the land; who being now placed in a high and spacious Orb, he scattered the Rays of Justice about him with great splendor. In this post he continued many years, manifesting in all his actions, an inflexible Virtue and Honesty; and indeed it fell out at least that he had an extraordinary occasion laid before him, for the proof and tryal thereof, upon which we find him as true as steel, for the greatest dangers could not affright him from his duty and Loyalty to his distressed Master, King Richard II, unto whom he faithfully adhered when most others had forsaken him." After the king was put to death by Henry IV, Sir John was banished and all his goods and lands confiscated for his loyalty to his royal master.

Apparently, King Henry IV sent Sir John to Waterford, Ireland, where he died in 1404. The lands he lost were in Cockington and

Clovelly in western England. But the story has a happy ending, not for that Sir John, but for his son, Robert, who was born about 1375. Again, Henry Grosvenor Cary repeated a story in his 1906 book from the tale of an earlier writer:

> In the beginning of the reign of Henry V (1413-1422) a certain Knight-errant of Arragon, having passed through divers countries, and performed many feats of Arms, arrived here in England, where he challenged any man of his rank and quality to make a trial of his skill in arms.
>
> This challenge was accepted by Sir Robert Cary, between whom a cruel encounter, and a long and doubtful combat was waged in Smithfield, London. But at length this noble Champion vanquished the presumptuous Arragonois, for which King Henry V restored unto him a good part of his father's lands, which for his loyalty to Richard II he had been deprived of by Henry IV and authorized him to bear the Arms of a Knight of Arragon, which the noble posterity continue to wear unto this day; for according to the laws of Heraldry, whoever fairly in the field conquers his adversary may justify the wearing of his Arms.

Henry Grosvenor Cary claimed an early coat of arms associated with the family consisted of a red chevron diagonally crossing a red shield, with three swans depicted. With Sir Robert Cary's victory over the Knight of Aragon at Smithfield, the Cary family coat of arms was changed to feature a black chevron across a silver shield, with three roses within the diagonal band, a stately swan atop a helmet, with a family motto below: "Sine Macula," which means "without blemish" or "without stain." Robert Cary—the Smithfield hero—had a brother of some note, James or John, who served as Bishop of Lichfield and Coventry. Henry Grosvenor Cary claimed this clergyman was also a dean of St. Paul's in London. Bishop James/John met with Pope Martin V (the Church of England was still two centuries away at this point) in 1419 and was appointed Lord Bishop of Exeter. But he lived only six more weeks and never took that seat.

A later Cary named William, who also became a knight, was born in 1437. He was known as the Knight of Cockington and a strong supporter of the House of Lancaster during the Wars of the Roses. At the Battle of Tewksbury on May 4, 1471, when William was thirty-four, the Lancaster army for which he fought was defeated, and to escape with his life, he and others took sanctuary in the local church. (That church sanctuary precedent had not worked for Thomas Becket 301 years earlier at Canterbury.) Soldiers and knights loyal to the House of York began negotiations through the barricaded church door and promised the Lancastrian remnant they would be pardoned if they would surrender. They did surrender, but all is not fair in love and war. William and the others were beheaded, their personal properties confiscated by the Yorkists. Later, King Henry VII—Henry Tudor—restored William Cary's property to his son, another Robert, born in 1460.

From this point, according to Henry Grosvenor Cary, the Cary family goes four different directions, with Charles Allen Cary's line coming through Robert Cary's son, William, born in 1495 in Clovelly. William was the son of Robert Cary's second wife, Agnes. Robert served as a knight and chief baron of the Exchequer under Henry VIII.

Ancient cousins from the other lines lived some interesting, triumphant, and tragic times over the centuries, rubbing elbows with English royalty, marrying well, owning property, fighting for king and country. Henry Grosvenor Cary's *Cary Family in England* recounted their highlights. He included, for example, Charles Allen Cary's distant cousin, the Rev. Henry Francis Cary (1772-1844) of London, who authored "the best translation of Dante which was ever written," self-published in 1814 but eventually demanding four editions. He served as a vicar/reader at various churches and spent more than a decade as an assistant librarian in the printed books department at the British Museum's library. He also authored a book on *Lives of English Poets* in 1846, plus other literary translations. But his Dante translation brought him prominence and earned this Cary a burial spot in Poets' Corner in Westminster Abbey, on the floor in front of the Wordsworth statue and near to Shakespeare's memorial.

Another of Charles Allen Cary's distant cousins, mentioned in Henry Grosvenor Cary's family history, is William Joseph Carey (1761-1801), a shoe cobbler who became an eminent Protestant missionary, most prominently to India. He was known for translating the Bible into Bengali, Arabic, Hindi, Sanskrit, and other languages, but his reputation included charges of colonialism and racism.

The text makes the case for a relative named Henry Cary authoring the music and lyrics to England's national anthem, "God Save the King," in 1740. Others dispute the song's authorship, but Henry Cary (1687-1743) apparently wrote some other poetry/songs ("Sally in Our Alley," anyone?). Perhaps a Cary's thoughts have prayerfully asked for divine protection over the sovereign of the realm going on three centuries.

With Cary family members consistently serving their kings and queens, property confiscation continued during the English Civil War as Oliver Cromwell's legions took over Cary grounds, including Cockington, in the seventeenth century. That incident may have played a role in John Cary sailing to America in 1634, only fourteen years after the Mayflower brought its first pilgrims to the East Coast.

In America, the Charles Allen Cary connection extended to sisters in greater Cincinnati in the generation just before the veterinarian's birth: Alice and Phoebe Cary, who gained a reputation for poetry in their lifetimes. Alice (1820-1871) and Phoebe (1824-1871) grew up on a farm ten miles north of the city and attended school only sporadically, and so were largely self-educated. But they loved to read, and after completing daily chores, they would burn candles long into the night to enjoy their books. In their mid-twenties, the women moved to New York City for work and to pursue their literary talents. Cary family memorabilia includes an 1891 edition of *The Poetical Works of Alice and Phoebe Cary*, published by Houghton Mifflin Company. This work includes more than 280 poems by Alice and more than 200 by Phoebe. There may be little to alert researchers into the interest Charles Allen Cary had in his cousins' poetical works—he most likely never met them—but one cannot discount the crusty-yet-cultured veterinarian having some level of appreciation: he and Emma named their daughters Phoebe and Alice.

Cary DNA apparently propels its incumbent to action. Regardless of who and what had come in his bloodline, Charles Allen Cary was born of intelligence, of an unceasing work ethic, and of a desire to solve problems. He was the man his times required. The collected glories and foibles of the human condition represented in previous Cary generations prepared a path for their bright young descendant from east central Iowa. He took a route with many opportunities but few guarantees.

CHAPTER FOUR

DR. CARY IN AMES

The environment and the society into which Charles Allen Cary was born in rural Iowa in 1861 was in part structured by a wave of agricultural advancements and organizing that had taken place in the half-century preceding his arrival. In the decade before his birth, for one example, the number of local and national agricultural organizations in America had more than tripled—from three hundred to almost nine hundred organizations acknowledged by the US Agricultural Society, a forerunner of the USDA, which itself was created by federal act on May 15, 1862. Further, the number of agricultural patents awarded in the United States totaled only forty-three as of 1847; but, within twenty years, that number had expanded to 1,778.[1]

During Charles Allen Cary's childhood, a series of public health disasters took place throughout the country, and the collective damage from these plagues may have focused a teenage Cary on pursuing a career in solving such problems. In no particular order, animal health crises of the era included:

Glanders. This lethal, infectious disease caused by a bacterium brought down vast numbers of horses employed by armies of both the Confederacy and the Union during the Civil War, and the spread of this disease continued long after the battles ended.

Texas Fever. Before and after the Civil War, Texas fever plagued the cattle world. Union forces' success in blocking trade and movement out of Southern markets served to build up vast communities of Texas fever-laden cattle, especially in lands west of the Mississippi River. When the war ended and cattle markets opened again, these animals brought the disease to markets back East and into the Midwest, to cattle with no immunity from the deadly microbe.

Equine Influenza. When Charles Cary was about ten years old, a particularly nasty strain of equine influenza paired with other, secondary infections to kill or severely weaken alarming numbers of horses in many communities, creating another public health disaster. One economic victim of this epizootic was the streetcar traffic of cities like New York and Chicago, which depended on horses to carry passengers at this time. L. A. Merillat and D. M. Campbell, in their 1935 work, *Veterinary Military History*, wrote of this problem: ". . . business dependent upon cartage was practically suspended where oxen could not be procured to make deliveries. No visitation of record equal in kind, scope, or virulence has ever occurred since in this country."[2]

Pleuropneumonia. Continued outbreaks of this disease in cattle caused heavy losses in many states after the Civil War, especially in Northern states and those east of the Mississippi River.

Hog cholera. This devastating malady also flared in increasing incidents, with annual dollar losses suffered by hog farmers in the multiple millions of dollars nationwide during the years following the Civil War.

Many of the diseases wrecking the food production and draft animal industries in nineteenth-century America also threatened the health, even the lives, of people. Rabies and glanders were well-known, deadly communicable diseases; and tuberculosis could be transmitted through meat or milk products to consumers, adding to the terrifying human mortality rate of tuberculosis (as discussed in Chapter 16). According to Iowa State University's Center for Food Security and Public Health, a division of its College of Veterinary Medicine, some species of the *Babesia* organism which brought about Texas fever in cattle can affect healthy people. Iowa State veterinarians contend, however, that cattle parasites seem to threaten only immunocompromised people, particularly those who have had their spleens removed.[3] Any transmission to people is extremely rare, but in the latter years of the nineteenth century, there was no clear understanding of whether tick fever was zoonotic, or communicable from animals to humans.

Mercifully, hog cholera—classical swine fever (CSF)—has presented no evidence to veterinary science in the past century that its virus can infect humans.[4] A different disease—swine influenza—may be transmitted from pigs to people, but such transmission has been rare.[5] There have been no reported clinical cases of people contracting equine influenza or canine influenza from normal exposure. There were some human volunteers who, when inoculated with an equine influenza virus, did become ill.[6] Of course, as readers in the twenty-first century would realize, a number of versions of avian flu have jumped from birds to people.

Medical experts—human and veterinary—in the days of Charles Allen Cary's youth simply lacked detailed knowledge of the nature and level of animal disease threats. These diseases ruined personal and regional economies and they killed animals. Some diseases killed people. Were other diseases lethal to humans? There were many more questions than answers in the late nineteenth century. Because of the spread and devastation caused by such varied, life- and economy-threatening afflictions, there never had been a time in America when more people were interested in getting a handle on these and other animal diseases.

There were some degreed veterinarians—Dr. Cary would later describe these as "graduate veterinarians"—in the country at this time, almost all of whom had earned their degrees in Europe. Veterinary schools had been granting degrees in places like Lyon (begun 1761), Turin (1769), Vienna (1777), London (1791), and many other overseas places for decades. The first veterinary training programs in the United States and Canada—privately opened and operated—began in Philadelphia in 1852, Boston in 1854, Ontario in 1862, New York in 1864, Chicago in 1865, and in Montreal in 1866. But these and many others, including McKillip in Chicago, would open and close.

By 1877, when Charles Allen Cary was sixteen, twenty-two colleges of the land-grant heritage had begun offering some level of veterinary science instruction. Somewhat conveniently for the Cary family, one such college was located in their state, a 114-mile train ride from Millersburg and presumably affordable for the family, or for young Cary himself, as he most likely worked and paid at least some of the bills.

Today, one can only speculate about Charles Allen Cary's reasons for setting out to become a veterinarian. The Cary family was long populated with people who worked hard and achieved significantly in various careers, many of them dictated by circumstances—farming, military, politics, etc. Charles Allen Cary, or anyone growing up in the

Midwest in the 1860s and 1870s, would have noticed that the livelihood of many people depended on animals in one way or another: cattle for meat and milk; hogs for lard and pork; sheep for mutton and
wool; chickens for meat and eggs; horses for transportation, either for
riding or for pulling a coach; oxen and mules for plowing or draying.
One can argue that, during the years of Cary's boyhood, animals'
importance for food and power was at its zenith. Diseases afflicting
food and draft animals threatened both income and the food supply of
those who counted on such animals for survival.

The opportunity to study animal health and veterinary science in
Iowa in the 1880s represented a means to several ends for Charles
Allen Cary. Such a path, he likely figured, would propel him toward
positions of leadership, authority, and respectable income, while providing the tools needed to solve problems affecting both people and
animals. Such a career would provide a level of mobility that an adven-
turous young man of this era of new transcontinental railroads and
transatlantic ships would have craved. Beyond these reasons, he obviously had a strong personal interest in working in animal health and,
as his career bore out, he was quite accomplished at it.

Cattle, sheep, and hogs were plentiful in Iowa during this era. Iowa, in
fact, was the nation's leader in hog production during Charles Cary's
teenage years.[7] During Dr. Cary's formative days on the family farm, he
undoubtedly heard about, and perhaps saw first-hand, the devastation
caused to the agricultural industry by the various diseases that killed animals, spread to and weakened others, and threatened humans. One
USDA report in 1875 estimated that farm losses nationwide due to animal diseases and deaths may have neared or surpassed one hundred million dollars per year. The need for trained veterinarians became increasingly clear to anyone impacted by such devastation.[8]

Exactly when Charles Allen Cary decided to become a veterinarian is
unknown, but his childhood coincided, in a sense, with the "childhood" of the profession of veterinary medicine in the United States. A
bright, inquisitive young man, Charles Cary possibly had awareness of
advancements in science taking place elsewhere in the world. As scientists like Robert Koch and Louis Pasteur made discoveries in far-away
places, and as the earliest crop of American veterinarians began to
make their mark, youngsters like Charles Cary gained inspiration for
pursuing scientific and medical discoveries. The following passage
from an 1889 USDA publication on hog cholera offers the flavor of a
spirit that may have spurred him and others on such a career path:

The suspicion entertained by those engaged in the study of diseases of man and the lower animals that infectious or communicable diseases are due to the living organisms of the lowest order, capable of rapid multiplication by the process of fission and spore-formation, has been transformed into conviction during the past ten years. A considerable number of the most common, most dreaded diseases have been proved to be caused by exceedingly minute, plant-like organisms known under the general name of bacteria. Among animals the micro-organisms causing anthrax, black quarter, tuberculosis, glanders, strangles, infectious pneumonia in horses and swine, and rouget in swine have been very thoroughly demonstrated. The opinion has been steadily gaining ground that in order to control infectious diseases we must learn their causes and the life history of the pathogenic bacterium found in each disease. These will suggest to us the measures that are most likely to prove successful in combating such maladies. Moreover, it is pretty well accepted today that the prevention of infectious diseases is the main thing to be arrived at in our studies, and that their treatment when they have once obtained a foothold is at best tentative and rarely successful. This is especially true of the lower animals. They are (in some diseases at least) always scattering the living virus and thereby endangering those still free from disease.[9]

While growing up on the family farm, perhaps young Cary learned of the reputations of some of the earliest legitimate veterinary practitioners, reputations made all the more obvious when contrasted with the more numerous "unqualified charlatans" referenced in this excerpt from a 1939 student publication at Iowa State University's College of Veterinary Medicine, reflecting on those dark days of previous generations:

Ninety-five per cent of the practitioners were unqualified, they were in the main charlatans, harpies, mountebanks, a preponderant group whose practices were unthinkably barbarious [sic] to say the least. Specialization was the rule; some were "horse doctors" and claimed no more than the name implies, some "cow leechers," who weren't so rash with their treatment; others like "Cowboy Charlie" traveled, giving free lectures to sell medicine; "horse dentists" were plentiful as were the "gelders." Surgery and therapeusis [sic] of even the qualified was at low ebb and asepsis was undreamed of. Anesthesia was in its experimental stage in human medicine, unknown in veterinary medicine.[10]

After attending what passed for local schools in or near Millersburg in the late 1860s and early to mid-1870s, Charles Allen Cary taught school locally for a time—possibly in the same school he had attended. He left the family farm probably in 1881 or 1882 for much larger Ames, 115 miles to the west in the center of the state, to pursue higher education at Iowa State Agricultural College. "Much larger" references Ames' population of between eleven hundred and twelve hundred citizens, about five or six times the size of Millersburg. Like Charles Cary's hometown, Ames in the 1880s was a relatively new settlement, having been established only in 1864, likely because of its location between Cedar Rapids and Council Bluff, towns connected by the first Transcontinental Railroad.

About the time Cary planned to enroll, Iowa State College offered a still-new four-year combined course in agriculture and veterinary science. Its entrance requirements were described in a book by one of its professors:

> Candidates for admission must be at least sixteen years of age. Before entering the classes they must pass an examination in reading, orthography, geography, grammar, and arithmetic. Candidates for graduation must be eighteen years of age or over; must have completed the entire course of study, and attained a standing of seventy-five per cent in all the studies pursued; and finally shall present an acceptable thesis upon some subject approved by the faculty. A graduation fee of five dollars will be required.[11]

Charles Stange—who would serve as dean of veterinary medicine at Iowa State from 1909 until 1936—noted in a history of the program that "the sophomore year was largely stock judging and the last year was devoted to veterinary science." He then quoted from the catalog of Charles Cary's time at Ames which provided additional details about the plan of study:

> The study and practice of Veterinary Science occupy 5 days a week during the senior year. Lectures are given on veterinary anatomy, physiology, *materia medica*, pathology, disease and treatment, surgery, sanitary science and practice.[12]

Charles Allen Cary earned his Bachelor of Science degree in 1885 and the Doctor of Veterinary Medicine (DVM) degree in 1887 when he was twenty-six. He completed his professional studies in a class of eleven. His DVM came only five years after Iowa State had begun granting the degree; before Dr. Cary's class was graduated, Iowa State had awarded only sixteen other DVM degrees.[13]

When Charles Cary arrived at Ames—or on the college campus just outside of town—to begin his studies in 1881 or 1882, he found a world vastly different from rural Millersburg: his fellow students numbered around three hundred—half again the population of his hometown—and most were young men, though a few women were enrolled. The campus was set on 120 acres, with an adjoining 860-acre farm. The central, stately Old Main building offered not only administrative office and classroom space, but lodging for many students. It's almost certain that Cary lived in Old Main during his time at Iowa State. Practically all out-of-town students—male and female—lived there.

The college featured relatively new physical and chemistry laboratory buildings, constructed about six years before his arrival for $16,000. There were telephones in various offices—the device had been invented only a decade earlier; a campus printing office; and an experimental kitchen, the first on a college campus in America and a facility in which domestic science majors honed their skills in making omelets, chicken pie, hot slaw, apple pie, soups, and fried oysters. Iowa State had a new creamery facility in its agricultural program, a sixteen-by-twenty-four structure wherein the milk from the college's fifty dairy cows would have been churned into butter, with student labor at the helm. Charles Cary would have taken plenty of turns at the butter churn. This facility produced all the milk and butter used on campus.

There was no charge for tuition, but if he was counted among the two hundred males living in student rooms in Old Main, Charles Allen Cary paid $2.50 per week for meals; $.40 per week toward steam heat and gas for the lamps; $.21 per week for incidentals; and $1-3 per week for his rent, though no explanation has been found that defines who paid $1 and who paid $3. Whether one had a roommate may have entered into the cost. The college asked $.50 per week for clothes washing and $5 per semester for a janitor's fee. Resident students supplied their own bedding. Undergraduate Cary would have roomed on the third or fourth floor of Old Main, as women students and their chaperone lived on the second floor. Early on, he probably lodged on the fourth floor, where most first-year men lived. As he progressed, he likely had a choice of a more studious environment on the third floor. The building's first floor was home to classrooms; the chapel; the

offices of the president and the treasurer; and the six-thousand-vol-
ume library, which was kept open between two and nine o'clock daily.
The fourth floor of Old Main also held the college's zoological and
geological museums, a feature that would recur years later when Professor Cary had a chance to construct such a facility at Auburn.

Iowa State students of the 1880s were required to attend daily
chapel service, and there was to be no card-playing, no use of tobacco,
and no drinking on campus. The college leadership would not put up
with "profane or obscene language," and by order of the Board of
Trustees, eternal and universal fuddy-duddies, "dancing on the college
grounds was prohibited." Students wishing to venture the mile-and-a-
half back into Ames were to register with the President's Office before-
hand and make sure any such travel would not interfere with their college exercises. Downtown, a theatre offered entertainment, and students could travel there either via stagecoach or a vehicle of some type
driven by "10-cent Billy," a local entrepreneur who charged a dime for
the round-trip, whether one was riding or sending a package.[14]

Studying was expected of all students in Old Main during the week
from seven to ten in the evening. A proctor made his or her—depending on the floor—inspection rounds at seven o'clock to ensure compliance. Weekend nights—Fridays, Saturdays, and Sundays—offered
more social time. The college sponsored four literary societies from
which students could choose. These societies met on Friday evenings.
As most students participated, Charles Allen Cary likely joined. One
student writing about the literary societies a few years later noted that
"orations . . . original essays, recitations, debates and music were given
by the individual members for the entertainment but mostly for the
edification of the other members." The writer suggested that, if the
society's business concluded with time available before "lights out,"
students would have launched a quick game to amuse and better
acquaint themselves, with "Pig in the Parlor" and "The Miller" the
usual favorites.[15] In addition to that "Pig in the Parlor" frivolity, baseball, football, croquet, and bicycle riding were popular among students; but time was limited for such extracurricular activities.

Young Cary's freshman undergraduate agriculture curriculum
included coursework lasting a couple of semesters in horticulture,
botany, practices in agriculture, vegetable anatomy and physiology,
physics-heat, English literature, advanced algebra, geometry, book-
keeping, rhetoric, German or Latin, drawing, composition, zoology,
and dairy. That agricultural practice course included a laboratory of

sorts: twelve hours of physical labor on campus that the faculty some-how connected to agriculture. To ensure students knew what they were getting themselves into, the college catalog prepared them with this friendly warning: "This institution can offer no inducements to the idler or self-indulgent."

Some of the required student labor undoubtedly was assigned on the campus farm, where the college herd included nineteen short-horns, seven Holsteins, a Jersey, forty-five high-grade cows, forty-five common cows, and a prized bull named Oneida Prince.

Charles Allen Cary and his fellow students pursuing the course in veterinary science spent untold numbers of hours in the company of Dr. Millikan Stalker (1841-1901), an Indiana native, former Tennessee school teacher, and 1873 Iowa State College agriculture graduate. While in school at Ames, he served as the first editor of the agriculture college's student newspaper. Remaining on campus after graduation to teach veterinary science, Dr. Stalker also served as secretary to the institution's Board of Trustees 1873-1876. Then, he left to further his credentials, enrolling in the veterinary science program at the first school in the country to offer such training: the New York College of Veterinary Surgery. He soon transferred, completing his studies at the Toronto Veterinary College in 1877 and earning something akin to a doctor of veterinary science degree. Returning to Iowa State, he began working as an instructor in agriculture and as superintendent of the college farm. He was promoted up the ranks in the veterinary program over the next couple of years, being named founding head of the program in 1879. The veterinary school actually considers its founding date as May 23, 1879, the day the Board of Trustees used the word "school" where previously they had used "department." Founding Dean Stalker wrote the first veterinary practice laws in Iowa and established the office of state veterinarian, which he held for the eleven years from 1884 to 1895.

Professor Stalker was described by L. A. Merillat and D. M. Campbell as "a one-man veterinary faculty,"[16] . . . "a man of engaging personality, a brilliant conversationalist, an exemplary citizen and the best public speaker on the college faculty."[17] The later veterinary dean, Dr. Stange, called Professor Stalker "a great lecturer. No one on the faculty of Iowa State College at that time had the ability to express himself in better and clearer English and could present his subject more effectively than Dr. Stalker. I never heard a man who was his equal as a conversationalist."[18] Dr. Stalker's anonymously written obituary described this life-long bachelor as having "a most charming personality . . . a master of good English and an entertainer and lecturer [of] high rank." In all these qualities, Dr. Stalker served as an early role model for the future Dean Cary, who carried these same traits.

One glimpse into the focus or direction of Professor Stalker's work with students such as Charles Allen Cary, and in his weighty writing style, may be found in a passage Dr. Stalker wrote in his first report as state veterinarian:

> The fact that the milk of tubercular cows is charged with the poison germs should cause it to be rejected in every instance as an article of food. As tuberculosis in man and in the bovine species is identical, the conclusion in inevitable consumption prevails to an alarming extent in this country and that this disease is frequently seen in cows that contribute to the milk and beef supply of our people renders the subject worthy of the most careful investigation by sanitarians.[19]

As Iowa State's veterinary school began and matured under Dr. Stalker over the three or four years before Charles Allen Cary arrived, veterinary work was accomplished in the former President's House, later called "South Hall," which had been built in 1868 and which burned down in 1912. This building became available in 1879 when College President Adonijah S. Welch—whose son, William, was in the 1883 graduating class in veterinary science—built a new home for himself and his family. In 1879 when veterinary science moved in, so did the college's program in botany. Veterinary students attended lectures and had laboratory work there, as remembered by College Physician Dr. David S. Fairchild:

> . . . in a small bedroom with one window which could be used as a laboratory (it was the best we could find). For larger classes we were permitted to use the front parlor when Professor Bessey did not need it for botany classes. We had three or four Beck student microscopes left over from Professor [C.E.] Bessey's laboratory, and a larger microscope, a Schrourer belonging to the writer, with 1/4 and 1/6 Hartnachs lenses. With this equipment and with specimens of tissues from the butcher shop, a few staining fluids and reagents, we were in position to study specimens of blood, connective tissue, muscle, etc.

To provide for the clinical and practical side of the veterinary work in the early days a barn located west of the Horticulture Department was renovated and called the Veterinary Hospital for the use of Professor Stalker. This was an exceedingly unpretentious building, only a barn at best, and a poor one at that, but here the first classes received their clinical training.[20]

The program's second home was called North Hall, occupied in 1881 by various agriculture programs, the veterinary folks, and the botanists. Dr. Cary would have attended lectures and laboratories in this facility both in his pre-vet and in his professional student terms.

Charles Allen Cary experienced both early settings in his Iowa State student days. When he completed his BS in agriculture in spring 1885 and prepared for formal studies in the still relatively new School of Veterinary Medicine, Cary and his fellow veterinary students surely were excited about the new Veterinary Hospital and Sanitary Building Iowa State was opening that year; though they may have paused at the $.60 fee each student was charged per semester to help toward the infirmary's operating costs. The hospital, measuring forty-five by fifty feet, cost $6,000 to construct and opened on June 1, 1885, at the beginning of Charles Cary's enrollment in the professional curriculum. This building replaced the smaller hospital space that had been made of the converted president's home, South Hall.

Dr. Fairchild wrote of the improved location and, in particular, of the daily grind:

The classrooms were in the Sanitary Building and occupied all the first floor. This building was erected at a cost of $4,000; the first floor veterinary, the second floor laboratory and hospital for sick students. The word hospital we were not permitted to use for fear it would convey the idea of an unhealthful location and endanger the future of the college. There was one lecture room, which would accommodate about 30 students, which was used by Professor Stalker for his lectures on physiology, histology, pathology and therapeutics, time so arranged as not to conflict. In physiology were the junior class in the general course, the textbook being Martin's "Human Body." Foster was used in advanced physiology. During the first four weeks of each year Dr. Fairchild gave lectures to the senior students in the general course on the anatomy and physiology of the brain, in the president's lecture room in the main building at 8:00 a.m.; a busy morning, four lectures in succession. Then came a general inspection every Monday and visits to sick students daily.[21]

Anticipating significant near-term growth in their veterinary school and in receipt of a request from new President Seaman A. Knapp—father of Bradford Knapp, who served as president of Alabama Polytechnic Institute during 1928-1932—Iowa State trustees in January 1884 had sent Professor Stalker to Boston to study plans for a veterinary hospital built in that city. By summer 1884, trustees approved $10,000 for a new veterinary facility, including both the hospital and Sanitary Building described above.[22]

The new hospital was a brick structure with 2,250 square feet over two floors. It offered "all the modern appliances for the treatment of diseased animals. The Sanitary Building houses offices and classrooms," promised the college catalog. Professor Stalker described the setting: "from a sanitary point of view this is one of the best, if not the best infirmary in the United States."[23] The hospital seemed a state-of-the-art palace to students in the late 1880s. It was lit by kerosene lamps, though Professor Stalker constantly lobbied higher-ups for those new-age electric lights that more upscale facilities were adding.

The new place represented a stark improvement to its predecessor, where in one large classroom sometimes as many as three veterinary science lectures occurred simultaneously. The new hospital also proved a good draw for the area's farms. By 1887, the team saw 250 patients, presumably half or more of those before Dr. Cary graduated that spring. One reality of this veterinary era, on which even the newest of facilities could not improve, was that animal carcasses were dissected only in the late fall and winter, during colder weather. Lower temperatures enabled preservation of the bodies. Costly embalming fluids were not available to the veterinary school while Charles Allen Cary trained.

Both of these facilities—the hospital and Sanitary Building—were used until 1926.[24] Clinical work still was conducted during Dr. Cary's time in school at the old hospital—the barn adjacent to North Hall—until the fire of 1912 made additional facilities necessary.[25]

In the national scheme of such programs, Iowa State had an early emphasis on veterinary medical training, with veterinary studies specified in the State of Iowa's 1858 legislative articles that established the institution. According to his early history of the program, Charles Stange wrote that Iowa State's program in veterinary studies was created as a response to a local agricultural and economic need: to assist those involved in the animal industry in their battles to control animal diseases. "Hog cholera was prevalent among swine herds, Texas fever

was not infrequent, and anthrax and glanders were commonly reported," Stange wrote.[26]

Iowa State graduated its first class of any kind in 1872, with students
enrolled in agriculture receiving a modest level of veterinary science
instruction. With its official beginning in 1879, Iowa State's School of
Veterinary Medicine became the first state-run veterinary college in
the United States. A number of privately run veterinary schools existed
throughout the country in those years, but as they all eventually
closed, Iowa State can be confirmed as the longest continuously operating American college of veterinary medicine, a designation in which
that institution deservedly takes great pride.

Iowa State's veterinary program required two years of study when
Charles Allen Cary enrolled, though the institution began a three-year
veterinary curriculum the year he graduated and added a fourth year
in 1903.

While Dr. Stalker tremendously influenced Dr. Cary's formal veterinary education, Cary had the added benefit of attending school—and
working side-by-side in the classroom, laboratory, slaughterhouse, and
on the college farm—with several outstanding veterinary students,
future stars of the profession. Four of those were named in Dr. Cary's
obituary, published in the *Journal of the AVMA* in spring 1935, as
being particularly accomplished and likely helpful and influential: Dr.
Sesco Stewart, Dr. M. H. Reynolds, Dr. George H. Glover, and Dr. W.
B. Niles.[27]

Canadian Dr. Sesco Stewart (1855-1918) moved to Iowa with his
family when he was seven, completed the Iowa State veterinary program in 1885, and after graduation took charge of the Bureau of Animal Industry's microscopic inspection of pork for trichina. He landed
in Kansas City in 1892 as a veterinarian and teacher at the Kansas City
Veterinary College. Dr. Stewart eventually was named dean of that college as well as secretary/treasurer of the college corporation. He was
considered "the pillar" of the KCVC. This college operated from 1891
to 1918, graduating nearly nineteen hundred veterinarians during
those twenty-seven years. Dr. Stewart was central to the organization
of both the Iowa and Missouri Valley Veterinary Medical Associations[28] and, on the national level, served as president of the American
Veterinary Medical Association in 1902-03 after having served as secretary of the AVMA for seven consecutive terms, from 1895 to 1902.[29]
Dr. Stange, in his history, described Dr. Stewart as "a big factor in the
development of the veterinary profession in the middle west."[30]

Also in Iowa State's class of 1885 was Dr. W. B. Niles, one of the early researchers whose work led to improvements in the effectiveness of hog cholera serum. Three years older than Dr. Cary and graduating two years ahead of him, Dr. Niles clearly made a sterling impression on Drs. Stalker and Fairchild. After graduation, Dr. Niles was invited to stay in Ames and work as a veterinary science "house surgeon" during 1886-87, Dr. Cary's senior year. Thus, Dr. Niles taught some of Dr. Cary's final-year rotations. The two men saw each other for the rest of their professional careers at AVMA meetings and perhaps other occasions. Dr. Niles left Ames in 1899 for a position in South Carolina with that state's Experiment Station, but returned to Iowa State in 1891 as a professor of veterinary science. He later affiliated with the Bureau of Animal Industry and became known for his research, particularly related to hog cholera. Iowa State's website notes that records are incomplete on the start date of veterinary research at the university, but that

> . . . probably the first work of a serious nature was taken up by Dr. W. B. Niles, when he became a member of the staff and devoted a part of his time to experiment station work. Dr. Niles, a very inquisitive scientist, was the first man west of Chicago to discover the *actinomyces* fungus in the tumors which it produces in cattle. This was in 1885, and Dr. Niles' graduation thesis was on the subject of *actinomycosis*. The first tuberculin to be used in the state of Iowa was injected by Dr. Niles in the McHenry herd at Denison, Iowa.[31]

Dr. George Henry Glover, who graduated the year after Dr. Cary, in Iowa State's Class of 1886, served as the first dean of Colorado State University's School of Veterinary Medicine when the program advanced from a department to school status in 1907. He would also serve as president of the American Veterinary Medical Association in 1910-11, a decade before Dr. Cary would hold the same high office.

Dr. M. H. Reynolds, Class of 1889, for years headed the University of Minnesota's veterinary science program and pioneered the development of veterinary policy regulations. Dr. S. B. Nelson, also in Iowa State's Class of 1889, established and served as the first dean of the College of Veterinary Medicine at Washington State University.[32]

College Physician Dr. David S. Fairchild was elected a professor in pathology, histology, therapeutics, and comparative anatomy in veterinary science in 1879. Years later, he reflected on both the primitive nature of the new veterinary program as well as its advancements, for which he attributed at least partial credit to the program's taking cues from long-established European programs:

> In those days we knew nothing about oil immersion lenses or substage attachments and our entire work in pathology, so far as the microscope was concerned, was pathological histology. As our work became generally known, several medical schools offered our students advanced standing in medical classes. Among them was Rush Medical College in Chicago. The relation of bacteriology to medicine was but little known. Pasteur was in the midst of his investigations and Lister was slowly bringing to the profession a knowledge of the relation of pathogenic bacteria to inflammation and their influence in wound healing.
>
> It is of interest to note that at about this same time the studies included in the course of some of the best European schools were physics, chemistry, zoology, botany, histology, physiology, anatomy, medicine, pharmacology, pathology, surgery, clinics, dietetics, obstetrics, veterinary police. These European schools in most cases were a century or more old when the Veterinary School was established at Iowa State College, yet its organizers and early teachers had the vision and, in spite of the advantages of age and prestige possessed by European schools and the greater development of the east (N.Y.), laid a sound foundation at a small college near a practically unknown village surrounded by the prairies of the middle west . . . all honor is due these pioneers.[33]

One of the many practices Dr. Stalker launched at Ames, which would be repeated in the Auburn of Dr. Cary's tenure, was the community clinic. At Iowa State, Dr. Stalker conducted a free clinic one afternoon each week, with each veterinary student required to participate. Area farmers were invited to bring their animals to the college farm for a diagnostic evaluation conducted by Dr. Stalker or one of the other faculty, with students observing or lending a hand. At Auburn later on, Dr. Cary would not charge the farmers for this service, and it seems certain that he patterned such generosity after Dr. Stalker, knowing students would benefit from every animal experience they had, and even a modest fee requirement might keep away a wonderful teaching case. Stange's book quoted Physician/Instructor Fairchild in a description of those clinics at Iowa State, which Auburn would mirror a few years later:

Free clinics are held one afternoon each week, where the students have an opportunity of seeing an extensive practice and acting as assistants in surgical operations. Animals taken into the hospital for treatment are placed under the care of some members of the class who treat them under the direction of the professor in charge. Students take this work in rotation, so that all become familiar with actual practice. The means of illustration in the classroom include skeletons, preparations of the various organs, plates, surgical instruments, collections of parasites and pathological specimens. Each student is required to dissect one subject.[34]

One other instructor at Iowa State Agricultural during Dr. Cary's college days merits mention: James Wilson (1835-1920) taught agriculture during Dr. Cary's time in Ames. Born in Scotland, Wilson served as US Secretary of Agriculture for sixteen years under Presidents William McKinley, Theodore Roosevelt, William Howard Taft, and Woodrow Wilson, though his tenure under Wilson lasted only a day-and-a-half. Along with US Circuit Court Judge John Bruce of Montgomery, James Wilson visited Auburn on December 1, 1897, speaking to cadets in Langdon Hall and having lunch with Dr. and Mrs. Cary in their new home on North Main Street. For the occasion, Dr. Cary invited several AAMC faculty members to the meal: Dr. P. H. Mell, Dr. A. F. McKissick, Professor F. S. Earle, Professor John F. Duggar, Dr. J. T. Anderson, and Professor B. B. Ross.[35]

Thirty years after Dr. Cary and his fellow students matriculated the veterinary program at Iowa State, another young man followed in their footsteps and earned the DVM in Ames. That graduate, Frederick D. Patterson (1901-1988), wrote in his memoirs, published posthumously in 1991, of his experiences in Ames, and while he came along a generation after Dr. Cary, Dr. Patterson's remembrances of his educational experiences shed more light on what the earlier students may have experienced:

. . . at Iowa State, particularly in the veterinary subjects, most classes consisted of lectures. There wasn't the abundance of textbooks that you find in colleges now. Instead, the professor told you what he thought you ought to know about his subject matter, and the student listened and took notes. Usually we were examined on what was said in the lectures; so I learned to listen very well and to take good notes.

In my freshman year, anatomy was the one course related to veterinary medicine. After gross anatomy of the whole body, we studied microscopic anatomy, examining each organ under the microscope to learn the structure of the organ in minute detail. We went next to physiology, the way in which the normal organ functions, and then moved on to pathology, what happens to organs when they are diseased. Another very important course was pharmacology, the study of drugs and doses, using *materia medica*, books on drugs. We had to master the administration of drugs in a syringe intravenously or subcutaneously, under the skin. Another part of our medical training involved learning how to restrain animals. Restraining a horse or a cow, for example, is quite an operation in itself. The animals had to be tied down and secured by the right method. If you didn't follow the right method, you got kicked!

We got to handle the dead animals in the first year. But the live animals we didn't practice on until Junior Clinics. Most of the surgery we did during our senior year.[36]

Dr. Patterson told of going to see an academic counselor on one occasion in his first or second year of veterinary school, and the counselor asked how he was getting along. "I seem to be doing all right," he told the official. "But I just don't have any time." The counselor responded with words that every veterinary student from Daniel E. Salmon to those currently enrolled on Auburn's Wire Road have come to realize: "You're not supposed to have any time. You're supposed to spend it all working on your subjects."

Frederick Douglass Patterson's memoir does not mention Dr. Cary or Alabama Polytechnic Institute, though he spent much of his career nearby. He earned not only his DVM but a master's degree at Iowa State, and later added a PhD from Cornell University. He joined the staff of Tuskegee Institute in 1928, heading its veterinary division. Eventually, he oversaw its entire agricultural program and still later, in 1935 at age thirty-three, he was named Tuskegee Institute's third president, serving in that role until 1953. He succeeded President Robert Moton, whose daughter, Catherine Elizabeth, he married. Dr. Patterson started a black Army Air Corps at Tuskegee, a group that evolved into the Tuskegee Airmen. Dr. Patterson established the School of Veterinary Medicine at Tuskegee in 1944, but perhaps he was best known for his founding role in launching the United Negro College Fund that same year. He received a Presidential Medal of Freedom Award from President Reagan in 1987, the year before he died. He is buried on the Tuskegee campus.[37]

CHAPTER FIVE

DR. CARY AND THE AVMA

Following his 1887 Iowa State graduation, Dr. Cary worked for about two years in the extreme southeast corner of Iowa in the state's southern-most town, Keokuk. He either joined an existing practice, or more likely launched a private, almost-exclusively large animal practice. One lure may have been Keokuk's medical college at that time. The College of Physicians and Surgeons began in La Port, Indiana, in 1846; moved to Madison, Wisconsin, the following year; then to Rock Island, Illinois, in 1848; and again to Davenport, Iowa, in 1849. The next move in 1850 was a bit more permanent, as Keokuk served as the school's home until 1908 when it was merged with Drake in Des Moines.[1] But any part this medical school had in Dr. Cary's decision to practice in Keokuk is unknown.

Keokuk's population of fourteen thousand when Dr. Cary arrived provided a new veterinarian plenty of work, especially when adding the surrounding farming communities. Keokuk sat along the Mississippi River, giving Dr. Cary an opportunity to take calls in Illinois as well, which would prove significant.

His stay in southeast Iowa was brief, though during this time Dr. Cary did manage to get himself appointed assistant state veterinarian. As his reputation grew, Dr. Cary was hired as a professor of veterinary science, with a key role in the Experiment Station, at South Dakota A&M, now South Dakota State University, from 1889 to 1892. Few records related to Dr. Cary's time in South Dakota survive. A tattered newspaper clipping from 1892 while he was in Germany reprints a letter he wrote as "veterinary editor of the *Dakota Farmer*," which references a regional agricultural magazine of the day. While at South Dakota A&M—in addition to teaching, research, and clinical duties—it appears he also was involved in outreach in the form of providing at least occasional copy to the *Dakota Farmer*.

At least once during his Brookings tenure, he apparently made the return trip to Iowa for professional purposes. The *American Veterinary Review*—forerunner of the *Journal of the AVMA*—reported in an 1889 issue that Dr. Cary, professor of veterinary sciences at South Dakota Agricultural College, was lined up to present a paper on "Bone Spavin" at the second annual meeting of the Iowa Veterinary Medical Association, held at the Savery House in Des Moines during September 3-4, 1889. If he made that trip—and Dr. Tait Butler's recap of the meeting does not specify whether Dr. Cary attended—he would have reunited with old pals Sesco Stewart and W. B. Niles, who were on the program as well. Not to mention, Iowa's State Fair was underway.

With experience in organized veterinary medicine on the state level in Iowa, Dr. Cary, the next year, in 1890, joined the national professional organization, the United States Veterinary Medical Association (USVMA), now known as the American Veterinary Medical Association (AVMA). Within this context, he was appointed resident secretary to the USVMA from South Dakota.

In 1891, surely inspired by time at his first USVMA convention in Chicago in September 1890, he contacted a number of South Dakota veterinarians and asked them to meet in Sioux Falls on September 24. Several responded, and they met in the parlor room of the Cataract Hotel and formed the South Dakota Veterinary Medical Association. Those gathered approved the organization's founding principles, authored by Dr. Cary:

> The objects of this Association are the mutual advancement of its members in veterinary science, the cultivation of fraternity, the elevation of the profession and the diffusion of the knowledge of veterinary medicine and surgery.

At that first gathering, "after an hour's time passed in hand-shaking and making acquaintance, order was called. The constitution and by-laws were read, adopted and signed by those present." Officers elected that day included President Cary, Vice President W. F. Keller of Sioux Falls, Secretary D. B. McCapes of Vermillion, and Treasurer E. K. Paine of Sioux Falls.[2]

Thanks to the Carys' daughter Alice maintaining a sense of her family's heritage and preserving many documents related to her parents, Dr. Cary's original membership certificate in the United States Veterinary Medical Association survives. Dated September 16, 1890, it is signed by then-USVMA President Charles B. Michener, Jr.; by the previous president of two years, Dr. Rush S. Huidekoper; by Dr. A. W. Clement, one of two vice presidents that year; and by Dr. William Horace Hoskins, the organization's secretary. September 16, 1890, marked the opening day of the USVMA's convention in Chicago. Dr. Cary was present, as he would be at most of these important national conventions during the next forty-five years.

Dr. Cary was particularly active and influential in the USVMA/ AVMA. His obituary in the *AVMA Journal* in 1935 detailed his heavy involvement from the time he joined the national association. "It is doubtful if any member of the Association held more offices or served on more important committees than Dr. Cary during his forty-five years of membership," the *Journal* tribute read, before providing the record of Dr. Cary's AVMA service. The breadth of his knowledge and the increasing respect he obviously gained among his fellow AVMA members shine through in that chronicle of service:

He first served as resident secretary of South Dakota (1891-92).

Upon his move to Alabama, he was appointed in 1893 resident secretary for that state, a position he held, with a few interruptions, until 1913.

His first committee appointment was to the Committee on Animal Food, 1892-93.

He was a member of the Committee on Intelligence and Education, 1893-94.

Four times he served on the Committee on Diseases between 1895 and 1904, and he chaired that committee in 1899-1900.

Six different AVMA presidents appointed him to the Committee on Resolutions during 1897-1928, and he chaired that committee during 1900-01 and 1917-18.

He was a member of the Committee on Publications during 1909-10.

He served on the Special Committee on Advertisements of Veterinary Remedies in 1912-13.

Dr. Cary chaired the Committee on the Reorganization of the Association during 1915-16.

He was a member of the Committee on Budget, 1919-20.

He served on the Special Committee on the Revision of the Constitution and By-laws during 1922-24.

Dr. Cary held membership on the Committee on International Veterinary Congress from 1928 through 1934.

He was a member of the Committee on Legislation for the five years between 1929 and 1934.

The Journal noted that Dr. Cary also served frequently on the Executive Committee: as a member during 1896-97; as chair during 1898-99; and as member again 1900-02 and 1914-15.

Dr. Cary also held office at the highest levels of the AVMA, accepting election as secretary of the national organization in 1898-99 and again during consecutive terms, 1913-14 and 1914-15; as one of five vice presidents during 1907-08; and as AVMA president during 1919-20.

Despite what must have been minimal institutional travel budgets, Dr. Cary attended the national conventions during almost all of his working years after 1890, a broad travel schedule not many in American society of those years could manage or afford. (It is certainly a possibility he paid his own way to some national or regional meetings, given the reality of state funding during his Auburn tenure.) Dr. Cary's *AVMA Journal* obituary noted his participation on the national stage and hinted at an excitable personality:

> A familiar figure at AVMA meetings, which he attended consistently for many years, Dr. Cary usually was a participant in every important debate. He was quite a forceful speaker, and there was never any doubt in the mind of any one as to where Dr. Cary stood on a question. Although it was his lot to be on the losing side, on more than one occasion, after an important issue had been debated, no one ever said that Dr. Cary was not a good loser.[3]

Convention dates and locations sometimes offered wonderful opportunities for learning and experiencing special events, even beyond the host cities' normal tourist and historic sites—especially for an educated and inquisitive man like Charles Allen Cary. Following are the dates and locations of USVMA/AVMA conventions during the Cary years, events of the time, and any details that have surfaced of Dr. Cary's involvement during those conventions:

1890 in Chicago. The meeting at which Dr. Cary received his membership certification was the twenty-seventh annual meeting of the national organization and was held at the new Auditorium Recital Hall during September 16-17. This gathering was billed by the USVMA as its "most important meeting . . . for many years" and by future president Dr. W. L. Williams as "the birthday of the true National Association of the United States."[4] These comments were based on the 1890 convention's more central location in Chicago rather than one of the eastern cities. In fact, from the USVMA's inaugural meeting in New York City in 1863 until the group met in Chicago, the conventions were held in New York City twenty-two times, in Boston twice, and in Philadelphia, Cincinnati, and Brooklyn once each. The organization put more emphasis on attendance at this meeting, chiefly in the form of a lengthy convention preview published in its magazine. The plea for participation paid off as eighty new members joined.

Dr. Cary would have appreciated these mid-September days in Chicago, seeing his old Iowa State comrade Sesco Stewart and meeting several of the day's heavy hitters, including USVMA President W. L. Williams and several former and future presidents: Charles Michener, L. A. Merillat, R. S. Huidekoper, Alexandre Liautard, Daniel Salmon (first American to earn the DVM), and other notables. He heard in the various sessions the latest thoughts on veterinary school education, specifically the national problem of inadequately prepared pre-vet students and the outdatedness of that era's textbooks; papers on Theobald Smith's work on the parasite causing Texas fever; on tuberculosis; on the work of the Bureau of Animal Industry; on jurisprudence; on treating horse hoof problems; and on meat inspection, among many other important topics.

Dr. Cary surely was hooked before the first scientific speaker took the stage. President Williams, in his welcoming address, threw down a gauntlet of sorts that a young veterinarian with a world of ambition would take to heart. Whether Dr. Williams' words made an impact on the other few hundred in attendance, one private in this army clearly heard and took as marching orders the astounding words of the organization's top man:

> Above and beyond all other reasons we welcome you here in the hope that your presence among us and our amalgamation with you will inspire the mass of this young and rapidly growing part of our profession to higher thought, to deeper study, to rapid, firm, enduring progress.

The outlook here for earnest, competent veterinarians, grows brighter and brighter every day. The general public is rapidly realizing his worth from an economic and humanitarian standpoint in the management of ordinary everyday accidents and ailments, and the State and nation are rapidly discovering the value and need of our profession from a national economic and sanitary view in controlling and eradicating those contagious diseases of animals which so often ruin the owner and cripple the finances of the community, or through other diseases, which in addition render the flesh of affected animals unfit for or dangerous as human food, or in that long list of diseases which are transmissible through the flesh or through contact from animal to man, usually of a very serious and deadly character.

The social standing, the emoluments, the honors to the competent veterinarian, must advance higher and higher at a rapid pace, while the incompetent, listless practitioner must find his room becoming more and more pinched and unsatisfactory.

We have at present in America but few prominent veterinarians who are really accomplishing something to elevate our profession, so few that they can be counted almost in a moment. Let them work as hard as they may, they can accomplish little towards placing our profession on a level with other learned professions in this country, or with the veterinary profession in many other lands.

We hopefully look to your society as the vital force, and to this day as the birthday, which shall place a whole army of earnest veterinarians in this wide field for observation, research, and thought, who, pressing forward harmoniously as one man, may yet during the lives of most of us place our profession on an equality with the veterinary or other scientific profession in any land.[5]

In the auditorium on the meeting's first day, Dr. Cary sat among the non-members. He signed on and likely paid his first year's dues that same day, and when the roll was called on day two, Dr. Cary answered as a member of the USVMA. His friend from the University of Missouri, Dr. Paul Paquin (see Chapter 6), attended, offering the motion to accept as members in the USVMA the graduates of Iowa Agricultural. This action confirmed the USVMA's recognition "of the Veterinary Department of the Iowa Agricultural College as a regularly organized and recognized Veterinary School."[6]

The meeting in the Midwest helped to shape Dr. Cary's career agenda. He heard talks on pertinent matters. He met some of the most prominent names in veterinary medicine of the day. After he had checked in as a member for the first time, he heard a lengthy and fascinating discussion among Dr. Paquin, Dr. A. W. Clement, Dr. Daniel E. Salmon, and Dr. Alexandre Liautard as they questioned-and-answered each other as to possible causes of Texas fever. This experience, given the heady standing of its participants, undoubtedly never left Dr. Cary's memory. Historian Dr. J. F. Smithcors linked the success of the 1890 Chicago meeting to "the change in the fortunes of the Association augured by the addition of new blood."[7] The USVMA decided to meet in Chicago again in 1893.

Even without the star-studded lineup of speakers, Dr. Cary would have appreciated the opportunity to attend the 1890 USVMA Chicago meeting. The Auditorium Recital Hall had opened the previous year, part of the rebuilding of downtown Chicago after Mrs. O'Leary's cow started the fire of 1871. A design of the famous architects Louis Sullivan and Dankmar Adler and situated at the corner of Michigan Avenue and Congress Street, the convention building was the largest in the country, and one of the most glorious and stately buildings from an architectural standpoint a young man from Millersburg, Iowa, could have imagined.

1891 in Washington, D.C. The move back east had an expected result: only five "western" veterinarians attended. The attendance of Dr. Cary—working in South Dakota at this time—is not recorded.

1892 in Boston. The convention was held during September 20-22, while Dr. Cary was in Germany, but his reputation already was beginning to grow in the members' minds. He was appointed this year to his first national job, a spot on the Committee on Animal Food.

1893 in Chicago. This convention, held October 17-20, was Dr. Cary's first USVMA meeting as a faculty member from the Agricultural and Mechanical College of Alabama. One hopes President Broun found funds to send his young veterinary scientist, who had been on campus about ten months at the time. One may assume he was there: Dr. Cary was appointed at this meeting to membership on the USVMA's Committee on Intelligence and Education for 1893-94.

A visit to Chicago for this convention tempted attendees to extend their stay as the World's Columbian Exposition, also known as the Chicago World's Fair, was in its final few weeks. At this fair, engineer George Ferris debuted his original 264-foot-high, thirty-six-car Ferris wheel. Also present were three full-size replicas of Christopher Columbus' ships—the Nina, Pinta, and Santa Maria—constructed in

Spain and sailed to America to mark the 400th anniversary of Columbus' trip to the new world.

The fair's fifteen hundred buildings included a twenty-acre "Palace of Agriculture," wherein were displayed some veterinary exhibits. President W. L. Williams acknowledged that "it is difficult for some industries or professions to exhibit their triumphs to a body of mixed visitors in such a manner as to interest and instruct a reasonable number of the passing throng . . . ." But J. F. Smithcors described the Bureau of Animal Industry's exhibits related to its work in eradicating animal diseases as "extensive and splendid." No American veterinary schools were represented among the exhibits, but the schools in France "had large exhibits," and American agricultural colleges "had a large and unified presentation consisting of models, skeletons, pathological specimens, and instruments used in teaching and practice."[8]

1894 in Philadelphia. A photograph taken during this meeting was reprinted in a 1927 edition of the *JAVMA* to promote the AVMA convention scheduled in Philadelphia later that year. Dr. Cary is pictured in the group standing outdoors at the University of Pennsylvania's School of Veterinary Medicine complex, at the corner of Pine and Thirty-sixth Streets in West Philly (now Hamilton Walk, in the heart of Penn's School of Medicine). The meeting itself was held at the Academy of Natural Sciences, at the intersection of Nineteenth and Race Streets. Dr. Cary in 1894 chaired the Education Committee, which provided his first opportunity to address his national colleagues at this meeting. In that speech, he

> recommended that each veterinary college have a full professor for each of eleven departments (including Physics and Latin). Too many teachers, he felt, were "practical M.D.s and theoretical veterinarians . . . not qualified to become expert professors in Veterinary Medical Colleges."[9]

1895 in Des Moines. Only twenty-five members were present as the USVMA convention began its three-day meeting on September 12, but Dr. Cary enjoyed a return to his home state. He again had the chance to speak as chair of the Committee on Education, suggesting that graduates of agricultural colleges with veterinary instruction be allowed a year's credit in recognized three-year veterinary colleges. The major issues of the gathering, however, were tuberculosis and some of the common diseases and injuries of farm animals the majority of that era's practitioners would have seen in a typical week. In Des Moines,

Dr. Cary had a chance to interact with national-caliber veterinarians such as James Law, Tait Butler, former USVMA President James L. Robertson, and M. H. McKillip. At this meeting, Dr. Cary was appointed to the first of his four terms on the Committee on Diseases, a committee he would chair in 1899-1900.

1896 in Buffalo. The record does not reflect whether he was present, but Dr. Cary would have taken some satisfaction in remarks made by Dr. William H. Dalrymple, a Scot who arrived to teach veterinary science at Louisiana State University at about the time Dr. Cary arrived in Auburn. Dr. Dalrymple "through his work and writings . . . became known as the 'father of veterinary medicine in the South,'" according to Smithcors, though many used that same commendation for Dr. Cary.[10] Dr. Dalrymple, who served five terms as a vice president of the AVMA before being elected its president for 1907-08, told the gathering in Buffalo that

> Veterinary medicine and surgery, in the more Southern States, are still in their infancy; but through the influence exerted by the reputable graduate the people are beginning to realize the value of intelligent aid in the care and treatment of their animals, in contradistinction to the illiteracy and superstition of the empiric, who is usually in the habit of compounding his mysterious nostrums at certain phases of the moon and performing his so-called operations under similar lunar conditions.[11]

1897 in Nashville. Tennessee celebrated its centennial for six months this year, including during the USVMA convention. Those attending could enjoy activities within an array of almost one hundred buildings designed in classical style. The only remaining edifice of the event is the re-created Parthenon of Athens, a tribute to Nashville's styling itself as the "Athens of the South."

The USVMA met during September 5-7 at the Tulane Hotel, where rooms were $1 per day and meals were $.50. The local committee for arrangements was composed of Dr. W. C. Rayben of Nashville, Dr. J. W. Scheibler of Memphis, Dr. Cary of Auburn, and Dr. W. H. Dalrymple of Baton Rouge. "Those in attendance complained about the food and the accommodations, but found local hospitality and the meeting a success."

At this meeting, Dr. Cary was appointed to the Committee on Resolutions, the first of six occasions AVMA presidents would enlist his help on this committee. Smithcors, in his recap of the meeting, said tuberculosis was "the major topic for discussion" and that a particular back-and-forth "between Drs. Salmon, Pearson, Law, Cary and Lowe— all future presidents of the Association—would be of interest today to anyone engaged in tuberculosis eradication."[12]

1898 in Omaha. The Trans-Mississippi Exposition—considered a World's Fair—took place in north Omaha from June 1 to October 31. The event's ornate grounds highlighted the economic, cultural, and artistic achievements of Midwesterners, a focus that should have captured the attention of an Iowan. An array of temporary buildings housed more than five thousand exhibits. The USVMA convened September 6-8, in the middle of the Expo. One major change took place at this meeting: the organization changed its name to the American Veterinary Medical Association—the AVMA.

President Daniel Salmon used his president's address to encourage furthering education among AVMA members, educating the public, and paying "more attention to meat and milk inspection, and the eradication or control of hog cholera, tuberculosis, Texas fever, glanders, sheep scab and rabies."[13] This meeting marked the first time an AVMA convention held a clinical examination program, which took place at a barn on Omaha's Capital Avenue. Surgeons in action during that clinical exhibition included Dr. George A. Scott of Independence, Iowa; Dr. L. A. Merillat of the McKillip College in Chicago; and Dr. W. L. Williams, the former AVMA president, of New York.

This meeting marked Dr. Cary's first substantial action with his national organization as he had opportunity to take part in a number of discussions. Dr. Smithcors noted that "the subject of meat inspection occupied a large part of the program" in Omaha, the highlight being presentations by a panel consisting of Drs. W. H. Hoskins, D. E. Salmon, Leonard Pearson, C. A. Cary, James Law and Sisco Stewart, "the president, a past-president and four future presidents of the Association."[14] The *American Veterinary Review's* recap of the meeting noted that Dr. Cary went "into the subject very thoroughly. He maintained that the butchers should pay the cost of inspection, and that under centralized system this could be done without perceptible cost to the consumer."[15]

After a discussion on the prevalence of osteoporosis in Tennessee, Dr. Cary suggested a method of treatment that had given him some good results—the injection of one-eighth of an ounce of barium chlorite intravenously once a week. During another discussion, he shared findings from necropsy exams he had performed on dogs that carried rabies. He was listed, too, as joining in the discussion following presentations by Dr. Roscoe Bell ("acute indigestion of the horse") and L. A. Merillat ("arytenoidopexy").

All of that input surely led to Dr. Cary's being one of the eight AVMA banquet attendees called on for extemporaneous, "felicitous speeches" to the dinner crowd. Unfortunately, no record was kept on what he shared on that occasion.

As he contributed solid ideas on a variety of subjects in the various sessions, Dr. Cary's star at AVMA began to rise. He served during 1897-98 as a member of AVMA's Committee on Resolutions, and during this Omaha convention was appointed to chair the Executive Committee for the following year. Other members were established fixtures of the profession—W. H. Hoskins, Daniel Salmon, and Sesco Stewart.

While at the 1898 meeting, Dr. Cary and others had opportunity to visit Omaha's Cudahy Packing Company to inspect an exhibit on pathological specimens collected by local inspectors of the Bureau of Animal Industry. One may assume the tourists spent the better part of a day at Cudahy HQ. Smithcors described that experience as "the most complete and extensive exhibit probably ever held in the world," though it's unsure exactly why he described it in such hyperbolic terms.[16]

1899 in New York City. AVMA met during September 5-7 at the Convention Hall on West Forty-third Street, and Dr. Cary most certainly attended—he chaired the Committee on Diseases this year and was listed for the first time as chair of the organization's Executive Committee. In New York, he heard a variety of subjects discussed by some of the nation's veterinary leaders. Of twenty-three papers presented, ten were by either past or future presidents or secretaries of the Association. In New York, AVMA used a local surgical clinic at the American Horse Exchange, at Fiftieth Street and Broadway, for its clinical sessions. A pathological exhibition was held at Eastman's Abattoir at Fifty-ninth Street and Eleventh Avenue. "All agreed it was a stupendous illustration of diseased tissues as found in the great slaughterbeds of the country . . . an object lesson in the immense domain of sanitary medicine," wrote the *American Veterinary Review*, before listing the eighty-six exhibited items (i.e., tuberculosis in lungs, ringworms, Texas fever, etc.)[17]

Dr. Cary, at this meeting, presented a paper on "Ulceration of the Stomach in Equines," and the *AVR* complimented him on "a manner that riveted general attention."[18] After his year of chairing the Executive Committee, Dr. Cary was asked to chair the AVMA Diseases Committee for 1900.

1900 in Detroit. Dr. Cary attended AVMA during September 4-6, with sessions at the Russell House—built in 1836 as the National Hotel—at the corner of Woodward Avenue and Cadillac Square. The Russell House was Detroit's leading hotel for half a century and the center of the community's social scene. In its heyday the gathering spot for those wanting the latest in Civil War battle news, it closed five years after hosting AVMA. Dr. Cary presented a paper on "Difficulties in the way of Municipal Meat Inspection in the South," and he heard a presentation by Dr. Cooper Curtice of Raleigh, North Carolina, on "Control of Cattle Ticks." Dr. Cary was re-appointed to the Executive Committee for 1900-01 and as chair of the Resolutions Committee.

1901 in Atlantic City. AVMA met during September 3-5 for its thirty-eighth convention. The setting was the Hotel Rudolf, described in a contemporary publication as "one of the palatial hotels of Atlantic City, which is known throughout the country." The Rudolf was then a six-year-old, five-story hotel on the Boardwalk, with Atlantic Ocean views. Dr. Cary updated his previous year's paper and spoke on "Some Obstructions in the Way of Efficient Meat and Milk Inspection." He likely had much to discuss with thirty-eight-year-old AVMA President Tait Butler, a year younger than Dr. Cary, whose 1891 letter to Alabama A&M College President Broun began the process which brought Dr. Cary to Auburn in the first place. When Dr. Cary was beginning his practice in Keokuk after graduating in 1887, Dr. Butler was practicing in Davenport, Iowa. In 1888, Dr. Butler spearheaded organization of the Iowa VMA and served as its president in 1889-90. Dr. Butler would hold faculty positions in Mississippi—he was Mississippi State University's first professor of zoology and veterinary science—Kansas, and North Carolina during 1891-1909. He was state veterinarian of both Kansas and North Carolina, and he worked during 1899 with the Bureau of Animal Industry. He served as editor and publisher of *Progressive Farmer* magazine for several years until his death in 1939. Dr. Cary was in good company in Atlantic City with the other speakers as well, sharing the speaker's stand during the three days with Drs. G. R. White, L. A. Merillat, Veranus A. Moore, and W. H. Dalrymple, among others.[19]

Dr. Cary was a member of the Resolutions Committee this year; when that committee's report was given, according to the *American Veterinary Review*, there followed "a very animated and prolonged discussion." The question-and-answer session on the committee's tuberculosis resolution alone "occupied several hours."[20] He was appointed again to the Executive Committee for 1901-02.

1902 in Minneapolis and *1903 in Ottowa.* Dr. Cary's presence unconfirmed.

1904 in St. Louis. A trip to the forty-first AVMA convention, held August 16-19, would have given Dr. Cary opportunity to attend the Louisiana Purchase Exposition, also known as the St. Louis World's Fair, held from April 30 to December 1, 1904. At the same time, a global athletics competition was staged in the area, and those events were later declared to represent the 1904 Summer Olympics, despite world politics making travel to the US difficult. Only about 10 percent of the six hundred and fifty-odd athletes competing in St. Louis that summer were from outside the States.

Forest Park, a 1,371-acre public park where the Louisiana Purchase Exhibition took place, hosted the diving, swimming, and water polo events on its man-made, two-acre Life Saving Exhibition Lake. In one of the great ironies in veterinary medical history, during the water polo matches, a number of cattle held near the lake for purposes related to the agricultural exhibition reportedly made their way into the lake not far from where the athletic competitions were taking place. The animals apparently stayed in there a while—it was August in St. Louis, after all—and did what cattle naturally do in pastures and ponds. Within a year, four water polo participants from the 1904 Games—all Americans—died of typhoid fever, their deaths linked to the cattle fouling the lake. Matters were not helped by the drain from the adjacent athletic housing emptying into the lake, pet dogs exercising and bathing in the same water, and exhibition-related bears also spending time in the lake.[21]

The veterinary meeting was conducted at the Monticello Hotel at Pine Boulevard and Kingshighway at the northeast corner of Forest Park, enabling attendees to slip over to the World's Fair or to some of the athletic competitions. Perhaps attending the national gathering for the first time in three years, Dr. Cary joined his compatriots of the Committee on Diseases to present what the *American Veterinary Review* called "a splendid report," chiefly because this committee with a different membership had failed to provide a report at recent AVMA meetings. The *AVR* report noted this committee had been stacked with animal health heavyweights who represented a diverse geography: Chairman Charles Higgins of Ottowa's Experimental Farm in Canada, and members A. S. Wheeler of North Carolina, Dr. Cary of Alabama Polytechnic, V. A. Moore of Cornell, N. S. Mayo of Kansas City, and A. R. Ward of California. Each provided a paper on a pertinent disease to be read and discussed at the meeting, and the result, according to the journal, was that "more work was accomplished at the St. Louis meeting than at any of its predecessors."[22]

1905 in Cleveland and *1906 in New Haven, CT.* No record of Dr. Cary's attendance.

1907 in Kansas City. This national convention was the largest to date, with 634 members and guests, at least double the number of any previous meeting. The KC convention was held during September 10-13, and attendees heard a who's who of speakers: James Law, W. L. Williams, J. R. Mohler, W. H. Dalrymple, and G. R. White.[23] Dr. Cary and Auburn colleague Dr. Ward Giltner jointly gave their latest paper on "Municipal Milk Inspection in the South," followed immediately by a paper by Dr. M. H. Reynolds of Minnesota on "Milk as Affected by Stable Practices and Subsequent Exposures." When discussion of these papers followed, the *AVR* reported, Dr. E. L. Quitman "then put a couple of knotty questions to Drs. Reynolds and Cary." Both speakers responded to Dr. Quitman, the *AVR* reported, "prompting considerable interest in the discussion."[24]

At this meeting in Kansas City, Dr. Cary was nominated for one of the AVMA's vice president positions; he was one of five elected to that level of office for 1907-08.

1908 in Philadelphia. The forty-fifth AVMA convention September 8-11 took place at the Hotel Walton at Broad and Locust Streets, about a quarter-mile west of Independence Hall. Dr. Cary was listed once again as a vice president of AVMA this year, and he must have been pleased at the selection of his Southern comrade Dr. W. H. Dalrymple of Louisiana State University as president.[25] This meeting was followed by two important meetings in Washington, DC: first, the meeting of the Association of Live Stock Sanitary Boards, followed by the International Congress on Tuberculosis, held from September 28 to October 12. Dr. Cary was so involved in Live Stock Sanitary Board work that he was almost certainly at that meeting. Adding to the likelihood of his attendance: the record reflects that Mrs. Cary attended AVMA with him in Philadelphia and that Dr. Cary attended and presented a paper at the International Congress on Tuberculosis. The globally famous Dr. Robert Koch attended this congress and presented to an overflowing crowd his paper on "The Relation of Bovine and

Human Tuberculosis." *AVR* reported that "practically every civilized nation was represented at this congress."[26] Dr. Koch died about eighteen months later.

1909 in Chicago. Dr. Cary, appointed to the AVMA Committee on Publications for this year, would have taken particular interest in one of the evening sessions during the September 7-10 meeting: a joint session with the Chicago Medical Society focused on milk and milk hygiene.[27]

1910 in San Francisco. Dr. Cary may not have attended because of the school's budget and the distance from Auburn. Likewise for *1911 in Toronto.* There is no record of Dr. Cary attending.

1912 in Indianapolis. At the forty-ninth annual AVMA convention held during August 27-30, Dr. Cary presented a paper on "Standard, Pure and Potent Biological Products." His chief point was recounted by Dr. Smithcors in his 1963 history:

> Speaking on the need for standardization of biological products, C.A. Cary charges in 1912: "The multiplicity of biological products that may be found on the market causes the public to open its mouth, buy, devour, suffer, get relief, or get no action, paying the price regardless of results. ... All that is required is a little pressure of the hypodermic syringe, and the mysterious biological product will do the rest." Lack of standardization, he emphasizes, has been the cause of tuberculin's having for some twenty years a "variable and checkered" history. The alternatives suggested by Dr. Cary are government manufacture and distribution, or government supervision of commercial production.[28]

In a seemingly related move, he also was appointed this year to a seat on the Special Committee on Advertisements of Veterinary Remedies, to "assist the editors of farm journals to purge their advertising columns of fake and misleading advertisements concerning proprietary preparations put out for the use of veterinarians and the public." The committee was chaired by Dr. N. S. Mayo, and its work led to, among other results, the London (Ontario) Veterinary Correspondence School being omitted from all periodicals, and many other questionable advertisers being turned down when they attempted to advertise in *Progressive Farmer* and other journals.[29]

1913 in New York City. This year marked the AVMA's fiftieth anniversary meeting. There was no mention of Dr. Cary in Dr. Smithcors' recap of the meeting, but Dr. Cary most likely attended. AVMA that year featured the most star-spangled lineup of speakers in its meetings to that time. Dr. Cary is listed as AVMA secretary for the next two years, suggesting he was present in New York to be elected to this post.

1914 scheduled for New Orleans. This year's convention was cancelled due to an outbreak of foot-and-mouth disease that ended up affecting roughly half of the country. As AVMA secretary, Dr. Cary was involved in planning this meeting, particularly as it was to take place in his region of the country. In that role, he likely was involved in whatever process was used to notify the membership of the meeting's cancellation.

1915 in Oakland. Dr. Cary continued his role as AVMA secretary at this meeting. He was listed in the *AVMA Journal* as one of forty-five Honor Roll members in conjunction with the Oakland convention, one of only four Southerners to gain this distinction. He also was selected this year to chair the Committee on the Reorganization of the Association, a committee that had first been appointed two years earlier with Dr. Daniel Salmon chairing and members including James Law and D. M. Campbell. The Oakland meeting took place between August 30 and September 2.

1916 in Detroit. Dr. Cary attended this convention, held during August 21-23, along with fellow Auburnites E. D. King, Jr., and W. W. Webb. The *AVMA Journal* listed Dr. Cary among the organization's Fellows.

1917 in Kansas City. At the fifty-fourth annual AVMA convention, during the second day's business meeting, the group elected Dr. Fred Torrance of Winnipeg, Manitoba, Canada, as its next president. Two other veterinarians were nominated for the top office and finished as runners-up: Dr. R. C. Moore of Missouri and Dr. Cary of Auburn.

1918 in Philadelphia. Dr. Cary was listed in the *Journal of the AVMA* coverage of this convention as chairing the Committee on Resolutions. He also contributed $25 at this time to the Liautard-American Veterinary Relief Fund. This fund honored the memory of Alexandre Francois Liautard, MD, VM, graduate of the veterinary school in Alfort, France, organizer of the New York College of Veterinary Surgeons, and one of the organizers of the United States Veterinary Medical Association. He was considered the father of veterinary medicine in America.

At this convention's second-day business meeting, Dr. Cary was nominated for presidency of the AVMA by Dr. Veranus A. Moore of the New York State College of Veterinary Medicine (Cornell). The subsequent edition of the *AVMA Journal* recapped the floor remarks as this business was conducted, and that coverage paints an interesting picture of the proceedings and Dr. Cary's stellar reputation. Dr. Moore commented from the floor as he nominated Dr. Cary:

> I have in mind a gentleman who has been a faithful member of this association for many years, a man who has seldom been absent from the meetings, who is from a section of this country that has been rather overlooked for a number of years: Dr. C.A. Cary of Alabama.

Dr. William H. Hoskins seconded Dr. Moore's nomination with further laudatory comments:

> I would like to second the nomination of Dr. Cary for the office of President. I recall that in 1890 this Association for the first time in its history held a meeting west of the Allegheny Mountains, and held it in the city of Chicago; and one of the three men who met us there at that time, and we went from the east in a goodly number, in proportion to our membership, was Dr. C.A. Cary. He has continued his membership from that day until this, and his membership now reaches over about thirty years. I can recall no meetings during that period of time at which Dr. Cary was not present. He has been a very active worker in the Association. We have never assigned to him a duty of any kind, no matter how slight it seemed, that he did not make an effort to perform it better than his predecessor. The annals and records of this Association will show many contributions of great value to this Association and of great value to the profession. He was for a long time a practitioner of veterinary medicine, and for many years a member of the teaching staff in several places throughout our country—at present at one of our schools in the South. There he is doing a vast work in connection with that school; and from what we have heard of the vast possibilities in the South in opening up a field to relieve the animal shortage, he has a great opportunity before him; and I hope he will receive this honor, of being elected President, especially as we may go to the South [for the AVMA convention] in 1919, and aid our brethren in the South in helping to open up that part of our territory. (Applause)

Two subsequent speakers nominated V. A. Moore for the presidency, and after a vote was taken, Moore had 184 votes to Cary's one hundred. When results were announced, a gracious Dr. Cary immediately asked for the floor:

> I want to move that this election be made unanimous, and I want to say this: that if a Northern man must be president at New Orleans next year there is no man I would rather have in the Chair than Dr. Moore (Applause), and when you get there, we will give you a gin fizz (Applause), the only one made on the New Orleans plan (Laughter).

At this Philadelphia meeting, Dr. Hoskins spoke on "The Trend of Veterinary Education" at one of the sessions, calling for standards in licensing exams, for cooperation and collegiality between state schools and private schools of veterinary medicine, for getting politics out of the state boards overseeing veterinary medicine, and for increased educational levels for high school students wishing to pursue veterinary medical studies. Dr. Hoskins' speech led to a spirited discussion—with a fair amount of disagreement. One would make a point, the next would accuse the previous speaker of missing the point or making a mistake in his thinking, the next would correct the previous view, etc. The discussion was headed toward launching a feud between rural schools and those located in metropolitan areas, with competing views on the merits of each. Dr. Cary is shown in the transcript as having the last word, and his comments from the floor offered insight into his character, his perspective, and his practical orientation:

> I want to say a word—let's get down to this thing. We are not going to settle the problem of education in five minutes and we are not going to change the facts. I have some idea of the conditions in New York and the South, and in Europe as well. I want to say that I have visited most of the prominent schools of this country and Europe and I have attended the clinics. I have never been in any one that has had all the things I thought it ought to have, or that they had a corner on this whole thing, or, in other words, have written up a monograph. There are some things in the country we never have in the city, and vice versa, and, no matter how much they argue, it is a fact. We have a condition in the South which you have not much of in the North. They told me when I started in our small town of 2,000 inhabitants we would not have any students. I have had all the clinical work we could use, just as much variation as any schools I have seen with this one exception—we do not have a great number of clinics. If I went to see Dr. Hoskins, to New York, I would not see many

things I see in my school. That is not a fault, not a fault of his school; it is a fact, nevertheless, and one we might get around—we find certain localities have their peculiarities in their surroundings and in their animal husbandry life. Just one thing I might mention. In Alabama, three years ago, there was not a carload of hogs shipped out. Last year, in the peanut region we shipped 2,300 carloads, an increase in production last year of fifty percent. These are facts from records made on these shipments. A good many of our men are doing more hog practice than anything else. Three years ago they could not have made a living in that neighborhood in that way. Yes, we want to get over this serious question and get together and do something and push things along. We are getting up into scientific areas, we want to get out and find these things, and so we are going to do something and not knock each other whether we have private schools or state schools. Some one says we are not getting what we ought to get. I believe you are getting all that is coming to you. Let us look the question squarely in the face and get to work.[30]

1919 in New Orleans. The group met November 17-21—the week before Dr. Cary's fifty-eighth birthday—at the sumptuous Grunewald Hotel, which forty-five years later would be the inspiration for Arthur Hailey's best-selling novel, *Hotel.* Dr. Cary served at this time on the Budget Committee. As the second afternoon's business meeting opened, President Moore asked for nominations for his successor. A Dr. Winchester immediately nominated Dr. Cary, with no elaboration. Dr. John Adams seconded this nomination, adding his thoughts on Dr. Cary:

Gentlemen of the American Veterinary Medical Association—and this is the American Veterinary Medical Association, as I understand it—not the Veterinary Medical Association of the University of Pennsylvania or Cornell or any other institution or association of the South or of New England, but it is the Veterinary Medical Association, the American Veterinary Medical Association, representing men from all sections and from all schools. Get that into your heads. Some men, I think, haven't gotten that into their heads yet. (Applause.) They seem to think this is an association for the personal gratification of ambition of sections of the country or schools or factions. The hope of the veterinary medical profession lies in the deliberation and the action and the work of this particular institution.

Just at the present time we are in a critical condition. We are just about to launch a movement that will in years—and less than a generation I predict—place American veterinary medicine on a plane with human medicine and the other sciences. We are far behind the medical science in Germany. It ought not to be and it won't be, but if we are not careful, gentlemen, our progress is going to be slow.

In this United States, represented in this Veterinary Medical Association, there is splendid timber for the officers of this society, scattered broadcast. When we choose a leader, the most forceful leader in our profession, we must look carefully that we are getting the best material. We want a man with a broad view. We want a man who knows the veterinary profession, a man with vision, a man who has the courage to carry out his convictions, and with friends, to work toward that objective.

Gentlemen, I have in mind such a man. He is not the only man. For twenty-seven years he has labored in the verdant, promising South. He knows the veterinary profession of the past. He knows the pitfalls that are to be avoided in the future. I, with pleasure, second the nomination of C.A. Cary. (Applause)

Another nomination came from the floor—the name of Dr. A. T. Kinsley. This action prompted another second to the nomination of Dr. Cary, provided by Dr. Cary's long-time ally, Dr. Tait Butler, who said:

Gentlemen, I can not let this opportunity go by, although I have no desire to weary you, or to make any long nominating speech; but I want to second the nomination of Dr. Cary for the simple reason that I feel that those who don't know him are apt to think less of him than those who know him intimately as I do. I have known him for thirty-eight years. During all those years the veterinary profession has had a staunch, straight, honest, loyal, enthusiastic supporter, a man who looks to the best interests of the profession, regardless of how it hurts himself or others. No profession has ever had a more loyal, a more true advocate and representative.

Further than that, like Dalrymple and Francis, he is a pioneer in the best work that has been done for the development of the live-stock industry of the South, and we of the veterinary profession today are in touch with a better knowledge and a better appreciation of the live-stock business, judging, feeding, etc., and every phase of it. Dr. Cary has been a shining light in what developments have occurred in the live-stock industry of the South. He has the respect, he has the confidence, of the live-stock men of the South, and if you elect him President of this organization today it will be the best proof that the veterinary profession has ever had because he is known over a third of the United States.

I want to say further that I know of no better veterinarian, with a broader vision, a broader or more accurate knowledge of the whole science of veterinary medicine. As a practitioner he has no equal, and he keeps abreast of the progress.

Further than that, Dr. Cary will hew to the line. He will have no favorites. There will be no cliques or factions that will have any standing with him if he is elected, because—and I have known him thirty-eight years—when it comes down to action, he hews to the line.

I want to say to you in conclusion, we don't ask you to elect Dr. Cary as a southern veterinarian; we ask you to elect him as an outstanding American veterinarian. (Applause).

Dr. Butler concluded by saying he also had known Dr. Kinsley since "before he ever studied veterinary medicine" and would know of "no better, no broader, no finer veterinarian living in America today," and that he would still be voting for Dr. Cary. At that point, caught up in the moment, Dr. Hoskins (who had lobbied for Dr. Cary the previous year) entered the fray, seconding the Cary nomination.

Mr. Chairman, I want to add another second to the nomination of Dr. Cary. I have been associated with Dr. Cary for more than a quarter of a century. There have been many times when we have differed in points of view, and many times when we have been antagonistic to each other and fought for our special hopes and aims in this Association; but I want to bear testimony that during the entire twenty-five years he has maintained the highest ideals of the Association and the veterinary profession of any man in this Association's history. I bear that testimony from close association with him. (Applause.)

The election went to Dr. Cary, 219 votes to Dr. Kinsley's eighty-seven. Charles Allen Cary was president of the American Veterinary Medical Association.[31]

1920 in Columbus, Ohio. The convention took place during August 23-27 at the twelve-story, 400-room Deshler Hotel, at the corner of Broad and High Streets, where today the twenty-five-story One Columbus overlooks the state capitol. The Deshler had opened four years earlier and proved to be "a central Ohio landmark . . . one of the premier hotels in the Midwest" for decades until it closed in 1969.[32]

As this was Dr. Cary's convention over which to preside, he and

Mrs. Cary hosted an opening night reception for the more than one thousand veterinarians and guests who attended. The event took place on Monday night, August 23, and, according to the *AVMA Journal*, "was among the most enjoyable occasions of the kind in the history of the organization. It was largely attended" in the Deshler's elegant ballroom. Dancing followed, and like good Presbyterians, Dr. and Mrs. Cary authorized that fruit punch be served to the guests.

The meeting gave Dr. Cary the opportunity to address the entirety of the organization, and his official presidential address, which ran several pages in the *AVMA Journal* of 1920, can be found in Appendix A.

One of the more noteworthy events of this convention was that the AVMA, during Dr. Cary's presidency, admitted to membership its first two African-American veterinarians: Dr. R. V. Gannon and Dr. J. G. Slade, both natives of Ohio and, at the time, both serving on the staff of the Bureau of Animal Industry. The vote to admit them to the AVMA was eighty-three to forty-eight.[33]

One additional note about the 1920 convention in Columbus: among many excellent speakers was one of Dr. Cary's protégés, Dr. B. T. Simms, API Class of 1911 and future director of the Bureau of Animal Industry. Dr. Simms spoke in Columbus on brucellosis, the first of several AVMA speaking opportunities he would have.

1921 in Denver. This meeting, held September 5-9, proved Dr. Cary's excellence in timing. Any presidential dance floor expectation for Dr. and Mrs. Cary in Cleveland was likely a picnic compared with demands on the new president, Dr. David S. White, who was cajoled into riding a bronco in a rodeo performance on the first day of the Colorado meeting.

1922 in St. Louis. AVMA met during August 28-September 1. Dr. Cary began a two-year term on the Special Committee on the Revision of the Constitution and By-laws.

1923 in Montreal. This meeting took place during August 27-31, and Dr. Cary was one of ten past presidents attending.

1924 in Des Moines. August 19-22. No reference has been found of Dr. Cary's attendance. As this meeting took place in his home state, he likely made every effort to be there.

1925 in Portland, Oregon. The meeting was held July 21-24. Again, Dr. Cary's attendance is not confirmed, but Oregon was home base for one of Dr. Cary's star graduates, Dr. B. T. Simms, who spoke on brucellosis control. One may assume Dr. Cary made a strong effort to attend.

1926 in Lexington, Kentucky, August 17-20, and *1927 in Philadel-*

phia, September 13-16. No record has surfaced of Dr. Cary at either of these meetings, but he likely attended each.

1928 in Minneapolis. This meeting was held August 7-10. During this session, Dr. Cary began a six-year appointment to the Committee on International Veterinary Congress.

1929 in Detroit. At this meeting, held August 13-16, Dr. Cary began a five-year appointment to the AVMA's Committee on Legislation.

1930 in Los Angeles. August 26-29. Dr. Cary's attendance is unconfirmed.

1931 in Kansas City, August 25-28, and *1932 in Atlanta*, August 23-26. Dr. Cary was present at each of these meetings, but he was not mentioned in the published recaps.

1933 in Chicago, August 14-18, and *1934 in New York City*, August 14-16. Again, Dr. Cary likely attended both of these conventions.

Dr. Cary also was active for many years in another national organization whose members' global aims mirrored his own: the US Live Stock Sanitary Association. He chaired its Committee on Tick Eradication during 1909-10 and was a member of this committee for most years the rest of his life. He also served the group through membership on its Committee on Legislation 1911-1914 and during 1931-32; on its Committee on Uniform Health Certificates during 1913-15; on its Committee on the Salmon Memorial, 1915-16; on its Committee on Live Stock Diseases, 1922-24; on the Committee on the Program for the AVMA, 1927-28; on its Committee on Policy, 1930-32; and its Committee on Regulations, 1931-32. Dr. Cary chaired the Live Stock Association's Committee on Meat and Milk Hygiene during 1931-32, and he served three terms as the organization's vice president: 1909-10, 1915-16, and 1926-27. Charles Allen Cary served as president of the US Live Stock Sanitary Association during 1927-28.

Taking part in organized veterinary medicine from the earliest times of his career served more than networking opportunities and continuing education for Dr. Cary. Ultimately, the strength of professional organizations proved key to his future plans. He may not have fully fathomed before he arrived in Auburn in 1892 the absolute necessity of organized veterinary medicine. But beyond the camaraderie he enjoyed, such collaboration would become one of his greatest allies in pursuing and reaching his goals, especially for creating consensus, building a team, training his students, and enlisting help to combat the deadly diseases he spent his professional life fighting.

CHAPTER SIX

DR. CARY IN COLUMBIA

After his 1887 Iowa State veterinary medical graduation, Charles Allen Cary worked at the veterinary practice in Keokuk, served for a time as assistant state veterinarian of Iowa, and in 1889 moved to Brookings and the South Dakota Agricultural and Mechanical College. His work in this faculty position consisted of teaching, research, and clinical outreach. His performance apparently attracted the attention of state government officials, one of whom asked Dr. Cary, probably during 1889, to serve as state veterinarian for South Dakota—heady work for so recent a graduate. However, there were few credentialed veterinarians in those days.

An eager learner, Dr. Cary spent the winter term of 1890 pursuing advanced studies at the University of Missouri in Columbia, likely having convinced his department or Experiment Station head at South Dakota, or perhaps the college president, of the benefits of furthering his abilities in treating animal diseases. His time in Columbia may have lasted as long as three months and may have served as a type of sabbatical during which he studied bacteriology and pathology.

The draw at Columbia for Dr. Cary was an opportunity to work with—and to learn from—Dr. Paul Paquin (1860-1916), a physician and veterinary scientist only a year older than Dr. Cary. Dr. Paquin, in

1885, had been appointed as Missouri's first state veterinarian. A native of Canada, Dr. Paquin joined the University of Missouri veterinary science instruction team in 1884 and launched the institution's program in studying diseases of livestock and poultry. He traveled in 1886 to Europe to study for several months under several world-renowned scientists, including at least part of this time in the laboratory of Dr. Louis Pasteur.[1]

During his time in Europe, Dr. Paquin wrote to someone back home:

> I study principally contagious diseases of animals at the Alfort Veterinary School under Messrs. Nocard and Trasbot, the former a collaborator of M. Pasteur. At the Hospital de la Charite, I studied under the well known Dr. Lantern, an authority on microscopic investigations of diseases. Later I shall follow for some time, I suppose, the laboratory of M. Pasteur.[2]

By 1889, Dr. Paquin had earned such a reputation that a scary incident involving him made national news, at least in the *American Veterinary Review*. That journal in 1889 alerted fellow veterinarians that "the young State Veterinarian of Missouri . . . who has for some time been making himself favorably known to his professional brethren by his scientific work, and a series of interesting investigations," had contracted a case of the potentially deadly glanders disease.[3] Thankfully, it wasn't glanders, and whatever ailment Dr. Paquin had picked up did not kill him.

By 1890, Dr. Paquin was serving as professor of comparative medicine and director of the vaccine lab at the University of Missouri Medical Department, as listed in the 1889-90 catalogue of the Missouri Medical College. A publication called *Medical Mirror* reported that he held the chair of pathology and bacteriology in the Medical Department of the State University of Missouri for many years, simultaneously serving as chief of the Sanitary Department of that state. In that role, he held authority over methods for controlling contagious diseases— on par with today's chief public health officers. He also published papers through the Missouri Experiment Station, addressing all manner of farm animal diseases, including hog cholera, anthrax, Texas fever, and glanders. During 1890, Dr. Paquin established and served as editor of a journal published from the Missouri campus: *Bacteriological World*, reportedly the only medical journal published in the English language at that time devoted exclusively to bacteriology.[4] In the years after Dr. Cary studied under him, Dr. Paquin authored at least four papers related to tuberculosis which appeared in the *Journal of the American Veterinary Medical Association*, which suggests that disease was also a focus for Dr. Cary during his time in Columbia.[5]

Dr. Paquin's obituary, published in the January 20, 1917, issue of the *Independent* newspaper in Kansas City, Missouri, offered further insights into his career and into specifics of his work that would have attracted Dr. Cary:

[Dr. Paquin's] medical studies began in 1873 at L'Ecole de Medicine et de Chirurgie de Montreal under Victoria University. He studied Comparative Medicine in Animals . . . at McGill University, after which he received a degree.

In 1883 or 1884 he was called to the Missouri State University to organize a State Sanitary Service for the study and control of contagious and infectious diseases of animals, in which he paid particular attention to contagious infections transmissible to man, and to dangerous meats and milk. It was in this position that his equipment as a Sanitarian and Pathologist was first brought prominently and favorably before the public, and the medical profession in particular, more especially by his work regarding tuberculosis and its transmissibility to children from tuberculous cows [sic] milk.

Very soon he was appointed a Professor of Comparative Medicine, Bacteriology, etc., for the Medical Department and the Agricultural College of the University.

While in this position he was delegated to attend the "Institut Pasteur," Paris, France, by the curators of the Missouri University and Governor Marmaduke. Pasteur was then at the zenith of his illustrious career as Chemist and FATHER of the Science of Bacteriology. He studied at Pasteur's laboratories and under his assistants at the laboratories of Cornil & Ranvoir, Paris Medical School; at the Museum of Natural History; and visited various other centers of professional education and practice in Europe.

On his return to the Missouri State University he established the first "Laboratory of Bacteriology, Pathology and Hygiene" in the West. It was the foundation of what has developed into several great laboratories and the department of preventive medicine at this progressive University.[6]

That "Bacteriology, Pathology and Hygiene" laboratory at Mizzou's Department of Veterinary Science was built in 1885 and represented the first vaccine-virus laboratory in the United States. Dr. Cary had opportunity in the winter of 1890 to train in this laboratory as well as in the department's veterinary laboratory, which had opened in 1887. In those years, Dr. Paquin and other staff veterinarians taught medical and agricultural students, conducted research on tick fever, and investigated livestock diseases throughout the state, including—but certainly not limited to—a July 1887 anthrax outbreak in Vernon, Missouri.

Dr. Cary would have been particularly interested in Dr. Paquin's take on how to stop Texas fever. A February 17, 2014, article by Randy Mertens, published on the University of Missouri's College of Agriculture, Food and Natural Resources (CAFNR) News website,[7] noted that Dr. Paquin, as head of the Missouri Experiment Station, oversaw research on Texas fever. Dr. Paquin already was consulting with Theobald Smith, MD and PhD, and Fred Lucius Kilborne, DVM, of the USDA when Dr. Paquin received a shipment of infected Texas cattle, brought by train under direction of Texas A&M veterinary faculty member Dr. Mark Francis.

Dr. Smith was a pioneer epidemiologist, bacteriologist, and pathologist whose many contributions to medical science were of far-reaching importance. Dr. Kilborne, a Cornell classmate of Smith's, was hired by America's first DVM, Dr. Daniel Salmon, as head of the Bureau of Animal Industry's Veterinary Experiment Station in 1885. These two—Smith and Kilborne—remain best known in veterinary circles for their work on Texas fever. They discovered the protozoan agent and its means of transmission by ticks, the first discovery of an arthropod linked with the transmission of an infectious disease.

Mertens' article reported on what the three investigators found after they began looking at blood samples from those Texas cattle:

> It was a critical clue that Texas fever manifested itself as a blood-borne disease. Drs. Paquin and Smith and Kilborne suspected that a microscopic protozoan was inhabiting and destroying red blood cells in infected animals. All three agreed that the disease was probably spread by cattle ticks. After sucking blood from an infected but immune animal, a tick would drop off into the grass and lay eggs from which would hatch young ticks already harboring the protozoan. Weeks after the original tick dropped from its longhorn host, its progeny were still capable of infecting other non-immune cattle. The disease died off seasonally when freezing weather in northern climates killed the ticks and their eggs.

Francis not only brought Texas cows to Missouri to study, but the ticks that infested them. Dr. Paquin and [Mizzou veterinary scientist John] Connaway pulled the insects from the Texas cows and applied them to certain Missouri cows while leaving others alone as a control. Cows with the ticks developed Texas fever. Finally, there was scientific proof.[8]

Charles Allen Cary recognized excellence and medical "can do" on the part of Dr. Paquin, as did the people of Missouri, who have remembered their outstanding doctor for his work. In present-day Columbia, Paquin Street, east of the university campus, bears his name. Paquin Park, a one-acre city space with an outdoor basketball half-court and picnic pavilion near the intersection of College and Paquin Streets, sits adjacent to Paquin Tower, a 200-unit, fifteen-story residential building specifically designed for low-income residents with disabilities and those sixty-two and older.

One glimpse into the environment Dr. Cary found when he spent time with Dr. Paquin may be gained from a letter to Levi Chubbuck, secretary of the state board of agriculture. Dr. Paquin wrote this letter from Columbia on November 6, 1890—many months after Dr. Cary had left town. Printed in the Oregon, Missouri-based *Holt County Sentinel* newspaper in its November 21, 1890, edition, the letter responded to a request from Mr. Chubbuck for an update on animal diseases causing problems in the agricultural community.[9] In the letter, Dr. Paquin said the most prevalent disease of the previous quarter, which was still active though declining as of early November, was aphthous fever in cattle, also known as foot-and-mouth disease. He confirmed that his team had "tested the material drooling from sore mouths and have failed to inoculate it. From these experiments and a large number of observations of various professional men and stockmen we have become convinced that the malady is not contagious."

Dr. Paquin referred to a published "circular letter on the subject" in which he prescribed treatment for this ailment in cattle. He also noted that "Black-leg exists in several counties but it seems . . . to a less extent than last year at this date." He acknowledged that some citizens had written to him asking for remedy for Black-leg, and he or his staff had responded to each. He discussed the problem:

We prescribe preventive inoculation which has proven so efficacious even among cattle in which outbreaks had already caused several deaths. Yet very few want to spend a trifle to save their calves. Some write as though they expected the State to prepare a remedy, pay for it and send it free of cost. The State has done her share in this matter by verifying the experiments of the French and proving Black-leg vaccination practicable and effective, and there are no funds at my command to manufacture medicines or virus of any kind at State expense for the benefit of comparatively few; besides there is no law authorizing such a course.

Dr. Paquin, in the letter, also mentioned glanders as having prevailed in various counties, and Texas fever not prevailing "near as extensively as last year in corresponding months," suggesting that Dr. Cary's time in Columbia offered plenty of opportunities—through on-farm inspections and laboratory testing, hands-on examinations, and interactions with other veterinarians on the front line—to further his knowledge of these and other diseases and how to fight them.

Whether the thought was prompted by his time at Mizzou or had begun in his mind before his time in Columbia, by 1891, Dr. Cary apparently decided to turn his focus to microorganisms and their damage to cattle and people. Despite a new wife and, by this time, a baby on the way, he made plans to travel to Germany for an extended time to study at the universities of Marburg, Berlin, and Stuttgart. At Berlin, he would spend time in a new infectious disease research laboratory under a man whose work he had apparently read, or read about: Dr. Robert Koch, who, more than a century after his death, is still considered globally as "the father of bacteriology."

CHAPTER SEVEN

AUBURN, THEN GERMANY

Dr. Cary likely spent time during 1891 acquiring the appropriate documents and making necessary preparations for temporary relocation to Germany for himself and Emma. Adding dimension to any planning, Dr. and Mrs. Cary learned during the summer of 1891 that Emma was expecting their first child, the baby due in April 1892. Sometime toward the latter part of 1891, after President Broun had corresponded with Dr. Tait Butler in Starkville and subsequently with Dr. Cary, Drs. Broun and Cary most likely met. Either through correspondence or during an interview that fall, or both, the two discussed President Broun's goals for the land-grant college at Auburn. The result was that Charles Allen Cary's near-term career plan took a detour that would change his and Emma's lives and the fortunes of a great many people.

Before Dr. Cary's temporary duty in Berlin commenced, during the first quarter of 1892, Dr. Cary arrived in Auburn at President Broun's invitation to begin a three-month stint as visiting lecturer in veterinary science in the Experiment Station of the Alabama Agricultural and Mechanical College.

The Special Collections and Archives Department at Auburn's Ralph Brown Draughon Library holds a number of papers and letters from

the Broun presidency, among them a copy of the letter President
Broun sent to Dr. Cary to confirm Cary's appointment as lecturer in
veterinary science for the first three months of 1892. That copy, on
API President's Office stationery, reads:

Auburn, Ala.   Nov. 16, 1891

    Dr. C.A. Cary
    Nauvoo, S.D.,
     Sir;-
    Your letter of Nov. 14th., stating that you ~~will~~ are willing to accept the
position of lecturer of Veterinary Science, as defined in my former communication, for three months, from Jan. 1st. to April 1st. for one hundred and fifty dollars ($150.00) per month, is received, and your proposi-
tion is accepted. You will please forward me a list of apparatus that you
will need, to cost say $150.00, with names of vendors, and I will endeavor
to have the same in the college by Jan. 1st. You will report here and enter
on your duties Jan. the first.
    Respectfully,[1]

The business letter format President Broun employed looks odd
enough to modern-day readers (see photo of letter in center photo section), but even more strange would be Dr. Broun's lining through a
word and leaving it that way, and his addressing Dr. Cary at Nauvoo,
South Dakota—not an actual place. Nauvoo was Mrs. Cary's hometown in Illinois, and the couple lived in Brookings, South Dakota. Nevertheless, the communication served its purpose. Apparently, Dr. Cary
had written to President Broun on November 14, 1891, to accept the
offer that had come via correspondence from President Broun previously. Searches in AU Archives have not unearthed those letters.
    Dr. Cary's personnel form from Alabama Polytechnic Institute, a
photocopy of which survives in the family papers, confirmed that he
spent the first three months of 1892 in Auburn, in a visiting
lecturer/scientist role. In that document, he noted that the "remaining
months of that year was [sic] spent in Europe." He initially filled out
that document, or at least dated it, January 1, 1907, a date which
appears across from his signature on the final of four legal-sized pages.
But he had crossed out the 1907 date and written beneath it, "modified
Dec 1919," beneath which is initialed "CAC."
    Another letter related to Dr. Cary's Auburn appointment remains in
the Cary family papers: a hand-written note from President Broun on

his presidential stationery to Dr. Cary, dated May 9, 1892, following that initial three-month appointment and before Dr. Cary took his family to Europe. That letter, as best deciphered, said:

Auburn, Ala.   May 9, 1892

Dr. C.A. Cary
Nauvoo Ill—
    My dr Sir
In reply to your ms of May 5th I beg to state that I will recommend to the Trustees your second proposition—to invite you to the chair of veterinary science & physiology from January 1st/93 to close of session June 15th – salary $1000 –
The Board will meet on June 13-14 when they will take position on this–& I will inform you of the result—much congratulations & best wishes for your son
    I am
    very respectfully
    yours
    Wm LeRoy Broun[2]

Piecing together the sequence of events in Dr. Cary's life: he practiced in Keokuk, Iowa, after his 1887 veterinary school graduation; met Emma Heck sometime between 1887 and 1889; accepted a positon in Brookings at the South Dakota Agricultural and Mechanical College and moved there in 1889; spent the winter of 1890 in Columbia, Missouri, possibly taking classes at the University of Missouri and studying and/or working under Dr. Paul Paquin; married Emma in November 1890; heard from and met President Broun sometime in 1891; spent the first three months of 1892 in Auburn, Alabama; became a father to Elwyn in April 1892; traveled to Europe and spent several months of 1892 in at least three locations in Germany, including studying under Dr. Robert Koch in Berlin; and returned to start a new job at Auburn by the beginning of 1893.

Among the preserved documents of Cary family holdings is a diary Dr. Cary kept during his travels in Europe in the summer and fall of 1892. The entries largely deal with his travels; where he, Emma, and baby Elwyn (and, for at least a part of the trip, some relatives) were going; what they found to see and do in those places; and his impressions of the people, locations, art, architecture, and the politics of the day in those great cities of Europe. His diary entries provided minimal detail of his scientific study and language work. (He studied German under a private tutor for some of the time that fall.)

Some highlights of those diary entries:[3]

Traveling from Antwerp, where among other things they had visited the zoo, the Carys arrived in Cologne [population 144,000 then] on Friday, July 8. Visited cathedral and art museum. Visited Cologne zoo and thought it lesser than the Antwerp zoo.

July 11, 1892 . . . took steamer to Koblenz. Lauded their eight-hour cruise along the Rhine as "one of the most pleasant trips of our journey— in fact, of our life." He was struck by people drinking beer during church service.

July 15th returned to Marburg via train. After church on Sunday the 17th, arranged a nurse for Elwyn and the rest went touring.

In Marburg on July 18, he and a companion [an uncle?] visited the slaughter house and the botanical garden. He made note that all animals killed there had to be inspected before their meat could be consumed.

July 22, 1892. In the afternoon, he and his uncle visited the Hygiene Institute and there saw Dr. Frankel's Laboratory. "Small but well equipped. Dr. Frankel is a very pleasant and fine man. Also saw Pathological Institute. Very fine pathological collection and an excellent building."

July 25 by rail to Berlin. Arrived 10:50 p.m.

July 26. "Spent most of day at hotel, but did get to go see a veterinary high school."

Berlin July 28. "Attended clinics. Bought some books."

July 29. "Met Professor Shrits (?) who kindly consented to look me up a place to study bacteriology. Visited the surgical and poly clinics & slaughter houses."

July 30. "Visited clinics etc."

Sunday, July 31, 1892. "Remained at home in forenoon: afternoon

Dearest and I [visited] the Thier Garten Park [Tiergarten Park] and the Zoological Garden. The zoo is very poor in most things except beer and music. The Antwerp and the Koln Zoo are the better and cleaner. Also New York. Beer Beer Beer—Beer everywhere."

August 1st 1892, Berlin Germany. "Attended clinics. Bought books."

August 2nd 1892. "Clinics & looked for baby wagon. Visited Rhorback's instrument house. Read and studied German."

August 3rd 1892. "Clinic very good today. Castration by Prof Dr. H. Moeller. Studied German the p.m. and evening."

Sep 24, 1892. Dr. and Mrs. Cary go in different routes today, she to Marburg, he to Munich, where he attended church in the morning, visited the English Garden and the veterinary school, and attended a Wagner opera that evening, "The Meistersinger von Nürnberg," which he pronounced "very lovely and beautiful."

September 28, 1892. Munich. He visited the slaughter house in the morning and the international art house in the afternoon. His take on the art museum: "I am no judge of art but I presume there was sufficient nudity to satisfy the taste and beauty of the art cultured and the curiosity of the layety."

Oct 3, 1892. Vienna, Austria. He wrote that upon arrival, all entering guests had their bags or trunks inspected, and any dirty clothes were to be collected, washed and returned to the owner. This was to keep out cholera. Dr. Cary had no dirty clothes upon his arrival.

Oct 6, 1892. Went to one of the finest opera houses in the world. There he heard "Manon," a French opera—costumes in the style of 1721. "The scenes, the singing, the orchestra were indeed grand."

10-8-92. "Today I visited the slaughter house and took several pictures of the veterinary college building erected in 1824. This school was founded in 1777. It is the second oldest on the continent, 2nd after Alfort."

Oct 10, 1892. Vienna, Austria. "Today I went to the vaccine laboratory of Dr. Hay ... where nearly all the human medical colleges etc are located. Dr. Hay vaccinated me in two places on both the right and left arm. I also procured vaccine for vaccinating Elwyn."

Dr. Cary also wrote at least a half-dozen letters that summer and fall of 1892 to the Jennings, Louisiana, *Reporter* newspaper, a publication that may have been owned, published, and/or edited by his father, telling of the family's trip, of the places they visited, and of his general impressions of Europe, which most of the paper's readers would never visit.

To offer a sense of what Dr. Cary encountered during this monumental trip, and to allow his own words to shed some further light on his large personality, his intellect, and his broad range of interests, following are excerpts from the half-dozen letters he wrote from Europe only a few months prior to beginning his lengthy tenure at Auburn:

As the North have imperfect ideas of the South and the South distorted ideas of the North, so the average American misunderstands the German and likewise the German at home forms an improper conception of the American. One must go to the home country of any people to understand them in their real unminimized and unmagnified condition.

Until recently it has been beyond the means of the moderately well-to-do American to cross the Atlantic and see things that ever remain on the confines of dreamland unless such a voyage be taken. To many a sea voyage is too dangerous to admit of venture. But the facts are that the majority of fears are frights. Our troubles have their origin and end in the mind. So with a sea voyage the dread is worse than the voyage. My wife and ten weeks old babe were not sea sick at all, but I must admit of going through three days of displeasure which was followed by a good hearty "staying" appetite.

Belgium like Holland and Germany is a perfect garden. Not a spot of earth goes to waste. Marks of the hoe, shovel, pick or spade re every visible. Natures resources are entirely consumed, utilized.

We remained at Marburg ... for two weeks. During that time I made several excursions on foot into the country surrounding Marburg. On one occasion I walked a distance of twenty-five miles, accompanied by an old man seventy six years old and four young girls. The facts are the old man and the girls withstood the long walk better than I. The reason therefor is obvious: people walk more in Germany for exercise, than in

America. On this long walk I passed through ten villages and also saw the country farms and roads, the forests and fields. Go where you will in Germany the earth is one perfect garden. There are no farm houses; the farmers all live in little villages.

The peasants or farmers are the most industrious I have ever observed. They would revolutionize the South quicker than all the host of Republican politicians of the North, who know? so much how to run the South. To be sure the peasants of Germany are in a sense slaves to constant work, but I honor the people who wear out instead of rusting out.

The convicts of the state should always construct roads in the state. While the American dislikes the "too-much-government" in European countries, the European can equally chastise the American on the too-much-individual-interest in American government.

A short walk into the country from any city will show one examples of man made forests of all ages. The oak, elm, the linden, the pine and the beach [sic] are the principal forest trees. North Germany with a climate that will not permit corn raising, can exhibit pine forest that will rival the beautiful "long leaf" pines twenty miles north of Jennings. Again, the Americans can learn a warning lesson: Plant forests now that the generations one or two hundred years hence may have timber for the necessities. But I nearly forgot the American idea. No future, no past, only the pulsating present!

Although the laborers, the common people are poor and hard worked apparently they are very happy. Their poverty and hard work does not drive away all joy. No doubt poverty exercises a bad influence on the morals of a people, but work is probably the greatest source of enjoyment. I am of the opinion that if the poor classes had plenty of good wholesome food and were not worked more hours than human nature can bear, the German lower classes would be a most happy lot of people.

Work, if not pressed by poverty or too much slavish drudgery, brings the greatest happiness to mankind.

I am now at the art center of Germany. At present the International Art Exhibition is open. As I passed through the Glass Palace wherein the fine paintings and statues from all nations are collected, I felt lost as it were, in a wilderness, a forest. I can look upon the beautiful figures, the variety of colors and forms, but why is this picture or that statue more beautiful to me; is more than I can tell in words. As Mark Twain said of Raphael's picture that he saw in Rome—there seems no soul, spirit or life essence manifested in the great works of art. If I could I would gladly give an extended description of the Art Exhibit, but it is best for me to keep within reasonable range of my narrow "ken."

While Munich is the center of painting, sculpture and music in Germany, it is also the greatest beer manufacturing city in the world. It holds the honor, or dishonor, of making the best beer in the world. But it is not difficult to obtain water to drink. The only trouble about water in this country is its impurity. In any thickly settled country, one thousand or more years old, all surface water is impure unless filtered or cooked. This will be so in America—in fact it is so in places. The methods of disposing of sewerage, of all refuse materials and of dead bodies must be radically changed or infectious diseases will reign in terror as cholera has in Hamburg. The refuse must be burnt or disinfected, the dead bodies must be cremated, in order to stay the ravages of disease and make the sanitary conditions more favorable to life. Superstition must yield to unquestioned scientific facts—truth. Look again at Hamburg! Typhoid fever is following in the foot steps of Cholera, because of the impure water supply. All the cities on the river above Hamburg empty their refuse, the sewerage into the river. Yes. I would recommend beer in preference to such death ladened water. Of course pure water can be obtained but not without difficulty and cost which the poor many times can not afford.[4]

Dr. Cary's hand-written letters of that season do not reflect any specifics on his studies, which seemed the primary reason he traveled to Germany in the first place. Long understood is that he spent time in the summer and fall of 1892 in the laboratories of Dr. Robert Koch, "the father of bacteriology." The gap in Dr. Cary's journal between the first few days in August and his entry of September 24 may suggest he was focused on his studies during those several weeks, with not much tourism getting in the way of his work.

Information from the Koch Institute's website describes Dr. Robert Koch (1843-1910) as a German physician who turned his attention and his energies toward disease research in the 1870s and eventually earned a world-wide reputation.[5] Dr. Koch launched experiments related to anthrax in 1876. He made microscopic drawings of organisms he viewed under the scope, and later was able to take photomicrographs in the late 1870s. Dr. Koch was appointed to the Imperial Health Office in Berlin in 1880. From this headquarters, he worked toward the bacteriological methodology that was "to prove just as useful for research into epidemics as it was for the development of preventive measures like disinfection."

Koch's paper on the *Aetiology of Tuberculosis*, presented on March 24, 1882, cemented his reputation for scientific achievement. The following year, he left for Egypt and India to study cholera epidemics in those nations. Dr. Koch succeeded in detecting the pathogen and in identifying the epidemic's cause.[6] His research focused on deadly diseases, chiefly tuberculosis and cholera, his goal to prevent infectious diseases or to discover and implement measures to control epidemics. As his reputation for success in studying these diseases and discovery at the highest levels spread around the world, undoubtedly, Charles Allen Cary and others in medical and veterinary medical training heard of the work of Robert Koch. The opportunity to go and learn from the master prompted Dr. Cary to go to Berlin.

Dr. Koch's work on tuberculosis included vaccination, but his hopes for determining an effective treatment or even a tuberculosis vaccine were dashed in 1890. Still, the success of Koch's staff at the University's Hygiene Institute and his own important methodological work led, by the end of the 1880s, to plans for a new institute to carry out research into infectious diseases.

About this time, or perhaps soon after, Dr. Cary began his own preparation for time in Germany. Koch's plans for the new institute were announced late in 1890, and the Royal Prussian Institute for Infectious Diseases opened on July 1, 1891, to showcase Koch's massive talents and leadership. Informally known as the Koch Institute even before its opening, its first location was next door to Charité Hospital, the largest and oldest hospital in Berlin.

The institute's Scientific Department was housed in a converted residential building known as "the triangle" because of its three-sided floorplan. Dr. Cary probably spent several months in this triangle, at work in the Koch Institute. There, likely on the second floor where Dr. Koch and the other scientists had their offices and laboratories, Dr. Cary gained insight into identifying and battling deadly diseases that he would use for the rest of his life. Dr. Koch would relocate the institute elsewhere in Berlin twelve years later, and a little more than a half-century later, the triangle building would be destroyed in World War II.

The hospital's clinical experiments and research laboratory were each under a director, both of whom reported to Dr. Koch. He first appointed as clinical director Dr. Ludwig Brieger (1849-1919), who over the course of a long career was an important contributor to numerous medical journals and an author of many essays and books dealing with pharmacology, pharmaceutical chemistry, bacteriology, pathology, and therapeutics. Dr. Brieger is remembered as an authority on each of these areas of medicine. Dr. Koch appointed as the laboratory research director Dr. Richard Pfeiffer, who earned a reputation for important discoveries in immunology and bacteriology.

While no known records exist of which scientists Dr. Cary studied under or with whom he collaborated during his time at the Koch Institute, some combination of Drs. Brieger and Pfeiffer and several other globally significant assistants working then under Dr. Koch were likely Dr. Cary's compatriots or supervisors during these months. Those others included Drs. Georg Gaffky (1850–1918), Paul Ehrlich (1854-1915), Emil von Behring (1854-1917), Shibasaburo Kitasato (1853-1931), Bernhard Proskauer (1851-1915) and August von Wassermann (1866-1925).

Dr. Gaffky would later serve as director of the Koch Institute and was renowned in his own right, having identified *bacillus salmonella typhi* in 1884 as the cause of typhoid disease.

Dr. Paul Ehrlich, physician and scientist, worked in hematology, immunology, and antimicrobial chemotherapy. He invented the precursor technique to gram-staining bacteria, which made possible distinguishing between different types of bacteria. This achievement enhanced scientists' ability to diagnose various blood diseases. Dr. Ehrlich, or perhaps others working in his laboratory, are credited with discovering arsphenamine, the first effective medicinal treatment for syphilis.

Dr. Emil von Behring received the 1901 Nobel Prize in Physiology or Medicine, the first such prize to be awarded, for his discovery of a diphtheria antitoxin. He was described as a "savior of children," a reference to diphtheria's significant cause of death in young people.

Dr. Shibasaburo Kitasato, Japanese physician and bacteriologist, is credited as the co-discoverer of the infectious agent of bubonic plague in Hong Kong in 1894. He was nominated for the Nobel Prize in Physiology or Medicine in 1901, based on his collaboration with Emil von Behring, though only von Behring was awarded the 1901 Nobel Prize.

Dr. Bernhard Proskauer, who headed Dr. Koch's Chemical

Department, is best known for development of the Voges-Proskauer test, a primary diagnostic test for enteric bacteria.

Dr. August von Wassermann made a name for himself through discovery of a universal blood serum test for syphilis, which was used globally for many years before superior test procedures were introduced.[7]

Many of the achievements and accolades of Dr. Koch's assistants took place in the years after Dr. Cary spent his time in Berlin, but the fact remains the future Auburn dean likely spent important, formative weeks, if not months, learning alongside some of the best medical minds of the world at that time. He would bring the knowledge gained in Berlin—as well as a working knowledge for speaking and writing German—back to the States and to his new world in East Alabama.

However Drs. Broun and Cary left things when Dr. Cary departed for Europe in spring 1892, President Broun knew he had found the man to build Auburn's program in veterinary science/veterinary medicine. In Auburn, President Broun made arrangements through the Board of Trustees to make Dr. Cary's position permanent, and a letter from President Broun that summer confirmed to the veterinarian his future:

> Auburn, Ala.   June 17-th. 1892
>
> Dr. C.A. Cary
> Nauvoo, Ill.,
>   Dear Sir:
>   The Board elected you Professor of Veterinary Science and Physiology. The duties to begin on January 1-st. 189[3]. with salary $1000.00 for services from Jan. 1-st. to close of session.
>   Respectfully,[8]

Soon after Dr. Cary received this letter from President Broun, he responded to accept the offer. His handwritten acceptance was drafted from Marburg, Germany, and reflected quite the chummy relationship the two apparently had developed in a short time:

> Marburg Germany   July 16 1892
>
> Presd Wm Leroy Broun
> Auburn Ala
>   Dear Friend:
>   Your letter, notifying me of the action of the Board, was received two days since. Please accept my sincere thanks for the interest taken

and work you have done, in my behalf. If you have made any arrangements as to class work for me—i.e., what classes I shall have and what terms or semesters—please notify me. My wife, baby and I landed at Antwerp, Belgium, July 7, 1892. Our voyage was very pleasant and without a storm. From Belgium we traveled by sail to the historic Rhine at Cologne. From Cologne by steamer up the Rhine to Coblence [Koblenz] and from thence by rail to this place. During the last 3 days I have walked through 10 ... villages that I might see and come in contact with the peasants and their work and homes.

We shall soon go to Berlin where I expect to remain most of my time while here. Any communications or letters will reach me by directing to Marburg in care of Rev. P. Heck.

There is a very fine University located here with almost 1000 students in attendance. I think in the course of a month I shall be able to take lectures.

It is very cool and pleasant here now—cooler than in Iowa or Ill. The country is very lovely and must be seen to be appreciated.

> Yours very truly
> C.A. Cary
> Germany
> c/o Rev. P. Heck[9]

CHAPTER EIGHT

THE AUBURN DR. CARY FOUND

M ost any intersection of time and place along the continuum of
human history offers a setting of conflict, people bringing to
their interpersonal relationships those qualities—selfishness, distrust,
greed, lust, fear—which we might call "baggage" or, charitably, "human
nature." The late nineteenth century in rural East Alabama presented
such a picture, given the influence of state and national, even global,
events. While the nation's economy had experienced positive growth
in the 1870s and 1880s, problems from the aftermath of the Civil War
persisted in the Deep South. Political battles over issues such as credit
availability, labor shortages, property taxes, and crop prices pitted
large landowners and planters against small farmers, with politicians
by necessity taking sides and muddying Alabama's political landscape.[1]
Post-war rebuilding and expansion of railroads—the overland shipping
and transportation leader of the day—proved a source of political
problems, with charges of fraud, bribery, and favoritism in this leading
industry. Financial distress among some railroad companies, including
corporate default, further sank the state's financial ship.[2]

As the century's final quarter arrived—with the state still in debt from
the war—tax revenues in Alabama began a significant slide. There were
at least two main causes of the revenue decline: first, the elimination of

taxes which, until 1865, had been collected on slaves owned and claimed by wealthier landowners; second, a series of property tax reductions the Legislature enacted in 1877 and 1880. Inadequate tax income resulted predictably in diminished quality of most every aspect of public life: education, road building and maintenance, government services, public health, and care for the indigent and mentally ill.[3]

Political parties in Alabama after the Civil War were splintered, with race relations, agricultural policies, tax rates, and innumerable other factors driving officials and citizens alike to side with either the Republicans, the Jeffersonian Democrats, the Bourbon Democrats, or an upstart movement from within the Democratic party: the Populists. Populism arose from a widespread belief that common people had lost their confidence in—and their standing in the priority of—traditional politicians, an opinion that would sound familiar to American voters of the early twenty-first century.[4]

All this political wrangling in Alabama resulted in a general sense of turmoil in many phases of its people's lives. Unemployment was up, farm prices were down, animal diseases threatened farm livelihood, politicians were seen as favoring wealthy individuals and corporations, and rural people—if not everybody—distrusted authority across the state. There was no money to support schools, to repair and expand roads, to help the lot of farmers and producers and small business owners, nor to take adequate care of the other areas the citizenry felt state government should oversee. Despair and hopelessness plagued many people. What could possibly attract an educated, ambitious, honest outsider to Alabama in the early 1890s? Welcome to Auburn, Charles Allen Cary.

With Dr. Cary first in Auburn during January-March of 1892, Emma took the opportunity to return to her parents' home in Nauvoo, Illinois, for that time, especially the later weeks of that winter, the final trimester of her pregnancy. Records show that Elwyn Allen Cary was born in Nauvoo on April 11, 1892, probably at the Heck home. A month later, on May 13, 1892, Charles Allen Cary was in possession of a United States passport to enable his travel to Europe, which seems to have taken place with his family beginning in June. The passport described him as age thirty; five-feet, seven and one-half inches tall; with brown eyes, auburn hair, a light complexion, and a small chin. Dr. Cary spent the better part of six months abroad in an intense schooling; he returned at year's end to the United States, prepared to alter the course of history.

During his visiting professor stint in Auburn, Dr. Cary became the embodiment of a plan long in President Broun's mind for building his increasingly capable land-grant institution. Two years earlier, when the board of trustees had held its annual meeting over several days in mid-June 1890—the school's Experiment Station by this time up and running—President Broun requested board approval for hiring a veterinary surgeon. He thus made the first official mention of veterinary science in conjunction with Auburn:

> To fulfill all the objects of the Experiment Station there will be required the services of a Veterinary Surgeon for the whole or part of the year. It is possible the services of an efficient veterinarian, who is connected with some other college, could be secured for a portion of the year and this for the present would satisfy our demands. If authorized correspondence looking to this end could be held with a competent professor of Veterinary Science, now engaged in another college with a view to delivering a short course of lectures on that science, at this institution. A lecturer might be obtained for small compensation who would prove beneficial to the college and Station.[5]

Minutes from the Alabama Agricultural and Mechanical College Board of Trustees' meeting of June 9, 1891, mention that "the election of a veterinary surgeon be postponed," suggesting that either President Broun had not yet found his man at that time, or had found a better man—Cary—than another he originally had in mind.

However, in the meeting the next day, Broun included these comments in his address to the board:

> The present condition of the college gives promise of increased usefulness in the cause of Education and demands careful consideration that its expansion should be in accordance with the requirements of the several acts granting its endowment, with what is best for the Educational interests of the State.
>
> I recommend that the following additions be made to the officers of instruction.
>
> 1st, a professor of History and Latin
>
> 2nd, That an adjunct Professorship of Modern Languages and History be made the Adjunct Professorship of Modern Languages and English
>
> 3rd, That there be appointed an Adjunct Professor of Electrical and Mechanical Engineering

4th, That there be appointed a professor of veterinary science

By the appointment of these officers the college will have increased ability to educate more thoroughly the youth who may come under its charge . . .[6]

The trustees liked what they were hearing from this president as he continued to mold the institution into the model of the land-grant force they had envisioned when they heard his 1880 commencement address. The minutes from the January 13, 1892, board meeting bring to fruition President Broun's plan for this first professor of veterinary science, as the president told trustees:

It is important for the interest of Agriculture, that the college should be provided with a Professor or Lecturer of Veterinary Science. Acting under authority given in a special resolution of the Board, I have with the personal approval of the Ex[ecutive] Committee, I have employed Dr. C. A. Cary to lecture on Veterinary Science for three months, beginning January 1st, at $150 per month and respectfully recommend that this action be confirmed and made permanent.[7]

At the Board of Trustees meeting of June 13, 1892, when Dr. Cary was soon to depart, was en route, or had arrived in Europe, President Broun reported on successes the young veterinarian achieved in his initial three months at Auburn:

Acting under authority formerly given by the Board, I appointed Dr. C.A. Cary of Illinois, a graduate of the Iowa Agricultural College in Veterinary Science, to lecture to the students during the second term from Jan. 1st to April 1st.

He proved himself to be a competent professor and instructive lecturer well informed in his department.

I recommend that the School of Veterinary Science and Physiology be established, the duties to extend from Jan 1st to June 1st. And that Dr. C.A. Cary be appointed to the position with a salary of $1,000.

There was purchased for the use of the department a human skeleton, and mounted skeletons of the horse, ox, sheep, and hogs; and also instruments for veterinary surgery.

The latter were used by the officer in the free clinics conducted at the Experiment Station as illustrations for the class.[8]

That report from President Broun to the trustees marked the first time the concept of a "school of veterinary science and physiology" was mentioned at Auburn, at least in the official record. There were, in the 1890s, seven privately operated veterinary schools in North America which offered three-year terms, and five private colleges offering veterinary degrees over two years. These schools all were located in major cities: New York (two), Boston, Philadelphia, Chicago (two), Montreal, Kansas City, Cincinnati, Toronto and Washington, DC (two). Efforts to establish varying types of veterinary schools beginning as early as the 1850s had all failed, most before they offered the first class.[9] The twelve private colleges operating at the time Dr. Cary first came to Auburn constituted the first successful schools in the country, but these were as much "for-profit" as they were for veterinary education. Drs. Merillat and Campbell offered an interesting thought about that:

> The truth is the United States did not have veterinary schools that were not tainted with outstanding imperfections from 1776 until 1920, or during its first 144 years. That brilliant men, men of achievement, and a workable veterinary service for the federal government and states, could have grown out of them under the circumstances, is one of the marvels of veterinary history—another American paradox. Necessity—a vast animal industry—was more of a factor in the making of capable veterinarians than were the schools. Great problems develop great men to solve them in all branches of human effort.[10]

A degree-granting veterinary science school at Alabama AMC would come about, but not for fifteen years. Meanwhile, across the country, some public institutions had developed, or were developing, such schools of veterinary science or veterinary medicine. Iowa State College, of course, where Dr. Cary studied, opened its veterinary course in 1879. The University of Pennsylvania opened its school in 1884. The program at Ohio State University dates to 1885. Cornell's veterinary school opened in 1896, Washington State University in 1899, and Kansas State University in 1905. Colorado State University and Auburn each opened veterinary schools in fall 1907. After those came Michigan State University (1910) and Texas A&M (1916).[11]

The treasurer's report for that board meeting in June 1892 detailed that Dr. Cary's $1,000 per year salary—which he would begin earning upon his arrival at the beginning of 1893—paled in contrast with some of the others: the biology professor earning $2,000 per year, and the

English professor, chemistry professor, history and Latin professor, and the electrical engineering professor each making $1,800 per year. The mechanic arts professor also earned more than Dr. Cary that year with a salary of $1,500. The first ($1,600) and second ($1,500) assistants in chemistry also were paid more than the veterinary science professor, but that would change soon.

Professor Cary clearly earned his salary and more, based on a report on the year's work in the Experiment Station, made to the president by agriculturist Alexander J. Bondurant and presented to the board that same day. Bondurant reported:

> Lectures were delivered to the students of the third and second classes on veterinary surgery and animal physiology by Dr. C.A. Cary and public clinics were held on the station grounds once every week, at which time the farmers from the adjoining county attended and brought with them stock to be examined and treated for any diseases or injuries.
>
> Much good resulted from these lectures made by Dr. Cary in different parts of the state in addition to the instruction imparted to classes at clinics held weekly.
>
> This work seems to have been popular and highly appreciated, and if it could be made a permanent course it should add to the efficiency of college and station work.[12]

A year later, in minutes for the board meeting held on June 12, 1893, the trustees again heard President Broun lauding his choice of a veterinary science lecturer in what amounts to a summary-to-date of Dr. Cary's achievements and a notice that they better act to retain this outstanding professor:

> The professor of physiology and veterinary science, Dr. C.A. Cary, of whom only six months' service was required, reported for duty on his return from Germany Jan 1st.
>
> In addition to his class work, he has on invitation lectured in different portions of the state on subjects related to veterinary science; having delivered in all 21 lectures; and has also conducted on Saturdays free clinics at the station. These have been generally well attended by the neighboring farmers.
>
> To retain the services of the present professor, who has proved himself in all respects competent, it is necessary to construct for the use of his department an inexpensive building.

The act of Congress establishing the Experiment Station requires that provision shall be made for the investigation of animal as well as plant diseases and their remedies, and in strict compliance with the law this professorship was established.[13]

The treasurer's report given to trustees at this meeting, referencing the year ending June 30, 1893, showed that President Broun approved of the work Dr. Cary was doing, as his salary was then listed at $1,800 per year, ranking him among the highest-paid professors at Auburn. During the following year, he would receive, courtesy of the board's approval, an additional $200 per year toward "commutation for house rent," which was common among the several most senior faculty members at the time.[14]

Later in the fall, from the minutes of the September 7, 1893, board meeting, Trustee Henry Clay Armstrong—member of the Alabama Legislature, State Superintendent of Education, and the son of the man for whom Armstrong Street in Auburn is named—proposed that $2,000 be appropriated for "erecting buildings and providing equipment for the department of Veterinary Science and that the location of said buildings be left with the Board of Visitors of the Experiment Station."[15] This motion was adopted, and the funds were used to construct the first veterinary building at Auburn. According to the first *Glomerata* yearbook published in 1897, this two-story building was located northwest of the college's main buildings at that time and

contains class-rooms and operating departments with all the conveniences that could be desired by the equine patients. The maimed and diseased horses for miles around travel here like pilgrims to Mecca; but they seek bodily, instead of spiritual, health; and under the skilled treatment of Dr. Cary they are soon restored to vigorous horsehood.[16]

The location was a sort of "no-man's land" adjacent to campus, on the south side of Magnolia Avenue. Acreage that became home to the first veterinary grounds was part of a plot the townspeople had bought from a local landowner during the Tichenor administration to give to the college. The arrangement supposedly had included a buy-back clause in the event the college did not need or could not use this property. Sure enough, faculty found the grounds unusable for their agricultural plans, but when the effort was made to transfer the property back to the seller, he insisted on paying only one-fifth of his earlier selling price. Trustees decided they would rather have unusable land than a bad deal, so they kept it. Cotton wouldn't grow there, but Dr. Cary didn't need good soil for his teaching and diagnostic efforts.[17]

President Broun reported to the trustees in June 1894 that a veterinary laboratory had been built at a cost of $1,944.50. The president provided board members with details of the facility and of the impact Dr. Cary's continued good work was having:

> The laboratory of veterinary science, constructed during the year, has been partially equipped. It contains a lecture room office, and museum, operating room and hospital ward for animals, and other special laboratory rooms.
>
> The free clinics, conducted every Saturday, have proved popular and valuable to the community adjacent, and also instructive to the students. During the year over 300 cases were treated by the officer in charge.[18]

One senses that Dr. Cary had a full say in the construction and equipping of this veterinary building, and it would come as a surprise if he had not influenced the president's decision to tell trustees at that June 1894 meeting ". . . it would be far better were the positon of State Veterinarian established in connection with the state Department of Agriculture, and the time of the office divided between the work of the college and the state."[19] The position of state veterinarian would be established, but not for several years, in 1907. That first veterinary building served the program for a decade, but later was moved a quarter-mile down Magnolia Avenue and given new life as a fraternity house and later as a private residence and boarding house across from Drake Infirmary. Its original location, by 1925, would be the site of Ramsay Hall, an engineering building.[20]

What a sales job President Broun must have done during those first days of meeting Charles Allen Cary, to recruit him to East Alabama in 1892. As an ambitious, well-trained, recently married veterinarian with plans to travel to Europe to study at the highest levels of biological science at that time, Dr. Cary was the type of man who would have been planning already where to go and what work to pursue after his time in Germany. And yet, in an hour or two, or over a day or two, President Broun the visionary persuaded Dr. Cary to alter his career plans at this critical moment and agree to launch a program where there was no precedent, in a part of the country he had never visited, with no guarantees the South would recover any time soon from the Civil War.

As 1892 drew to a cold close, Dr. and Mrs. Cary returned to the States and made arrangements to reach Auburn, Alabama—Dr. Cary coming a few weeks before Emma. The Auburn they found must have given them pause for re-evaluating their decision. Auburn in the 1890s had fourteen hundred residents, a few buildings, churches, a school, a few stores, a handful of places to eat, private homes with their out-houses, and a college that had ambitions if not many students. Dirt streets were bumpy from horses pulling carriages, carts, and wagons. The place was sometimes foul-smelling. Homes were lit by lamps—electricity in residences was almost twenty years away. Here and there, along some streets, were installed modest lights, kerosene lamps set on eight-foot poles. Auburn Mayor Thomas Wimberly had persuaded a young electrical engineering graduate named Arthur St. Clair Dunstan to put these lights in place, and they provided modest illumination in the evenings. They also became an occasional target for some of the more enterprising cadets, who would put gunpowder at the base, attach a fuse, light the burner, and retreat a distance to watch their destructive results. Residents didn't know from night to night whether the closest street lamp would provide an evening's light or a brief explosion.[21]

In 1890s Auburn, drinking water for man and beast came from wells. Food was grown locally. The college had land for use as pastures and for agricultural experiments, a priority of the president. The train depot saw regular-running trains, if only five or six times a day. Auburn residents of the twenty-first century can travel ninety minutes to Atlanta's international airport and be in New York or Honolulu or Paris within hours. Auburn in 1892 had a train to take one to Mont-gomery or Atlanta; from there, one could travel to almost anywhere in the country. Conversely, most any book or equipment could be ordered and delivered to Auburn. Access to travel and receipt of necessities had to be a huge selling point to Charles Allen Cary—as was the essentially blank slate President Broun had given him for building a veterinary program.

Dr. Cary arrived in Auburn by way of a Richmond & Danville train. He disembarked at the depot—the second such structure at that loca-tion, and a building that would burn down from a lightning strike in 1904. On likely one of the final days of 1892, he stood along the short path—later called Mitcham Avenue—that connected the north end of

Main Street and Gay Street, recently named for a local man who sold ninety acres to the college for an Experiment Station farm. Dr. Cary walked into the depot through doors with a wooden sign reading "Auburn" over the entrance. If nature called, he visited the outhouse a few steps beyond the building's west end. If he required a porter, a black man—maybe old Ephiram Drake himself—would have been summoned to bring his horse and cart. But Dr. Cary likely arrived with only a few belongings in a bag or two. His family's furniture and other possessions came later, nearer to the day when Mrs. Cary and Elwyn arrived. Dr. Cary already would have made those arrangements for trunks, crates, bedding, etc.

Taking his bearings, bags in hand, Dr. Cary looked down the hill, down the dirt street to the south, to see the town's business district. He saw on Main Street's (today's College Street's) east side headed toward the Magnolia Avenue intersection: two grocery stores in between vacant stores, a barber shop, a butcher shop, a general store, a hardware store (possibly operated by Mayor Wimberly's successor, J. W. Harris), and the drug store on the corner, possibly run by George H. Dixon, druggist and pharmacist. Or maybe at the time, it was Bragaw's Drug Store. Not too many years later, it would get the name of Toomer's. Somewhere in there was T. A. Flanagan's store, which sold boots, shoes, dry goods, clothing, caps and hats, and goods one could order from the nationally famous Wanamaker's in Philadelphia. Flanagan's offered cadets uniforms and other accoutrements—desired or required. In the midst of these establishments was—or later stood—Jackson's Kandy Kitchen. Around the corner was C. P. McElhaney's Livery, Feed, and Sale Stable.

A long plank walkway stretched from the intersection up the street, fronting each store. Each merchant constructed the walk in front of his shop, so various segments were not uniform plank width or height. If there were no customers, Dr. Cary may have seen merchants taking a break in front of their stores, sharing the latest family or church news.

The west side of north Main Street offered another grocery, perhaps W. B. Gullatte's store, with its dry goods and "all kinds of can goods." Also along this western side of the street was Mr. Holifield's store, located "at the old drug store place," a cobbler, another meat market, another general store and grocery, and a photo shop. The Thomas Hotel was next, and immediately north of it, the McElheney Hotel—later called the Jones Hotel. Perhaps Dr. Cary lodged in one of those for a time before his family arrived. At the intersection nearest to where he stood, across Main Street, was a cotton warehouse. In the middle of the dirt street, three-quarters of the way to the intersection with Magnolia, Dr. Cary would have noticed a gathering spot—perhaps a horse-and-carriage stopped at that moment—where drivers allowed their horses a well-water break. Another well was found around the corner on East Magnolia in front of a new Episcopal Church building, the Church of the Holy Innocents.

Farther down, rising above the modest skyline of downtown Auburn, stood the imposing Main Building, by far the tallest building for many miles, which in years to come would be named for a local who became Governor William James Samford. For the time being, it was known as the Main Building, which it was, but it was not the first. Old Main, the original, had stood on that site for thirty years from its construction in 1857 until a fire began in the basement's northwest corner around four o'clock in the morning on June 24, 1887. The Main Building Dr. Cary saw—built from some of the bricks of its burned predecessor as well as new bricks made at the Pinetucket house two miles to the southwest—had been standing for only five years as he arrived, but its stately clock tower was visible from the depot, and its two-ton bell—hoisted into place by an industrious local named John Frazier Heard—could be heard for miles as it tolled each quarter-hour. A white picket fence ran along the building's east side, parallel to the dirt Main Street, with a row of trees on either side of the street.

On the north side of the impressive Main Building, Dr. Cary saw another campus structure, the recently named Langdon Hall. Constructed many years earlier, this building once sat a few blocks away, at the corner of today's Gay Street and Magnolia Avenue, where it served as the Auburn Masonic Female College's auditorium. After the Female College closed following the Civil War, the building was relocated—in pieces—in 1883 to its present site next to Old Main, then the Main Building, later Samford Hall. By the time of Dr. Cary's arrival, Langdon already had received a major makeover, with its exterior now bricked and its old Italianate style chunked for a Greek Revival look. Four massive columns adorned and supported a new front porch, reached by a dozen steps from ground level. Langdon Hall—named for an Auburn trustee and secretary of state from Mobile named Charles Langdon—would be the home of Dr. Cary's first Auburn office. He, Dr. George Petrie, and a few other faculty were housed on the first floor of Langdon in the 1890s.[22]

As Dr. Cary looked down Main Street that December day in 1892, several yards from the intersection of Main and Magnolia sat a smaller but elegant-looking structure, built only four years earlier, which served as the chemistry laboratory building. It joined the Main Building and Langdon Hall to form the chief facilities of the main campus as Dr. Cary arrived, not counting faculty housing and an Experiment Station plot a healthy walk to the south. His veterinary building would be the fourth. That chemistry laboratory building (later used for art and music instruction) remains—today called Hargis Hall, headquarters of Auburn's Graduate School. It remembers Estes Hargis, MD, (1895-1966), an Auburn student of 1915-17 who studied medicine at the University of Pennsylvania and who later worked alongside Dr. Will Mayo, founder of the Mayo Clinic.

Other streets fed off Main and Magnolia, with commercial buildings and houses situated in rows in various directions, but as Dr. Cary got his bearings in his new town, the sight of the academic center must have encouraged him. At least this unknown place had three impressive buildings, and the president had told him of adequate pasture land beyond the campus. In addition, faculty members enjoyed nice-for-its-time housing along the streets adjacent to campus, including Faculty Avenue by the Main Building. Dr. Cary also remembered President Broun's promise that, if Dr. Cary came to Auburn, Auburn would provide him a veterinary building. And, he knew, William LeRoy Broun's word was solid.

The record has not been uncovered as to the exact date Dr. Cary rolled into town late in December 1892, but surely he was in place by December 31 to report for duty on New Year's Day. He likely had a first-hand view of a massive downtown fire that destroyed commercial property, though not along Main Street. The chief publication of the time, *The College Index*, a local monthly news magazine, detailed that fire in its January 1893 edition:

> On the night of December 31st Auburn was visited by a disastrous fire—the third within the past six months. This time the fire started (it is supposed from a hanging lamp) in the Masonic Building. The flames quickly spread to some adjoining buildings, and before the fire could be stopped it had destroyed five buildings. If it had not been for a heavy rain it is highly probable that the whole of the business portion of the town would have been burned. This narrow escape is a strong argument for the organization of a fire department.[23]

The College Index also noted Dr. Cary's arrival on the Agricultural and Mechanical College faculty, though this notice did not appear until the June 1893 issue. The magazine reported:

> Dr. C.A. Cary has been made professor of physiology and veterinary science. Dr. Cary spent a number of months last year in Germany pursuing studies in his special line, and he is amply equipped for the work he has to do here. As veterinarian of the Experiment Station he is enabled to do a species of work that will be specially appreciated by the farmers all over the State.[24]

When Dr. Cary arrived in Auburn prior to beginning his work on January 1, 1893, he came alone. Emma and baby Elwyn stayed a time with her parents in Illinois. Her travel dates are unclear after all these decades. An article in the *Lee County Bulletin* from 1944—a yellowed clipping included among many papers and other items preserved in an array of boxes and trunks in the attic of the Cary home and taken out after the death of Alice Cary Pick Gibson in 2006—was authored by Emma Cary herself and detailed her remembrances from fifty years previous. We can attribute the misspelling of her married last name to a typesetter's error. And oddly, she would have arrived in 1893, not 1894 as she remembered, and their stay in Europe was a part of one year, not two. But those details aside, Emma Cary provided a unique perspective on her initial arrival into Auburn as well as a glimpse of the village at that time. A portion of what she wrote in that article:

> In the year 1894—fifty years ago—a young man elected professor in the Alabama Polytechnic Institute hired a horse and buggy to meet his wife and baby son at the railway station in Auburn, Alabama. They had just returned from a two years' stay in Europe where this young professor studied bacteriology in Berlin under the celebrated Dr. Koch who discovered the tuberculosis bacillus. The young man was Dr. Charles Allen Carey. [sic]
>
> Young Dr. Carey had some misgivings about the first impression his wife might have of our new home town, so he instructed the driver not to drive us up the main street but to detour East to Gay, and then drive West to a residence where now stands Duncan Hall.
>
> We were domiciled in two rooms, taking our meals with the Claytons, an Episcopalian family that had a house full of college boys. In those days all college people considered it their bounden duty to help house the 250

college students then attending Auburn College. There were no dormitories or fraternities then.

Life in those days was easy and care-free, with no seeming annoyances. The houses put up at that time were built on stilts or brick pillars; so that the air circulated freely and blew away the termites. There were no lawns to mow—as grass those days did not grow under trees—so we had to decide between the trees and Bermuda grass. We preferred the trees.

There were no servant problems. One . . . family could supply more help than was needed. Old Uncle Joe would carry in the water and the wood for Aunt Liza the cook; one of the [children] would take her bundle of sticks and sweep the yard; another would fill the kerosene lamps and get the lanterns ready for our "black-out" nights when the moon was not shining. They would provide our tables with all the vitamins we needed but of which we had never heard.

Our College President, Dr. Broun, when once asked why they had located the college here, replied, "For its healthfulness of climate and poverty of soil: any experiment succeeding here would succeed anywhere in the State."

There did not seem to exist at that time any sympathetic communication with such evils as strikes, sabotages, rivalries, or income taxes. It seemed that the sun shone more brightly, the atmosphere was filled with the fragrance of china berry blossoms. Japonica, honeysuckle and kiss-me-at-the-gate were entrancing. The mocking birds, accompanied by all the others, sang most lustily. Perhaps there was too much leisure and contentment for progress—in a material way. This even tenure could not continue much longer. Ideas and notions began to enter our consciousness.

One day we were told that we were to have a football team at our college. A dashing young man by the name of George Petrie was elected to serve as coach. He served for two years. Some exciting times followed this innovation, especially when our students celebrated their victories with a bonfire at the railway station. They would tear through town like an avalanche, carrying before them fence rails, boxes, barrels and boards from sidewalks—where there were any; and merchants often contributed a share, even adding kerosene to their donations. Property owners would guard their gates, fences and chicken houses lest next morning they find desolation. The boys would ignite this huge pyre on the arrival of the train. One night we were told, a woman travelling from the North saw the fire and students half clad performing their Indian dance around the blaze, and she fainted, thinking it was one of those Southern lynchings she had heard about.[25]

Thus, the Cary family was reunited in the early days of 1893 at home in Auburn, at first in two rooms of a house along today's Mell Street, located where Duncan Hall now sits, but in 1893 a short walk from the headquarters of the Experiment Station. Whether sooner or later, Dr. Cary arranged, for his family's second Auburn home, a house east of the Main Building and a couple of blocks over, a five-minute brisk walk east from his family's initial, temporary lodging. This second house faced east near today's northwest corner of Gay Street and Miller Avenue, a short walk from either the Main Building or to his experiment farm. The family lived in this second house for a few years before moving in 1897 to North Main (College) Street into the house now known as the Halliday-Cary-Pick House. (Dr. Cary bought the late Major Halliday's 1851 house—used by Union troops as a hospital during the Civil War and as a recovery place for Confederates after the war—and four surrounding acres at public auction for $1,625 on February 2, 1897, according to family papers. Two years later, Dr. Cary purchased additional land, a large tract to the north and west to serve as his farm, a section of town today known as Cary Woods.)

The Carys became key people in the village from their arrival. In addition to Dr. Cary's veterinary work, the couple quickly became involved with a local conversation club which brought together college and community adults for shared study and social occasions. The civic service-minded Emma also would become an early leader, even president, of the Auburn Woman's Club, and she would play a significant local role in the fight for suffrage in the early twentieth century.

Soon after their arrival in Auburn, given the episode of spiritual commitment in Emma Heck Cary's hometown church two weeks after their wedding more than two years earlier, Dr. and Mrs. Cary made sure to affiliate with a local church. They placed membership with the Auburn Presbyterian Church, located then at the corner of Main Street and Faculty Avenue in what is now the Auburn University Chapel. The young couple had a short walk on Sundays from their home to the church services.

Auburn Presbyterian Church was established on June 16, 1850, when an area presbytery sent Minister William H. Moore to hold evangelical services for a group of Presbyterians who were meeting on a regular basis but had not yet formalized as a congregation. This group was led by Edwin Reese, who along with his wife, Sarah, were charter members of the West Point, Georgia, Presbyterian Church in December 1837. Reese moved to the newly settled Auburn after that time, built a plantation, and became a trustee of both the Auburn Female Academy and the East Alabama Male College. Reese's thirty-two slaves made the bricks used in building the structure that became the first Presbyterian Church, later the Auburn University Chapel. At the church's first meeting, Reese was elected and ordained one of the group's ruling elders, a church office to which Dr. Cary would be elected in 1896. The Carys never met the Reeses; Sarah died in 1865, and Edwin in 1877. However, the Auburn Presbyterian Church they helped establish would bring Charles Allen and Emma Cary into close contact with a number of important Auburnites of the late nineteenth century: George Petrie, a member there for more than fifty years; A. J. Bondurant, a colleague of Dr. Cary's in the Experiment Station; local bookstore owner R. W. Burton; and Mathematics Professor Bolling H. Crenshaw, who later lived across the street from the Cary family on North College Street.

The Presbyterian congregation was led at the time of the Carys' arrival by Rev. C. A. Baker, Opelika's full-time minister who preached at Auburn once a month. Charles Allen and Emma didn't have long to know him: he died August 7, 1893. From the time of Baker's death through the first months of 1894, the congregation's ruling elders preached. Dr. Cary's appointment as an elder came in 1896, so he likely was excused from pulpit duties during this era, though it's hard to imagine the locals would have passed up a chance to hear from a bright Christian man of his local prominence. During 1896, if not before, Dr. Cary began a long run as superintendent of the Presbyterian Church's Sunday School program. Also in 1896, the group welcomed its next preacher: J. J. Woll, who was also the Opelika minister. Woll filled in monthly for three years but left the area for Virginia in 1899. A year or so later, he was shot and killed at age thirty-two by a lawyer who had an uncharitable reaction to something Woll preached.

During these early years, Auburn Presbyterian Church membership hovered around twenty-five, but with the coming of the next minister, a twenty-six-year-old named Thomas Johnston Hutchinson, who arrived in May 1910, membership grew to around seventy in five years. Hutchinson was an advocate of family prayer, and he preached against drinking and dancing. Apparently, his audience was keen to hear these messages. As membership grew, some felt it was time for a larger building. A plan was hatched to trade the building and location to the YMCA for another lot a block east, at the corner of what is today Thach Avenue and Gay Street. Some in the congregation believed the college-front location was too good to give up. While it is unknown where the Carys fell on this issue, the group went through with the swap plan and, by 1917, began meeting in the new location a block away. The Auburn Presbyterian Church still meets there today.

By the 1920s, the City of Auburn began paving some streets, but the Presbyterian Church was expected to pay for the cost of paving Thach Avenue and Gay Street where those streets bordered church property. Someone in the congregation led opposition to this approach due to cost; but, as both Dr. and Mrs. Cary would show, time and again, support for wise use of taxes for progress in the community, one would assume they heartily approved of paved streets and of paying one's fair share. The Presbyterians eventually paid for paving a portion of Thach Avenue in 1928, but several years passed before they turned over funds related to paving their portion of Gay Street.

In 1926, the Carys and others at church welcomed new minister Samuel Burney Hay, who served the congregation in this capacity until 1948. He was the minister at the time of Dr. Cary's death in 1935. The dean's funeral service, held in Langdon Hall to accommodate the crowd, was largely an API and veterinary community event, but Brother Hay had a role in that service and likely in the graveside memorial that followed.[26]

In 1893, however, Charles Allen and Emma Cary were settling into their new community of friends. After they moved from the Mell Street house to the Gay Street/Miller Avenue location, their neighbors on Gay Street a few blocks to the north included President Broun and, next to him, Professor J. T. Anderson. Turning west on Faculty Avenue, neighbors a short walk up included: Dr. John Hodges Drake, III, the college and town physician, on the east side of Main Street; and across the street, General James Henry Lane, the Confederate officer who taught civil engineering and whose daughter would marry Dr. Petrie and live next door; Professor Leroy Stafford Boyd, son of former East Alabama Male College President David French Boyd; Professor Patrick Hues Mell, whose house sat close to where today's Mell Street intersects with Thach Avenue and who later served as president of Clemson University; Professor John J. Wilmore, who devoted more than fifty years to teaching and administration in Auburn engineering; and Professor Charles Coleman Thach, who would be named president of API after the death of President Broun and for whom the street later was named.

President Broun, a masterful administrator and planner, was excited about the start-up of the veterinary science program he had long wanted to add to the curriculum. He had not wasted time in arranging for the arrival of his newest star faculty member. An inventory of the Veterinary Department's chemicals and instruments, written in a flowing longhand cursive and dated March 31, 1892, listed a number of items as procured, most or all before Dr. Cary began his initial three-month appointment. One can assume this inventory resulted from President Broun asking Dr. Cary for his "list of apparatus that you will need" in that November 16, 1891, letter. The paper being dated on the final day of Dr. Cary's visiting lecturer appointment may mean this list reflected the assortment of veterinary supplies in place as Dr. Cary left town. The inventory included:

Medicines in Experiment Station Office

Epsom Salts	20 lbs.
Sodium Sulphate	10 lbs.
Sulphate of Iron	5 lbs.
Sulphur	5 lbs.
Nux Vomica	1 lb.
Salicylic Acid	1 lb.
Boracic Acid	2 lbs.
Barbados Aloes	1 lb.
Chlorate of Potash	2 lbs.
Zinc Sulfate	2 lbs.
Lead Acetate	1 lb.
Potassium Nitrate	4 lbs.
Hyposulfite Soda	1 lb.
Bromide Potassium	1 lb.
Tinnic acid	4 oz.
Calomel	1 lb.
Sulphate Cinchonidia	4 oz.
Hydro Chlorate Cocaine	1/8 oz.
Muriate Pilocarpine	30 grams
Sulfate of Errine	3 grams
Oxide Potash	¼ lb.
Lunar Caustic	1 oz.
Cantharides	1 oz.
Per Iodide of Mercury	1 oz.
Glycerine	1 lb.

Muriate Tincture Iron	1 lb.
Sweet Spirits of Nitra	2 lbs.
Fluid Extract Belladonna	1 lb.
Crystalized Carbolic Acid	1 lb.
Tincture of Iodine	4 oz.
Chromic Acid	1 oz.
Croton Oil	1 oz.
Tincture of Digitas	½ lb.
Chloroform	3 lbs.
Vaseline	1 lb.
Raw Linseed Oil (in cans)	2 gallons
Iron Mortar and Pestle	1
Large Spatula	1
Alcohol	1 ½ gallons
Muslin for Bandages	5 yards

Instruments (in Box at Agricultural College Museum)
(one each of the following items)
Open Molar Cutter
Closed Molar Cutter
Molar Extracting Forceps
Pair Handles for Cutters and Extractor
Set, H & D Floats and Tooth Files
Tooth Chisel
Half Tooth Forceps
Crooked Front Tooth File
¾ inch Trephine
Castotome
Metal Mallet
Bone Gauge or Scoof
Green's Mouth Speculum
Schaefer's Ecraseur
Nose Speculum
Bone Drill with Complete Set of Drills
Two-ounce Hand Rubber Syringe
Horse Catheter
Dozen Assorted Surgical Needles
Nearly Fool Spool of Surgeon's Silk Thread
Paquedine Thermo Cautery with Two Platinum Points—All in Special Case—Valuable—$80

Pair Scissors 6 in. Curved on Flat
Right Drawing Hoof Knife
Left Drawing Hoof Knife
Embryotomy Knife Slide Catch
Spring back Castrating Knife
Tenotomy Knife Straight Long Handle
Sharp Pointed Scalpel Hard Rubber Handle
Broad Blade Scalpel Hard Rubber Handle-Slide Catch
Sharp Pointed Curved Bistoury Hard Rubber Handle-Side Catch
Probe Pointed Curved Bistoury Hard Rubber Handle-Side Catch
French _____ Catch Artery Forceps
Fricke's Slide Catch Artery Forceps
Bulldog Artery Forceps
Aspirating Needle & Trocar with Rubber Bulb Attachment
Set of Baker's Casting Hobbles & Chain
Self-Adjusting Tracheotomy Tube

Apparatus—at Museum

Artificial Hoof (in case in Agricultural Museum at College)	1
Charts of Drawing of Teeth of Horse and Ox	4
Chart Drawing of Alimentary Canal of Horse	1
Chart Drawing of Alimentary Canal of Ox	1
Large Canvass Chart Drawing of Horse's Foot, Horse Shoes	1
Box of Anatomical and Pathological Bones (at station in box)	1
Set of 5 Charts printed at museum at college	1
Two Kidneys (Diseased, Preserved in Alcohol at Prof. Atkinson's Laboratory)	
Human Skeleton	1
Horse Skeleton	1
Ox Skeleton	1
Sheep Skeleton	1
Hog Skeleton	1

CHAPTER NINE

STARTING UP A VETERINARY PROGRAM

L ike the college president who hired him, Dr. Cary already had a
plan when he arrived at Auburn. This plan evolved through the
experiences he gained during his years at Iowa Agricultural College, in
veterinary practice at Keokuk, at work in South Dakota, and in the laboratories of Columbia and in Berlin. He aimed to build not only a veterinary science instruction and animal research program, but also, in
the short term, to begin addressing some of the major diseases that
had long affected public health and the nation's agricultural industry,
notably tick fever, hog cholera, and tuberculosis. He also would seek to
elevate his academic program into a degree-granting college on par
with the excellent school he had attended at Iowa State; establish the
office of state veterinarian, the office he had held in South Dakota; and
pursue, through an organization of veterinarians on the state level,
public policy through the Alabama Legislature, to ensure that adequate and necessary practices were protected and advanced in a society that was not given to trusting authority.

Joe Yeager and Gene Stevenson, longtime Auburn agricultural faculty members and administrators, in their comprehensive history of the
university's agriculture program, *Inside Ag Hill*, wrote of Dr. Cary's
early days:

During Cary's first year at Auburn, in addition to his regular classes, he gave lectures at the college chapel each Saturday. He also gave clinical instructions outdoors when weather permitted. Operations were performed and treatment given to diseased and injured animals brought to the [Experiment] Station.[1]

As he began his professorial work, Dr. Cary lectured at 8:00 a.m. twice weekly for two hours in the Main Building, then in his Veterinary Building after its completion. His students may have been late on a regular basis. The Main Building's bell rang at 7:15 each morning to wake the world, and cadets were required to line up for roll call in front of Langdon Hall before a short 7:45 a.m. chapel service each day, including Saturdays. They also had daily roll call at noon and before supper time for several years. Dr. Cary's students took active part in clinical practice three to five hours most days. His classroom presentations focused on such vital issues as anatomy of the horse and cow, diseases common to horses and cattle, equine lameness, minor surgical practices, actions and uses of common medicines, meat inspection, practices for protecting the health of man and of domesticated animals, post-mortem examination practice, dissection, and general pathology.

Dr. Cary had his students purchase a copy of Martin's *Human Body*—the same text he studied at Iowa Agricultural—for learning human anatomy, a copy of Hough and Sedgwick's *The Human Mechanism*, and Huxley's *Physiology*. He may have enlisted the help of his friend, fellow Presbyterian elder and downtown Auburn business owner Robert Burton, owner of Burton's Book Store, for ordering those and other required texts.

Two other longtime Auburn chroniclers, Kaye Lovvorn and Jerry Roden, both of whom served as editor of the *Auburn Alumnews*, collaborated in 1970 on a short history of the veterinary medicine program. They described Dr. Cary's typical daily appearance as wearing "a uniform blue serge suit, starched collar and derby hat." From that formal, no-nonsense appearance came a man on a mission:

> By all accounts, he was a tough taskmaster, but Dr. Cary asked no more than he gave. For years, he arose at daybreak and went to work on his farm near Auburn. He returned home for breakfast and then drove his two-wheel cart to campus where he taught an eight o'clock class. An hour later, he drove to the depot to catch a 9:18 train to Montgomery,

where he performed his duties as state veterinarian. When he came back to Auburn on the eight o'clock train that night, his secretary—a male student—met him, and they disposed of the day's mail. Then Dr. Cary went home to supper. About 1926, Dr. Cary replaced his horse-drawn two-wheeler with one of Auburn's first automobiles. A busy man, he always started in high and routinely burned out his clutch. A local mechanic tried to tell him how to use low gear and save clutches. As he jerked down the road, Dr. Cary responded, "Don't tell me how to drive my car."[2]

Historian Redding Sugg, Jr.—son of the College of Veterinary Medicine's third dean—also wrote a description of Dean Cary in his 2004 essay in the Veterinary College's *Quarterly*:

Dressed as for a 19th-century costume drama, Dr. Cary wore a frock coat, standup collar, walrus mustache, and thick hair waving down over his collar. His piercing eyes were fairly caught in Mrs. Moore's portrait [which hangs in the lobby of Greene Hall, outside the entrance to the Cary Veterinary Library at the College of Veterinary Medicine], and his Midwestern accent was exotic to our Alabama ears. We boys had to have bulldog pompadours, a sort of crewcut just long enough to part; college boys kept their hair short, and of course rats [first-year API students then] had no hair at all. One day somebody, no doubt a vet student, placed a sign in Dr. Cary's car reading Helpfully, Uncle Billy Askew's Barber Shop. Haircuts 10 Cents."[3]

Uncle Billy's was a downtown Auburn barber shop/shoe repair. One of Uncle Billy's advertisements in the *Plainsman* from the mid-1930s proclaimed haircuts for $.30, shoe shines for $.05, "GOOD HOT DOGS and GOOD HAMBURGERS" for $.05, plus ice cream, candies, cakes, fresh cold milk, cold drinks, hot chocolate, and hot coffee served with whipped cream. "The best coffee found anywhere in the world, FIVE CENTS." They also offered dry cleaning and pressing as local representatives for Sunshine Cleaners. There was no address given in the ad, but Billy's was located "across street from campus."

Responding to a 1991 letter from Dr. H. C. Morgan '55, then associate dean for administration and academic affairs at the veterinary college, Redding Sugg, Jr. wrote that he remembered Dr. Cary "distinctly" from his boyhood. "I was 13 when he died," Sugg wrote. "I found him intimidating, with that handle-bar moustache, long hair over his collar in the era of the bulldog pompadour, rather peculiar accent that origin of which I don't know, and piercing eyes. Did he really wear a frock coat—I seem to remember that he did." Sugg admitted Dr. Cary projected "something of the rather eccentric effect."[4]

With Dr. Cary's arrival and with some level of attention then placed on veterinary science instruction, twenty-five students enrolled in his first veterinary science class. Many, if not all, of the students in his early classes would have taken part in Dr. Cary's efforts in clinical cases and outreach on the campus. Some of the diagnostic and instructional work with live animals soon was conducted a few hundred feet west of the Veterinary Building, on grounds outside the barn and stables Dr. Cary had constructed at the approximate location of Auburn's Textile Engineering Building, rebuilt and repurposed in 2018 as the Gavin Engineering Research Laboratory. Additional hands-on animal work likely took place on the 225-acre campus Experiment Station farm where a barn and a small dairy were located near the present-day Samford Avenue/Mell Street intersection, near the President's Home and the Hill Dormitories.

That Experiment Station farm was meager at the time of Dr. Cary's arrival, but he did find a setting much improved from what it had been. The land had been farmed previous to the 1890s but was abandoned because of low yield and erosion. The Experiment Station became active in earnest in 1883, after the Alabama Legislature authorized the A&M College to receive one-third of the proceeds from state fertilizer sales so experts at Auburn could conduct some basic research on the fertilizers used in Alabama.

President Broun had directed that the site be upgraded to further this work. Buildings and fences left from the previous era were either demolished or repaired, pine thickets were cleared out, ditches filled in. A water supply was made available. Dairy equipment was purchased and installed. Quality Jersey cows were brought in—the 1897 *Glomerata* bragged on "a herd of the finest Jersey cattle to be found in the South."[5]

Additional barns, a silo, office space, and work rooms were constructed. Meteorological equipment was acquired. The location was being built still when Dr. Cary left in the spring of 1892 for his trip to Europe. That spring, a ten-horsepower motor was added to furnish power to run the cotton gin, threshing machine, and feed mill. The stable and pig pens were repositioned to more suitable locations, and a windmill was erected to move water through pipes to a new barn and to cattle and hog lots. With all these improvements, the Experiment Station farm was in much better condition when Dr. Cary returned at the beginning of 1893.[6]

Dr. Calvin W. Schwabe, a 1954 graduate of the College of Veterinary Medicine at Auburn and later an eminent public health veterinarian and administrator, said during a 1992 celebration marking Dr. Cary's centennial year of arriving in Auburn, the dean "quickly established himself as an energetic man of action guided by a deep faith in the limitless potential of the mostly rural people who were then the 'backbone of America.'"[7] That faith in the rural people began at Auburn with teaching veterinary science to the sons of farmers, but quickly expanded as Dr. Cary spread his work in a rippling effect through society.

Dr. Cary built his veterinary program first through coursework for his students, but soon added Saturday free clinics to involve and benefit area farmers and their animals, all the while lobbying for and seeing to completion a series of buildings that gradually moved the program's center to the west on the campus. He advanced veterinary medicine's place in the Deep South through hiring a series of assistants to help with the teaching load, research demands, and clinical caseload. He also generated worlds of good will and political points beyond the campus borders through his appearances during several years at Farmers' Institutes throughout Alabama, in which he taught farmers and conducted clinical examinations and treatments—including surgeries—on their animals, at times for hours on end.

In the 1894 Annual Report of the Experiment Station, which President Broun presented to college trustees, Dr. Cary most likely contributed this description of his Saturday clinics:

> These lectures were always delivered in connection with surgical operations, or with the examination and treatment of cases having internal or constitutional diseases. This clinical work was given for the special instruction of the farmers and students. The practical cases formed excellent object lessons for instructing the students and farmers in the most practical and scientific ways of treating sick and diseased animals.[8]

What caliber of hands-on veterinarian was Dr. Cary? By the middle of his career, he had gained such a national reputation that he was appointed in 1919 to a three-person Committee on Methods of Teaching Surgery of the Association of State and Provincial Veterinary Colleges. This committee's detailed recommendations for aligning surgical training in the nation's veterinary colleges were published in that spring's issue of the *Journal of the AVMA*.[9]

One man who later walked in Dr. Cary's shoes as dean at Auburn described a focused, talented, and dedicated servant. Dean Emeritus John Thomas Vaughan, interviewed in the *Auburn Veterinarian* in 2013, spoke admiringly of his predecessor:

> The record is pretty sketchy in places. But from 1892, when Dr. Cary came to Auburn and worked without any permanent credentials until 1907 when the school was established, that entire time, he might have had one assistant, two at most. No one to help. What he did, he did singlehandedly: taught class after class, worked in the laboratory, provided care to animals. There was the time he went somewhere and lectured all day long and then operated on a whole raft of animals. These weren't dogs and cats. These were horses and mules, every now and then cattle. He was doing surgeries and castrations, foot infections, lameness, a multitude of whatever came along. These were large animals, and he was using whatever help could be drafted on site. No tranquilizers, no antibiotics, almost no anesthetics, very rudimentary anesthetics. Restraint was purely physical, with some psychological restraint.[10]

Occasionally, one can find a comment that one of his students may have written about Dr. Cary's diagnostic and surgical skills. But those are rare. One glimpse into his clinical skills may be found in a report he made to the June 1906 issue of the *American Veterinary Review*. Dr. Cary's paper on "Diaphragmatic Hernia in a Twelve-Year-Old Mule" is included in that issue's section on "Reports of Cases." That report reveals the thorough nature of Dr. Cary's handling of a single, representative case:

> The mule had been resting for 10 weeks with what appeared like gonitis in the left hind limb, but had been treated for bone spavin and sesamoiditis. During this time it ran in a lot with a few horses, and occasionally had access to a lot where cattle were fed cotton-seed meal and hulls. On two or three occasions it had colic attacks, which yielded to the ordinary domestic remedies of soda, etc. What seemed to be a fourth attack of colic called me to the case on March 23. I found the mule without fever, normal pulse, and suffering from colicky pains, manifest by uneasiness, getting up, lying down, etc. In the left rib region four ribs were fractured and a marked

indenture, as often found in cases of osteo-porosis. The lameness history, the broken ribs, and the colic from indigestion, led me to suspect osteoporosis. The mule was sent to the hospital and was treated for colic and in the course of 24 hours seemed to be free of pain and eating grain and hay. The broken ribs being movable and sensitive, I expected pleurisy might develop. On the third day my assistant called me to see the pumping breathing of hydrothorax. Hence, we waited a few hours and the labored breathing disappeared and respirations became nearly normal. The temperature was then 103 to 105 F., and pulse rapid, 80 per minute. That night the mule died. Post-mortem revealed a rupture of the stomach; quite a quantity of food in abdominal cavity; abdomen full of red serum; peritonitis; liver, spleen and kidneys engorged with blood. Thorax, quite a quantity of res serum, but not as much as was found in the abdomen. Pleura was only slightly inflamed. Lungs almost normal. The double colon and caecum were in the left lung cavity; not strangulated nor inflamed, and contained apparently normal semi-liquid material and no more gas than usual. A piece or fold of the mesentery and omentum had at some previous period passed through an opening between the spleen and stomach and another opening on the left side of the tendinous portion of the diaphragm and become fixed to the inner surface of a fracture of the 11th rib. The hernia opening in the diaphragm was 2½ inches in diameter, and the opening between the spleen and the stomach was about the same size. The edges of each opening were smooth and entirely healed, showing that they were not recently made.

No doubt the immediate cause of death was the rupture of the stomach.

But how could a twelve-year-old mule do hard dray work up to within ten weeks of its death with such a diaphragmatic hernia?

Possibly it occurred some time during the ten weeks.[11]

Dr. Cary authored another paper which the *American Veterinary Review* published in a 1910 issue, a recap of twenty recent cases of "roaring" in horses and mules he had seen at Auburn. In this paper, Dr. Cary noted that he had tried surgical methods developed by both L. A. Merillat and W. L. Williams. These included cases from local farms as well as animals referred to him by veterinarians in St. Louis; from West Point, Georgia; and from Birmingham. The details of those cases indicate that Dr. Cary maintained a hands-on approach to his work during even his busiest times of involvement with administering the veterinary college; serving as state veterinarian; conducting the Farmers' Institutes; solving public health and political issues related to

Texas fever, hog cholera, and tuberculosis; and in his duties as a frequent officer of the American Veterinary Medical Association.

Saturday clinics or not, during 1894, Charles Allen Cary was still low man on the Auburn totem pole, so he was not exempt from the occasional mundane assignment. One such example was covered in the old *Orange and Blue* student newspaper, forerunner of today's *Auburn Plainsman*, in its November 21, 1894, issue. Montgomery during November 8-16 hosted a Southern Exposition, an event likely closer to a state or county fair than to the World Expo that Dr. Cary had visited in 1890 in Chicago. Nevertheless, expectations soared. The *Vernon Courier* newspaper predicted in its September 27, 1894, edition that "The southern Exposition which is to be held in Montgomery from the 8th to the 16th Nov. promises to eclipse anything of the kind ever held in the state." With that level of hype, President Broun wanted his budding college to have an impressive presence in this affair, with all disciplines featured. Dr. Cary was the man he selected to make that happen. He proved a good choice. The campus newspaper account makes for a fascinating recap of the Agricultural and Mechanical College's exhibits:

> The exhibit of Polytechnic Institute at the Southern Exposition in Montgomery is the most extensive and varied that the Institute has ever made. It occupies the entire end of the main building, and has been very artistically arranged by Dr. Cary who is in charge, assisted by Messrs. Trammel and Hammack.
>
> Commencing at the right, the first department is that of Mechanics. In this the most noticeable exhibits are, a ten horse power steam engine made by the students, and student work illustrating the course of instruction in wood work, forging and machine work. Some of the work in ornamental turning is very beautiful, showing both taste and workmanship. The next exhibit is that of the department of Electrical Engineering. This contains a dynamo made by the students which has been in use for some time, furnishing power to run the cotton gin, thresher and other farm machinery at the experiment station. It also contains many other specimens of student work and of instruments used in the Electrical Laboratory.
>
> The next exhibit is that of the Department of Civil Engineering. It contains several sets of instruments, and some very fine models of bridges now in use on prominent railroads. But the most attractive feature is the

beautiful drawings, very handsomely mounted. These drawings are student work in Architecture, Mechanical and Machine drawing as well as in Civil Engineering. They illustrate the course in drawing, and the method of instruction. Many of them were on exhibition at the World's Fair at Chicago, and attracted much notice and commendation. Suspended from the walls is the diploma and the medal awarded for the exhibit made at the Paris Exposition. This exhibit has been highly complimented by Engineers and other competent judges.

The central exhibit is in an alcove in which are a set of German Models illustrating descriptive Geometry and a large number of Photographs of the College buildings, laboratories, apparatus, etc., the football teams, and the Faculty. The photographs are so arranged as to give a very pleasing effect, as well as to furnish much information as to facilities of the College for instruction. The alcove is always thronged with interested visitors.

The exhibit of the department of Biology next to the left of the alcove has cases of insects and a fine display of mounted Alabama birds. Then comes the exhibit of the department of Botany and Geology. The exhibit of foreign cottons grown on the College farm, consisting of stalk, leaves, boils and the cotton, is both novel and instructive. This exhibit attracts unusual notice. Probably no similar exhibit has ever been seen in the country.

In the department of Agriculture, there are all kinds of Agricultural products raised in the South and a great variety of seeds put up in jars, etc.

The special feature is the Tobacco, both in the leaf and in the manufactured form. Experts say these specimens compare favorably with the best tobaccos of Virginia and North Carolina. It is said that even young ladies asked for some of the "Golden Plug," presumably for their sweethearts. The last exhibit is that of the Veterinary Department. This contains several skeletons of domestic animals from Ward's Celebrated Establishment, also fine papier-mache models of the organs of animals in their normal and in diseased conditions, and many other objects of interest too numerous to mention.

This exhibit attracts universal attention and is thronged with visitors. It is a revelation to most visitors and will doubtless be of great benefit to the College in enlightening the public as to the extensive facilities furnished for higher technical and scientific education. A pleasing attraction is the large sign painted and decorated in college colors, and the tasteful manner in which exhibits are arranged.[12]

The *Opelika Morning Post* described the college exhibit as "highly praised by many visitors . . . one of the great attractions at the Exposition." But its report also noted that Dr. Cary and Professor Trammell had to spend, most likely, hour after hour packing up all that stuff and shipping back to Auburn the vast array of pictures, apparatuses, skeletons, and tobacco samples.[13] Such was the dues-paying required of a young faculty member.

Fresh from his impressive showing at the Montgomery Expo, Dr. Cary in 1895 began developing plans for an actual hospital space near the veterinary building. Again, he earned the trustees' and President Broun's support for this facility; and, in 1896, Dr. Cary supervised construction of a hospital building that provided five large box stalls and four open, single stalls. An upstairs area was utilized for feed storage. Dr. Cary may have had someone bring in a cat or two to live in the hospital to help keep the inevitable mice and rats at bay, as Auburn for many years had a most active and populous rodent society—even besides freshmen. (For ages, in a tradition that has since gone away, Auburn's first-year students were known as "rats," and most agreed to purchase and to wear while on campus the small orange and blue beanie that was referred to as a "rat cap.")

The Veterinary Department had use of an adjacent six-acre parcel, which today represents the heart of the northeast section of campus (largely that area along West Magnolia Avenue fronted by Ginn College of Engineering facilities). This land was divided into lots, pens, and paddocks. One lot within this compound held two sheds where, combined, 175 cattle, oxen, horses, and mules could be housed. These sheds were used for short-term housing for animals brought to campus for diagnosis and treatment as well as for isolation of animals suspected of carrying infectious disease. What may strike the modern reader is that the always-muddy surroundings of Dr. Cary's veterinary realm did not stand out. Auburn's streets were unpaved at this point, and many homes surrounding the campus had backyard animals that gave nearby yards a look similar to the on-campus pastures. Still, perhaps from the standpoint of aroma, this West Magnolia area did stand out.

As he learned from his Iowa State days, Dr. Cary used Saturday clinics chiefly for instruction. In fact, the API *Catalog* from 1901-02 specifically stated that, "Free clinics are given every Saturday for the benefit of students in veterinary science." Benefits to locals were secondary, though Dr. Cary recognized that having animals brought in from area farms was an excellent way for him and his team to ascertain the general health status of Alabama's cows, horses, mules, and hogs.

Institutional records of Dr. Cary's Saturday clinics in those early days of the program probably no longer exist, but one source offers insight into the events that took place. In the Auburn University Library's Special Collections, two notebooks survive from the time, each page containing the handwritten notes of C. L. Jenkins, who either observed or took part in Saturday clinic proceedings. The *Glomerata* yearbook at Auburn from 1900 listed a Clarence Luther Jenkins from Talladega among "special students," enrolled for instruction but not a member of any of the degree-seeking classes. He is not found in the *Glomerata* yearbooks on either side of 1900. Whatever brought Jenkins to Auburn, he spent his Saturdays that fall of 1899 and the following winter of 1900 attending Dr. Cary's Saturday clinics, taking notes on each case.

Jenkins' notes include the names of the animal owners, where they were from, the type of animal brought, each animal's age and presenting problem, and notes about the recommended treatment. Nowhere in the notebooks does he mention Dr. Cary or any other professor or fellow student. But during those weeks—a dozen Saturdays from September 23 through December 9 of 1899 and a like period from January to May of 1900—Jenkins recorded the activities.

Owners came from mostly local communities: Auburn, Opelika, Sandy Hill, Hatchechubbee, Ridge Grove, Chewacla, Motts Mill, Society Hill, Notasulga, Roxana, Loachapoka, Tuskegee, Gold Hill, Tallassee, Alliance, Salem, Floyd, Cusseta. The animals were common to rural areas of the time and place: horses, cows, mules, a few dogs. The injuries and illnesses were also what would be expected: bladder trouble, warts and tumors, lameness and dental problems in horses, lack of appetite, general lethargy. Some of the recommendations seem appropriate for medicine in the present time, with the various pharmaceuticals suggested. Other treatments sounded oddly elementary: "Remove the tumor with the knife." "One of the stitches irritates the skin. Remove the stitch."[14]

Jenkins' records show that each Saturday differed in the nature of cases made available to students. The number of cases also varied, from two or three cases in the final two clinics of the year to fourteen and seventeen cases on a couple of Saturdays. The clinics seemed to average eight to ten cases per Saturday, and these included castrations. There is no mention of the location of these clinics. While Dr. Cary kept some animals at the Experiment Station farm, located in the vicinity of today's President's Home and the Hill Dorms, an AU

Archives photo from the period shows a group gathered for an examination of a horse, with one of the old veterinary buildings nearby. This
photo suggests these Saturday clinics were held on the grounds outside the veterinary buildings in the area of campus where today sit
Ramsay Hall and the Harbert Civil Engineering Center.

Years after he had launched them, Dr. Cary offered his perspective
as to the value of Saturday clinics when the *Orange and Blue* ran a
brief article written by him in its issue of March 31, 1909:

> Some knowledge of veterinary science is of great value to every farmer.
> Therefore, any live course in agriculture should have in it some instruc-
> tion in exterior anatomy; work in some parts of descriptive anatomy;
> some lessons on lamenesses, on the recognition of the more common
> diseases of farm animals, and along lines of hygiene, sanitation, and
> methods of preventing diseases. Up to this year the agricultural course
> was so arranged as to require all agricultural students to take up the
> above named lines in veterinary science. But the new arrangement
> requires only one-half as much as formerly, and gives the students in ani-
> mal husbandry a chance to elect and take more than was previously
> required. The Saturday free clinic of the regular three-year course in vet-
> erinary medicine and surgery is open to the agricultural students for one
> or two years. This clinic gives the student opportunity to obtain practical
> instruction by seeing and taking part in the inspection, diagnosis, and
> treatment of many diseased animals. Students who have completed the
> four years' agricultural course and have taken all the special work in vet-
> erinary medicine and surgery can finish the regular three-year course in
> veterinary medicine and surgery in two years.[15]

Dr. Cary's Saturday clinics served untold numbers of farmers and
their animals over the years, and the clinical work was not limited to
Saturdays. Farmers from near and far brought their injured or ailing
animals to the Veterinary School for diagnosis and treatment on a regular basis, and we can rest assured that those on staff did their best on
each case. But in veterinary medicine, then and now, wins and losses
occur. One case that was probably memorable for several years took
place in the fall of 1912, and the *Orange and Blue* reported—in its
usual unique style—on the sad results in its October 12, 1912, issue:

> Mule Electrocuted at API Clinic
>   A mule was brought into clinics by a man for treatment and owing

to the nature of the disease, was advised to leave the mule here for at least two weeks, which he did. Monday, September 30, the mule was operated on, and the patient stood the operation well and was placed in the hospital ward, where grass was plentiful and left there to let the wounds heal. But while eating in innocence Tuesday, after wounds were healed and patient showing all symptoms for the better, one of the wires that carried the current from the power house to the hospital and to other parts of town, fell from a pole under which the innocent animal was eating grass and struck the animal upon its head. The mule was killed instantly, we suppose. He was lying caught in the wire when found dead. The body was carried to the dead house and there prepared for the funeral which was held Thursday evening due to the late coming of the ones necessary to such work here. We all extend our sympathy to the owner and are truly sorry of his loss.[16]

Tilling the Soil

C. L. Jenkins' accounts of Saturday clinics describe some aspects of Dr. Cary's working environment in his earliest days in Auburn. Another source in the Auburn University Library also offers insights along this line, a book published in 1908 called *Tilling the Soil for Profit and Pleasure*. This work billed itself as "a compendium of agricultural science and practice on field, orchard, and garden crops, spraying, soils, the feeding and diseases of farm animals, dairy, and poultry raising in the Southern states." A single volume of more than 560 pages, the book was edited by James Clyde Adams and published by the Austell Publishing Company of Atlanta. Mr. Adams enlisted the help of Dr. Cary in a 135-page chapter on "The Horse," the great majority of which Dr. Cary wrote. Dr. Cary's introduction to this section—the book calls this section "the horse department"—in itself served as a sort of promotion of veterinary training:

> These chapters on the diseases of the horse are written that they may help farmers and horsemen who are not within reach of qualified graduate veterinarians. They may help the ordinary man who has not the technical knowledge of the graduate veterinarian. The more the farmer or the stockman knows the better he is able to see the necessity of employing a specialist or one who is expert in operating and treating live stock. Much of the following pages is written in terms that are not considered scientific. But it has been my aim to leave out all technical terms as far as possible in order to make the meaning plain to the average man. The treat-

ment suggested for the different diseases is not the only one that may be employed; but is one method selected, often times, as the one that may be used with the least difficulty and expense by the farmer.[17]

Dr. Cary's horse "department" offered a comprehensive overview of equine anatomy and detailed descriptions of many ailments that horses can contract, along with the veterinarian's view of best treatment practices. Anatomical descriptions suggested what potential horse buyers should investigate before purchasing. Another section detailed birth and delivery of foals. The text was accompanied by highly skilled medical illustrations, though the artist was not named.

Within this incredibly detailed book, Dr. Cary offered insight into one strategy he used in getting his program off the ground—with direct mail and the use of newspapers. At least one of the newspapers that ran his open letter to farmers was the *Weekly Age Herald* published in Birmingham. Its issue of January 25, 1893—less than a month after Dr. Cary officially began his permanent post at Auburn—carried his invitation to farmers to write to him about eye problems in their livestock.

> During January, 1893, the Veterinary Department of the Alabama Agricultural College issued about two hundred circular letters containing questions related to eye diseases among domestic animals; these were mailed to farmers and stockmen in all the counties of Alabama, and they were also published in many of the daily and weekly papers of the State. The principal question in the circular letter read as follows:
>
> "Are horses and mules in your beat or county affected with what is commonly called moon-blindness? If you have had such an eye disease please state how frequently it occurs, and what is your view of the cause of it?"
>
> I received in all nearly 125 replies. From these replies I have obtained the following records on periodic ophthalmia or moon-blindness . . . .[18]

Dr. Cary revealed the farmers' responses to his survey effort. He noted that from the free Saturday clinics he and his students held "during the first three months of 1892 and during the same time of 1893, 21 cases have come under my observation."

In his first years of heading the veterinary science program at Auburn, Dr. Cary lectured on the anatomy and diseases of horses, cattle, hogs, and other animals found on the farm, including dogs. He explained and then performed surgeries. He enlightened his student audience on the merits of the various medicines they used, or which he introduced to them. He explained the methods and necessity of meat and milk inspection. He demonstrated post-mortem examination techniques and what to look for when dissecting domesticated animals. Dr. Cary's students learned every minute, soaking in every word he said. Dr. Calvin Schwabe, the Auburn graduate who made a name in public health, never studied under Dr. Cary, but knew some who had. He said, related to Dr. Cary's teaching style, that, while, in his view, Dr. Cary would not be considered a distinguished researcher,

> . . . he was a man very well-informed and up-to-date about science ... an educator especially gifted in transmitting knowledge practically to people who could use it ... on occasions an important synthesizer of new knowledge from varied sources, a person whose lifetime academic accomplishments included instances of stimulating significant research advances by pointing to and indicating the possibilities from juxtaposing or linking different lines of research . . . . [19]

In addition to his classroom and field clinic lectures, Dr. Cary joined the ranks of his fellow API faculty on occasion to present public lectures on areas within his realm of expertise. Historian Dr. George Petrie spoke often on global events. President Broun the physicist lectured on the mechanics of hearing. According to the *Orange and Blue* published on February 5, 1896, for example, "Dr. Cary gave a very instructive as well as interesting lecture last Friday night on the 'Development of the Mind.' He is a thoroughly entertaining lecturer and we always like to hear him." This lecture took place in Langdon Hall on January 31, 1896. Dr. Cary supplemented his talk with stereopticon images, pictures projected from dual lenses, one atop the other. The stereopticon—sometimes referred to as a "magic lantern"—was, in essence, an early version of the slide projector, used for entertainment and academic and missionary purposes before the arrival of moving pictures. Variations of this apparatus dated to the 1860s, and some were advertised in sales catalogs of the day. Where Dr. Cary acquired one, and how he produced the images he showed, is anyone's guess.

A few years later, Dr. Cary held the stage again. The *Orange and Blue* dated January 31, 1900, reported that "The lecture in the college last Saturday night by Dr. C. A. Cary on 'Respiration' was both instructive and interesting. Dr. Cary, as we all know, is a man of great knowledge, and a most interesting talker on all subjects connected with his work. Had it been more generally known that he would lecture no doubt there would have been a larger crowd out to hear him." This talk, apparently inadequately advertised, took place on January 27, 1900, again in Langdon Hall.

The school paper devoted a good bit more attention to Dr. Cary's next on-campus public lecture, a show-and-tell talk on blood circulation chronicled in the February 27, 1901, *Orange and Blue*:

Last Friday evening Dr. Cary gave in the college chapel the first of his two public lectures. The subject was "The Heart and Blood."

Instructive facts were presented in an interesting way, and at the conclusion of the lecture many in the audience gathered around the desk to examine the diagrams, models and specimens. The lecture gave a brief outline of the anatomy of the heart, arteries and veins, and discussed the relation of the cavities of the heart to the great blood vessels, and the peculiar action of its valves. Next he showed in a graphic way the form and composition of the red and white corpuscles and pointed out their probable uses. An interesting experience was related of an observer who after two weeks upon a high mountain noticed that the number of red corpuscles in his blood had increased from 5 to 7 million per cubic millimeter. This might explain the great benefit that invalids sometimes receive in high altitudes.

He then discussed the causes for the circulation of the blood. Many interesting facts were pointed out about the contraction of the heart, the elastic power of the arteries and the suction in the large veins and the auricles of the heart.

By an analysis of its beat the professor then showed that the heart rested more than half of the time; but the faster the beat the smaller was the proportion of rest and the greater the danger of exhaustion or failure, as in some cases of high fever.

The nervous mechanism of the heart was next treated. This, said Dr. Cary, is not yet well understood. In some animals nerve cells have been found in the heart itself. When the heart of a terrapin or crawfish is cut out, it will if kept warm and moist beat for hours. The apex of a terrapin's heart will continue to beat after it is severed from the rest, and yet no nerve cells have ever been found in that part of it.

There are nerves that retard the heart's beat and others that accelerate it. But in view of the fact that it is so often spoke of as the seat of emotion and affection it is interesting to note that its nerves are chiefly motor, that is such as produce motion, and very few if any of them are censor, that is such as produce sensation or feeling.

Dr. Cary's second lecture will be given Friday night, March 1st, at half past seven. His subject will be "Diseases of the Blood."[20]

Dr. Cary's public talks were more than simply interesting diversions for the locals to attend; they focused on relevant science and medicine. The best example of this may be his October 1, 1897, address on smallpox and yellow fever. Smallpox had been killing people worldwide long before this time, and there appeared no end in sight of this plague. A smallpox outbreak in Montgomery that fall drove home the message. The *Opelika Morning Post* reported that "a large audience was present and gave the lecturer a very attentive hearing. The lecture was a clear, simple and forcible presentation of the subject, full of facts and statements that would attend to allay the fears of many in these panicky times."[21] The *Post* was so impressed with the timeliness of Dr. Cary's comments that the paper reprinted the entirety of the speech over two issues that month, at the top of its front page.

Dr. Cary's specific counsel to his students occasionally may be found in forgotten corners of Auburn, and an article from the *Plainsman* issue of November 16, 1923, serves as an example of how he guided students. The reporter covering a recent student veterinary association meeting recounted the dean's advice on how his students might approach their studies, which in essence stressed personal commitment, if not the rules of grammar.

> According to Dr. Cary there is no iron clad rules for the study of Veterinary Medicine and the success of the student depends upon how well he can adapt himself to the surrounding conditions. There are too many things during the present time to attract a young fellows attention, is the view of the Doctor. Several other points relating to students life and good citizenship after leaving college were stressed by the speaker.[22]

One comment related to "things" that attracted his students' attention, reportedly made by Dr. Cary, was shared by Dr. Wilford Bailey, a 1942 graduate of the program, during his speech at the College of Veterinary Medicine on November 15, 1992, when the College marked the centennial of Dr. Cary's arrival. This comment shed more light on the level of disdain with which Dr. Cary viewed such distractions.

"Less time should be wasted on football, other games, holidays and numerous idle periods," Dr. Cary reportedly said. "If exercise and development are required, let them be in the form of constructive work in gymnasiums, military drill, etc."[23]

While his student C. L. Jenkins did not mention him by name in his diary that survives, another student who trained under Dr. Cary did keep a diary that found its way to the Draughon Library Special Collections and Archives. Franklin A. Clark (1898-1973) kept regular notes of his time as a student at Auburn in the 1920s as well as his prior experience as a machine gunner in World War I and later as a dairy inspector with the federal government. Dr. Clark, from Andalusia, Alabama, enlisted in the US Army in 1917, was sent to France, and was wounded in July 1918 in the early days of the Second Battle of the Marne. He returned to the States and was discharged in February 1919. He then enrolled in API's course in agriculture, graduating in 1923, and followed that with enrollment in the College of Veterinary Medicine. He earned his DVM in 1924, worked a year with the Alabama State Health Department, and then spent seventeen years—1926-1943—with the federal Public Health Service. That work took him throughout the country inspecting and reporting on dairy operations. After retirement from federal work, he returned to Andalusia and farmed until his death at age seventy-five in September 1973.

Dr. Clark's papers in the Auburn Special Collections speak to those activities that occupied his mind then: class football and baseball games, his troubles with understanding college women, going to church on Sundays, and the day-to-day classes, lectures, and veterinary clinical work that took up his time. He included a few anecdotes related to Dr. Cary and to student work in veterinary school. In a letter to his father back in Andalusia dated February 18, 1923, Clark wrote:

> Next week we are to have a pretty busy program here. Thurs the 22nd we have a class football game, a review with Gov. Brandon on the reviewing stand, a lot of speeches by him and others. Also that night our meeting, the Alabama Veterinary Medical Association, will begin a three days session. The next night (Fri.) we give a banquet to the visiting vets. We are excused from most of our classes to attend the lectures at this and they run practically all day and way into the night.[24]

Clark's entry for February 19, 1924:

> Just the usual humdrum of class work. One operation at clinics. Dr. Cary

doing a tenotomy. In Jr Surgery this morning he started talking about diagnosis and applying this to life, success, etc. Made a very good lecture.

Apparently, Auburn received a big snow in the middle of that March, and Clark related in his diary entry of Friday, March 14, 1924, a couple of incidents that give further, if brief, insight into the world of the veterinary faculty—and that of mischievous undergraduates—of the day:

> Snowed on some last night and this morning was still about 3 inches deep. So must have been at least 6 in. full in all. Went to class at nine. When passed Serum Plant Drs. Sugg, Winters & Wingate came out to bombard me with snowballs. Of course I stopped to mix it, and when I stooped over once too quickly, tore my trousers for about nine inches in the most critical place. But luckily had on my raincoat so didn't let this bother me.
>
> Back at 2 to clinics. Dr. Cary came in raveing. Some boys were on his building uptown throwing snow on those below. He came along and went up to run them down. The last one down took the ladder away and left Dr. Cary up there.

Eventually rescued, Dr. Cary spoke on this episode the following day, as Clark in his diary entry for Saturday, March 15, 1924, reported that "At clinics Dr. Cary raved at length again . . . ."

Two weeks later, Dr. Cary apparently was still feeling the slight and may have taken his frustrations out on poor Clark, whose diary entry for Saturday, March 29, 1924, noted that he "read until nine and [then went] to clinics. Dr. Cary came in late and tried to run me to death. But must try to please him for a while for may want his help before long. At least want his approval of my thesis."

Clark's entry for his diary on Saturday, May 10, 1924:

> Up at 6:30 and studied jr surgery til 8:45 . . . Then to vet building. Sat around til nearly 10. Dr. Cary came and decided to give us clinic exam . . . Wrote 16 pages on the exam. Got my milk notes back . . . made 90 and got some praise.

For May 12, 1924, Clark wrote about that day's class with Dr. Cary: "studied 'til 8:30 and over to take exam on milk. Was long but very practical/wrote 15 pages on the 10 questions."

Clark's diary entry for April 14, 1924, revealed his focus as his graduation neared as well as additional insight into his relationship with Dr. Cary:

> Studied milk inspection til nine, then to three classes. Dr. Cary called me off and said that he had told Dr. Welch of my fitness for the state milk inspection job and that he had made arrangements for me to see him Wed when we are down there.

Franklin Clark landed that state milk inspection job after his spring graduation, launching his career in that important service. His diaries, at least from his time as a veterinary student, revealed in only a few entries that Dr. Cary was exceedingly busy with outside activities at this time. Dr. Cary, on occasion, was described as out of town or late for his lectures, undoubtedly the result of his being central to so many aspects of public health. Clark's entries depict a professor who demanded much from his students, but one who worked on their behalf to help them find employment or to direct them in their studies, and who praised them when their effort warranted a pat on the back.

A couple of additional sources suggested the preparedness of Auburn's veterinary students, at least a part of which can be credited to their chief professor and dean. A State Demonstration Extension agent named L. E. Newman, referenced in the *Auburn Alumnus* of January 1918, said of those who studied under Dr. Cary:

> Students from Auburn are showing up mighty well in war service examinations. In almost every instance where a former Auburn man is examined he receives a commission. The Auburn men have shown up as being far better fitted for Army veterinary service than the graduates from the Northern states. The reason is thought to be that the Northern universities are so well equipped that when the men get away from the equipment they cannot do their best work; that the Auburn men have no such equipment but have as good practical training and theory, with the result that they have had to learn to work without such elaborate equipment.[25]

And following Dr. Cary's death, in a letter to API President Luther Duncan, Dr. T. H. Ferguson, a veterinarian from Lake Geneva, Wisconsin, who had come to Auburn at Dr. Cary's invitation to speak to students, stated in memorial tribute that ". . . Dr. Cary's methods of veterinary education prepared his students to serve the Southern live stock and sanitary requirements better than any other veterinary institution of which I know."[26]

Another example of Dr. Cary's students taking their Auburn training and leading productive, helpful professional lives can be seen in the career of E. D. King, Jr., a graduate from API's veterinary class of 1916. (King's name appears elsewhere in this volume as he joined Dr. Cary for trips to various professional meetings and visited at Auburn to take part in Annual Conference on occasion.) An article about him in the May 18, 1928, edition of the *Plainsman*, "Former Auburn Man Receives Mention," detailed Dr. King's career and suggested both his own capabilities as well as the level of education he secured under Dr. Cary and other faculty at Auburn:

In a recent issue of the magazine, "Certified Milk," there appeared a picture of E. D. King, Jr., '16, with the caption, "Successful Promoter of Milk Week." Dr. King received this honor for the splendid manner in which he promoted "Milk Week" in Valdosta, Ga., where he is Meat and Milk Inspector.

Born on a farm near Mobile, Ala., Dr. King received his early education at the Lower Peach Tree High School and Southern Business University of Mobile, and taught in . . . Monroe County before he was twenty-one years of age. In 1916 he completed a course of Veterinary Medicine at . . . Alabama Polytechnic Institute, serving that year as president of the college veterinary society. He commenced practice in Mobile the same year, but in October 1917, was called to the colors and served with the Veterinary Reserve of the U.S. Army with the rank of Second Lieutenant. His duties took him to France where he was in active service in the battles of St. Mihiel, Aisne-Marne and Meuse-Argonne.

Returning to the United States in the spring of 1919, Dr. King resumed general practice at Mobile, remaining there until 1920, when he became Meat and Milk Inspector at Valdosta.

He has since been Commander of the Valdosta Post of the American Legion and is Resident-Secretary of the American Veterinary Medical Association. He is also Chairman of the Publicity Committee of the Southeastern States Food and Drug Officials Association. His career has included lecturing at several important educational institutions and the delivering of addresses and papers before meetings of many veterinary associations. Dr. King is regarded by his profession as one of the most dependable authorities on food hygiene.[27]

Another significant way in which Dr. Cary supported his students was in helping those not from Auburn to find lodging when school was in session. He and Mrs. Cary—in a practice shared by many college faculty members and other local folks—allowed students to board in their home once they were settled in their North Main Street (North College) house bought in 1897. Dr. Cary reconfigured part of the home's attic space to provide lodging for a dozen or so veterinary students in a time when out-of-town Auburn students had few or no housing options. The students each had a small bed space and plenty of opportunity to bump their heads when they arose each morning. That housing plan lasted a decade or so, with Dr. Cary—and perhaps Mrs. Cary—regularly using a broom or other long-handled device to knock on the ceiling when the boys upstairs were getting too loud and rowdy and keeping the Cary children (who, by 1904, numbered three: Elwyn, Phoebe, and Alice), plus their early-rising parents, up late.

Dr. Cary eventually solved the housing problem to the satisfaction of all parties by building next door a separate house which came to be known as "Cary Castle." The nickname may have arisen because of the home's unique shape and because, in the early years of the twentieth century, it offered what passed for luxury living for college students. Cary Castle, which still houses Auburn students next door to the Cary House, had twelve bedrooms, and each lodger had a private outdoor woodshed in which to keep wood for his fireplace. Whether those who christened the dormitory Cary Castle knew, that name was fitting because of the ancient Castle Cary connected with Dr. Cary's ancestors in England.

Dr. and Mrs. Cary's philanthropy and care for Auburn students were continued by their descendants, as the Cary family home, the Halladay-Cary-Pick House, was gifted in 2011 to Auburn University by Frances Pick Dillard and her children. Fran Dillard was the daughter-in-law of youngest Cary daughter Alice Cary Pick Gibson, who was the last family member to live in the house after 100 years of Carys residing there.

Looking back on Dr. Cary many years later, one of his former students—J. Alec Barger, DVM, of Pass Christian, Mississippi—in a December 1, 1962, letter to Auburn Dean James E. Greene, wrote:

> If one were asked for a word that might symbolize Dr. Cary, it could well be "courage." For we recall that when he assumed the double

responsibilities of Dean and State Veterinarian in 1907 that glanders, dourine, sheep and cattle scab, cattle tick fever, hog cholera, bovine tuberculosis, and brucellosis were among the diseases which were existing in our midst, and all out of control, and that each of these in its self was an inhibiting factor in our livestock production and development.

Dr. Cary was the first of those who called attention to this situation.

However, the manner of control which he and other leaders in thought suggested brought on controversies of no small distinction.

We are all cognizant of the results that have accrued from the control measures which were instituted; but since all of that is history, what interests us at this late date is in reflecting upon the verbal and political battles that took place in getting the job under way.

Issues of a controversial nature posed no deterent [sic] to Dr. Cary. He maintained that one should be privileged to take any position that he could defend—and he did.

When aroused, the apparent, docile and half-timid man became firey [sic] eloquent, and his vocal chastizement [sic] of those who opposed his views was the cause of gratification, and we may say, even amusement to his followers who were many.

For several years this verbal war broke out anew when any sizeable gathering of veterinarians and livestock men took place. Dr. Cary, however, "stayed in training" and his followers increased until one might say: "There was no organized opposition to rational disease control measures."

In the presence of student and relatively unlearned veterinarians, (and in the latter group there were many of us.) Dr. Cary was a sympathetic and patient teacher, as he attended our State Association meetings, and presided over the question box for hours.

To us, the name Cary means dedication, in all its applicable ramifications, and the memory of him is pleasant indeed.[28]

Adding Facilities, the DVM, and People

Auburn's college library was housed in Old Main from its earliest days, even after the great fire of 1887 and the rebuilding of today's Samford Hall. Dr. Cary added to its holdings by authorizing the purchase of many books and subscriptions to numerous domestic and international veterinary science journals. Dr. Cary's time in Germany influenced the collection as he brought in journals he had discovered abroad, including publications from France, Germany, and England. Among those he ordered, or persuaded the administration to add, were the *American Microscopial Journal; Archives de Zoologie Experimentale; Archives Fuer Microskopis-*

che Anatomic; Centralblatt Fur Bakteriologie; Fleming's Veterinary Journal; Journal de L'Anatomie et de La Phisiologie; Journal of Comparative Pathology and Therapeutics; Journal of Morphology; Journal of New York Microscopial Society; Journal of the Royal Microscopial Society; and *Quarterly Journal of the Microscopial Society.*

He supplemented the collection with government-published animal health texts and other volumes he found through interactions with peers at national and regional meetings. Many of his personal veterinary books came to the collection shortly after his death, a gift of his widow. Some of these—including Dr. Cary's personal copies—held place on the shelves of Auburn's Draughon Library at the time of this writing, with Dr. Cary's attractive signature on the inside pages.

Facilities were important, and Dr. Cary realized he needed far more in the way of classroom, laboratory, clinical, and research space than what he inherited in the modest building and the allocated barn and paddock space at the Experiment Station farm. With what one can assume was the complete support of President Broun, Dr. Cary convinced the administration and trustees of the need for newer, more modern, and expanded space for his work and that of his assistants and students in building the veterinary program.

Records indicate that the first true veterinary building on the Auburn campus was constructed in early 1894 along Magnolia Avenue (about where the Ramsay Hall engineering building later would be constructed) near, as the 1897 *Glomerata* described, the northwestern corner of campus. This wooden structure, which served Dr. Cary and his colleagues and students until 1924, consisted of nine rooms over two floors, including a lecture room, Dr. Cary's office, four laboratories, an operating room, and what was referred to as a museum: a room in which Dr. Cary kept skeletons of a horse, ox, sheep, hog, and a human, as well as many preserved animal organs, likely kept inside jars filled with that wonderful new product that originated in the laboratories of Russia, formaldehyde (the plastination process being decades from development).

The API *Catalog* describing these laboratories for prospective students noted that "quite a collection of diseased tissues and animal parasites are found in connection with the lab." In time, as funds became available, Dr. Cary outfitted his laboratories with three New York-made Bausch & Lomb and two Winkel microscopes—possibly single-scope apparatuses made in Gottingen, Germany—as well as sterilizers, autoclaves, incubators, and all the necessary and available equipment required in bacteriological work.

While building his facilities, Dr. Cary still was involved heavily in work across campus at the Experiment Station farm. Records from trustees' minutes of June 12, 1894, showed a motion approved by the board related to Dr. Cary: "The Professor of Veterinary Science shall have charge of experiments related to food and care of animals at the Experiment Station, and also, investigations relating to their diseases, remedies, etc." Whether this new policy settled some campus turf battle that had erupted or merely put on paper officially what Dr. Cary had been doing, his already-established authority on campus animal research and clinical examinations and treatment was made clear to all.

The following year, Dr. Cary expanded his students' education through post-mortem examinations in a new dissection room, which he had built onto the veterinary building.

A few years into his Auburn work, Dr. Cary authorized the following overview description of his program for the 1901 API *Catalog*:

The sophomore class studies human anatomy, physiology and hygiene during the entire college year.

It is the aim of the department to give the students practical and real knowledge of the gross anatomy and functions of the various parts of the human body. Due attention is given, also, to the laws of health—the conditions most favorable to a continuous healthy action of the organs of the human body.

Instruction is given by lectures and by text-books, supplemented by blackboard drawings, charts, models of organs, a human skeleton and by dissections of some of the smaller animals (dog, cat, etc.)

Martin's Human Body is used as a text and reference book, and several other works on anatomy, physiology and hygiene may be consulted in the college library.

Students in the agricultural and chemical course of study, during the entire junior and senior years, devote to this work two hours per week in the class room and three hours per week at practical clinics. Instruction in veterinary science and art is given by lectures.

The lectures are arranged with special reference to the students who are interested in horses or other domestic animals; also to those students who contemplate studying human or veterinary medicine. While it is not the aim to give a complete course in veterinary medicine, we attempt to present the general principles of comparative medicine with such special applications as are adapted to the conditions and wants of the students.

Special attention is given to the exterior anatomy of the horse, while comparative anatomy is presented mainly in connection with the study of the diseases of the different apparatus of the horse or other domestic animals.

Lameness in the horse, minor surgery, the actions and uses of the most common medicines, the principles and practice of comparative medicine, and the ways of protecting the health of domestic animals, are considered in as plain and practical a manner as the time allotted to each subject will permit. Post-mortem examination and the dissection of domestic animals are used as object lessons in the study of general pathology and anatomy.

The senior class in pharmacy devotes three hours per week, during the first and second terms to the study of therapeutics; and three hours per week during the third term to class room and laboratory work in bacteriology.

To the post-graduate student this department furnishes work in histology, pathology, bacteriology, meat and milk inspection. This work gives students who contemplate studying medicine excellent preparatory work along that line. Such students may devote their entire time to work in this department with the approval of the faculty.

Histology includes methods of injecting small animals, collecting, fixing, hardening, embedding, section cutting, mounting, staining, examining under the microscope, drawing and describing the different tissues.

Pathology is studied in the text and reference books and morbid histology embraces naked eye and microscopic examinations of diseased tissues in the laboratory. Quite a collection of diseased tissues and animal parasites are found in connection with the laboratory.

The laboratory is well fitted for the study of bacteriology. Bacteriological analysis of water, milk, sputum, pus, diseased tissues, and of soils can be made. All of the practical operations in the preparation of culture, media, sterilizations, inoculations of small animals, straining, microscopial examinations, may be learned. In the laboratory are 3 Bausch and Lomb and 2 Winkel microscopes, each of which is supplied with oil immersion objectives, 2 oculars, Abbe condenser, and iris diaphragm. Sterilizers, autoclaves, incubators, and all the necessary apparatus required in bacteriological work are to be found in the laboratory.

The department of physiology and veterinary science is now located by itself in a building which consists of a two-story portion containing four laboratory rooms on the second floor and a lecture room, museum and office on the lower floor; and a one-story part which contains an operating room.

The building is supplied with water and gas and the laboratory is now equipped for work. The museum contains the skeletons of the horse, the ox, the sheep and the hog, and a human skeleton. It also contains a collection of pathological and anatomical specimens, and one of animal parasites.

The new veterinary hospital building contains five large box-stalls, four open single stalls, an office and a feed room on the lower floor; the upper floor is used as a storage room for hay, fodder, etc. The hospital is supplied with fresh water.

A new brick and cement dissecting room (16x32) has just been completed. It is supplied with extensive north sky-light and with water and gas.

Every Saturday during the college year the department conducts a free clinic for the benefit of the students in veterinary science and art. Clinical cases have been various and numerous, giving the students opportunity to see and study many diseases and lameness and to become proficient in minor operations.[29]

Dr. Cary's overview—probably the most extensive description he wrote about the school he built—mentioned lectures devoted to human anatomy and the presence of a human skeleton in the museum collection. This object was central to an incident that involved a number of students who, one presumes, were enrolled in programs other than veterinary science. That adventure warrants a brief recollection.

One night in 1899 or 1900, with genius overflowing and surplus time on their hands, several non-veterinary science cadets hatched a plan, as students before them and after them have done. Half of the group would make its way to the train depot and remove the adjacent outhouse, repositioning it at the intersection of Main Street and Magnolia (today's Toomer's Corner). The other half would sneak off to "Vet Hill" and enter Dr. Cary's second-floor laboratory—what reason would he have had to lock the door?—to borrow the human skeleton. These events took place in the hours after midnight, when student inspiration always reaches its zenith.

Meeting up with their treasures with only the moon to illuminate their actions, these gallant undergrads set the outhouse in the middle of the dirt intersection and positioned the skeleton inside, on the seat, posed—balanced—hunched over with skull resting in hand, a pose not dissimilar to that already appearing in the studio of a French artist named Rodin half a world away.

The student artists then retreated to the nearest shadows to await the town's awakening and its response to their work. An hour or three later—what suspense it must have been for these comedians—the first rays of daybreak illuminated their handiwork as a few Auburn folks began to venture into the village. The early-rising citizens, of course, noticed the addition of a centrally placed outhouse, and after a while some began to approach it. The first to arrive meekly knocked, but hearing no response, one of the locals eased open the door. They must have paused to soak in the view of a human skeleton sitting on the pot in the middle of the street. After several people surely had a good laugh about this discovery, someone who recognized the components likely suggested that the outhouse and skeleton be returned to their respective places. No word survives on whether the students received appropriate prizes for their inventiveness.

Interestingly, the young man who 'fessed up years later was a seventeen- or eighteen-year-old undergraduate from nearby Hatchechubbee named Holland McTyeire Smith. This ne'er-do-well, who received his BS from API in 1901, joined the Alabama National Guard before pursuing a law degree in Tuscaloosa. He later practiced law in Montgomery, where his father was a well-known attorney. But the younger Smith decided life in the Army offered more excitement. After all, as his late-night Auburn activities proved, he was accustomed to far greater shenanigans than mundane lawyering offered. Holland Smith would later commission into the Marine Corps, become its highest-ranked general, and earn the nickname "Howlin' Mad" by troops serving under him in the Dominican Republic in 1916. He would direct Army, Navy, and Marine amphibious training as World War II approached, work that made possible successful landings in both the Atlantic and Pacific, which led to his being known as the father of amphibious warfare. Smith earned distinction for brilliant commanding of major battles in the Pacific during World War II, including Iwo Jima. General Smith, ranking with General Robert Bullard and General Carl E. Mundy, Jr., among the most highly decorated of the many military men who have come through Auburn, in 1945 received an honorary doctor of laws degree from API, all links to the outhouse/skeleton affair forgiven.[30]

From the time of his arrival at Auburn and into the first several years of the twentieth century, Dr. Cary taught students whose degree programs were in agriculture. But as he had earned the DVM degree at Iowa State, his goal—and the goal of the by-now-deceased president who had hired him—was to establish a degree-granting college of veterinary medicine. That academic structure was approved by the Board of Trustees at API on June 3, 1907. Minutes from that day's trustee meeting record, in understated terms, that "After studying the entire field and after full consultation with the head of the department, a three-year course in veterinary medicine has been established. This is the first of the kind offered to Southern students. It is advocated with enthusiasm by the professor of Veterinary Science, who anticipates much good from its establishment."[31]

The board's action that day not only authorized a DVM-granting curriculum—the first in the United States south of Pennsylvania—but was considered the official founding of Auburn's "School of Veterinary Medicine" and the appointing of Dr. Cary as its first dean. However, the "school" designation is blurred by the fact that Dr. Cary's program, from its early days, appeared to be called "department," "school," or "college" interchangeably. While the Alabama Polytechnic Institute *Catalog* listed Charles Allen Cary as professor of physiology and veterinary science and state veterinarian in the 1907 and 1908 editions, by the 1909-10 version, Dr. Cary's title had expanded to include "Dean of the Faculty of Veterinary Medicine and Surgery." In order of appointment, he was listed after fellow deans George Petrie, Bennett Battle Ross, and John Jenkins Wilmore.

Two years after the trustees approved API's DVM degree program, at commencement exercises probably held in Langdon Hall in spring 1909, Dr. Cary surely watched with pride as his first few—the exact number is ambiguous—Auburn graduates took their places to receive diplomas that confirmed the first API-trained doctors of veterinary medicine.

No record has surfaced of that 1909 commencement, and the few places one could look to specify Auburn's initial veterinary graduates do not align. The 1909 *Glomerata* lists seven members of the Class of '09 studying veterinary medicine. The College of Veterinary Medicine displays, in the lobby of its Greene Hall administrative building, photos of six members it considers the first graduates of the program, and the inaugural issue of the Auburn Alumni Association's *Alumni Quarterly* in 1912 asserted there were four veterinary graduates in 1909. The API *Catalog*, which may be considered the most authoritative of these sources, listed five DVM recipients (all of whom are included below except for James Ernest Threadgill of Marengo County). The seven listed in the 1909 *Glomerata* were:

William Rufus King Beck of Camden, Alabama, who served as both president and vice president of the student veterinary medical association and who, according to an issue of the *Auburn Alumni Quarterly* in 1912, went on to study medicine in Birmingham;

Armstrong Hill, a Sylacauga native and member of Sigma Alpha Epsilon fraternity who played on the API football team, served as vice president of the student veterinary association, and earned recognition in the *Glomerata* for his habit of bumming smokes from professor and future dean Dr. I. S. McAdory. He worked early in his career as a meat inspector in Montgomery;

William Monroe Howell of Baker Hill, Alabama, a Sigma Nu who won a medal for his work with the debate society and who served as president of both the student veterinary association and the Websterian Literary Society. He would spend the early years of his career as chief meat and milk inspector in Valdosta, Georgia;

Percy Wilbur Hudson, an Auburn native who also served a term as president of the veterinary medical student group;

Isham Smith Ingram, another Auburn native, a vice president of the student VMA who would be dead by 1912;

George Bascom Sparkman, from Tampa, Florida, a Delta Sigma Theta fraternity member, an Auburn football player, member of the *Glomerata* board, and president of the Florida student group at API; and

John Bowles Steadham, also from Auburn, a Sigma Theta Epsilon member, active in the German Club and in the API Band and "one of the best known and most popular fellows in college."[32]

The events and ceremony held to mark API's 1909 commencement have been lost to history, but a recap of the 1912 commencement three years later in the first *Auburn Alumni Quarterly* described a dignified, high-minded event:

> The seniors marched into Langdon Hall in a body, all clad in the gray and white dress uniform. After the diplomas had been awarded they were called to the front of the stage and there stood an attentive group while Dr. Thach gave them a few words of encouragement and godspeed.[33]

With these graduates that spring day in 1912 were eleven new doctors of veterinary medicine as well as special API student Phoebe Cary, Charles and Emma Cary's daughter, who received her bachelor's degree a year later and began her career as a French and domestic science teacher at Wilcox County High School in Camden.[34] (Phoebe Cary Shoemaker would become a two-time API graduate, earning a master's degree in 1943 in the School of Home Economics, today's College of Human Sciences, with a master's thesis on "Nutrition Education of Low-Income Groups" still shelved in Draughon Library.) Miss Cary would be the lone female graduate in spring 1913 and serve as both class historian and class poet. The *Glomerata* that year extolled her qualities:

> . . . she is one of the most brilliant students in the entire class. She is one of the most loyal members of the general course, and the male members of that course all believe she is "beyond compare."[35]

Not as lengthy in its description, another comment survived from this era of the founding dean as to his take on the growth and direction of his program. Dr. Cary, while serving as president of the Alabama Live Stock Association in 1910, included these thoughts in his address to that membership's convention in Montgomery that year:

> The Department of Veterinary Medicine of the API is young and needs much to make it complete, but it is growing and the time is not far distant when every county seat and every town shall have a graduate veterinarian to look after the diseases of livestock as efficiently as the doctors now look after the diseases of man.[36]

As the scope of veterinary medical work grew under Dr. Cary, and as Auburn was able financially, it became a priority for Dr. Cary and for the institution to bring on board additional faculty members. To that end, in 1897, Dr. Cary hired one of his recent agriculture graduates, W. J. Nixon, as assistant in veterinary sciences.

A revolving door saw Dr. Cary's assistants arrive and depart during the subsequent years. Some may have found the dean impossible to please or the workload too daunting. Perhaps some departed for other reasons: higher-paying jobs, advancement opportunities, or the brighter lights of larger cities. Whatever the individual cases, a number of lieutenants served under Dr. Cary for varying lengths of time in the early years of the program.

Another of his early hires as an assistant was 1898 graduate Bishop "Bish" Billing Warwick, who came to Auburn from Talladega and apparently impressed the boss. Dr. Cary brought him on board as an assistant in veterinary science shortly after Warwick's graduation.

In 1899, Dr. Cary hired Bailey Edgar Brown as assistant professor of veterinary science. In 1902, he brought on board Frederick Greenville Matthews in this position. API's 1901-02 *Catalog* lists Matthews as a Lee County native and enrolled as a graduate student; thus, Dr. Cary may have hired Matthews upon his graduation, if not before.

One of Dr. Cary's most notable hires came in 1904 when he enlisted as a general purpose staff member a local African American named Luke Sales, called by everyone for many years "Dr. Luke." Hired as a janitor and all-around handyman for the original veterinary building, Dr. Luke spent more than half a century in the employment of the college, handling an array of tasks for the benefit of Dr. Cary, the other faculty, and students. His work ranged from running errands; holding animals during exams; stocking equipment, medicines, and feed, and retrieving those when needed; and disposing of animal carcasses.

Auburn veterinary students from the earliest days into the middle years of the twentieth century found Dr. Luke a constant of their world. When the Class of '52 compiled a booklet at the time of its graduation which reviewed the members' four years at Auburn, those providing text for the publication included a charming paragraph about Dr. Luke:

> Of course, it's impossible for any veterinary student from API to recall the post mortem room without seeing in mind at the same time "Dr. Luke." Dr. Luke was brought here by Dr. Cary and is as much a part of the veterinary school as any fixture in the school. He evidently is immune to all diseases that man can contract from animals. He has certainly been exposed to more than most of us will ever see in a lifetime of practice. The odor of cooking meat, burned hair, etc., is associated with Cary Hall and with that we have a vision of Dr. Luke—furnace blazing with door open and Dr. Luke standing in blood and water up over the top of the sole of his boots, cutting the rest of the carcass up to throw in the furnace fire.[37]

Luke was apparently not only a loyal and capable employee, but also a character of the highest order. One tale suggested Luke was on one occasion taken into custody by local law enforcement, suspected of murder. One version of the story incredibly had Luke disposing of the victim's body in the incinerator normally used to burn animal carcasses. The story goes that Dean Cary acknowledged that Luke was perhaps not the most innocent of parties, but explained to the sheriff, "We have to have him at the college." And Luke, the story goes, was given some level of suspended sentence and paroled into the responsible oversight of Dr. Cary. The reliability of that legend never has been confirmed, but its various renditions hold rank among old-time Auburn veterinarians.

Redding Sugg, Jr., in his essay in the summer/fall 2004 *Auburn Veterinary Quarterly*, came close to verifying such a story, noting that Dr. Luke, "the major-domo and man of all work on Vet Hill, had served time for a crime of passion and had been paroled to Dr. Cary years earlier."

The historian Dr. Sugg—a boy growing up in Auburn during some of Dr. Luke's heyday—described Luke and one of his enduring memories of this soldier in Dr. Cary's army:

> Very dark, he spoke a Gullah dialect and was said to be a voo-doo priest with power in Summer Hill, the black community just off the Opelika Road where he lived. It was he who did the pole-axing at the slaughter house, and we assured ourselves that he drank ritual blood. He fell ill after my father [Dean Sugg] became dean. Daddy went to his house, realized he was dying, and on the instant tried to lift him to take him out to the car and to the V.A. Hospital, the only available place a black man could be properly treated. Luke demanded to be put down, declaring that it wasn't right that Daddy should carry him. He kept a farm bell on a post in his yard. This was rung, and two young men appeared, carried him to the car, accompanied him to Tuskegee and into the hospital.[38]

One insightful wag, clearly affiliated with the veterinary program either as a student or staff member, authored a poem honoring Dr. Luke. The anonymous copy cited here was discovered in a veterinary medicine scrapbook compiled by long-time associate dean Dr. H. C. Morgan, Jr. '55 and found in his home almost twenty years after Dr. Morgan's death in summer 1998. The poem, called "Dr. Luke's Retreat," chronicles Dr. Luke's role in the process of disposing of animal carcasses in the college's incinerator, located for years behind Cary Hall on main campus. It begins:

> Oh, let us speak of Luke's retreat, that strangest darkest turn,
> Which stands behind Old Cary Hall, so mysterious and stern.
> It lies within an open place, with open arms it waits
> For patients who aren't leaving by the customary gates.

The poem concludes:

At certain times one sometimes finds a patient in this place
Who limply lies with glassy eyes receding in his face,
Who doesn't seem to breathe at all, who doesn't make a sound,
Whose temperature it seems to fall, whose pulse cannot be found.
A quiet state, a final page, a dream within the making;
A silence deep, an empty sleep without the fear of waking.
But no one states or intimates that maybe he's expired,
For anyone can plainly see that he is simply tired.
It isn't wise to analyze, to shed an explanation,
For this is just a new disease, of infinite duration.
But if you look within the book, upon his progress sheet,
You'll find a sign within the line—"Discharged to Luke's Retreat!"

In the early twentieth century, African Americans often were hired for the grunt work and the dirty work at institutions like API. The world had many miles to go at that point. While politically impossible at the turn of the century for any dean at API to hire an African American into a professional position, Dr. Cary should receive a modest amount of credit for putting race secondary to achievement and scientific benefit on at least one significant occasion. While this incident did not result in any major civil rights breakthroughs at the time, Dr. Cary's inviting Dr. George Washington Carver of Tuskegee Institute to speak before the Alabama Live Stock Association's state meeting in Birmingham in 1903 was a bold move on the host's part.

Dr. Carver served as director of the Tuskegee Experiment Station at the time; and, in this role, he frequently met the professional agricultural staff at Auburn. He and Dr. Cary struck up a friendship of sorts. The two consulted on a regular basis as Tuskegee did not employ a veterinarian at this time. It did not hurt that both Drs. Carver and Cary were alumni of Iowa Agricultural College. According to one biography of Dr. Carver, he arranged on a few occasions for Dr. Cary to visit Tuskegee to diagnose ailments in livestock as well as to lecture to agriculture and animal science students.

Dr. Cary, too, would have been familiar with Dr. Carver's work as the latter's reports or bulletins were published through the Agricultural Experiment Station, and those bulletins typically were exchanged among institutions.

Dr. Carver's relationship with Dr. Cary, Dr. Carver's professional reputation, and Dr. Cary's confidence in the caliber of work Dr. Carver was doing led to an invitation for Dr. Carver to read a paper at the Alabama Live Stock Association's 1903 meeting in Birmingham. Dr. Carver obviously was pleased with the invite, and Dr. Cary, the Live Stock Association's president, acknowledged that the request was "quite unique as [the Association] is a distinctly Southern organization."

The day of the meeting arrived, and Dr. Carver spoke on the livestock work in progress at Tuskegee. President Cary followed him to the podium to "most heartily endorse every word" and to urge those present to visit Tuskegee. Birmingham reporters described Dr. Carver's speech as "one of the most interesting of the addresses delivered" at the meeting.

But that moment, progressive as it was, still had an edge to it. Dr. Cary admitted that he had been "very fearful at first" about the reaction of the all-white group to his inviting Dr. Carver to participate, but had decided "to make the venture as someone must at some time, somewhere." The Live Stock Association meeting attendees' response was "a great and agreeable surprise" to its president, as he noted that an overwhelming majority of those present had "personally thanked him for the innovation."[39]

Dr. Cary's agricultural and veterinary associates helped advance his educational efforts. Due to his packed schedule, Dr. Cary depended on his assistants at Auburn to help with classes, laboratories, and clinical cases. In 1906, Dr. Cary hired another pair of professionals, Dr. Ward Giltner from Cornell and Dr. C. T. Butler. Dr. Giltner, in particular, proved a worthy colleague of Dr. Cary's and went on to a highly distinguished, as well as tragic, career. Dr. Giltner left Auburn after only two years for an appointment as professor of bacteriology at the veterinary college at Michigan State University. He later chaired MSU's Department of Bacteriology and, in 1923, was appointed as the college's dean, a post he held until his retirement in 1948. During his deanship, Dr. Giltner remained chair of the Department of Bacteriology. During that time, he more than tripled the size of the Michigan State faculty and oversaw a program that excelled in research. Like his early boss at Auburn, Dr. Giltner was active in the AVMA on a national level for his entire professional career, his name appearing time and again in recaps of AVMA convention activities. Michigan State's veterinary program, for years, was headquartered in a building that had been named Giltner Hall in his memory.

Dr. Giltner's family tragedy came in December 1936, when his daughter Elizabeth was shot dead in the family's East Lansing home by a close female friend as the two women sat at the dining room table addressing wedding invitations. Elizabeth, twenty-five, engaged to Captain David Babcock, an instructor in Michigan State's ROTC program, had invited Hope Morgan to the house to help address the invitations. The mentally ill Morgan later told police she "felt like killing someone." Because of Dr. Giltner's respected position as dean of a veterinary college, this tragic story hit papers nationwide, including the *New York Times.*

However, Dr. Giltner's two years with Dr. Cary were tragedy-free and highly productive. The experience set him on course for a number of important contributions to veterinary medicine, starting in Auburn and culminating during his long career in Michigan. When Dr. Cary hired Dr. Giltner to head up his Department of Bacteriology within the veterinary program, Dr. Giltner brought a broad knowledge that fit well with Dr. Cary's ambitions. With Dr. Giltner added to the staff, Dr. Cary was able to advance the curriculum. By 1906, Auburn students could take instruction in obstetrics, infectious disease, parasites, toxicology, and urine analysis as well as meat and milk inspection. When Dr. Cary spearheaded a reorganization of the Alabama Veterinary Medical Association in 1907, the new members elected Dr. Giltner as vice president and Dr. Cary as secretary/treasurer. Dr. Giltner served on the Alabama VMA's executive committee during his final year in Auburn, assisting Dr. Cary closely in getting the organization headed in the right direction. When Dr. Giltner left for Michigan, Dr. Cary hired Dr. L. E. Case to succeed him.

While these several assistants came and went during those early years, Dr. Cary also made use of the students in veterinary science for much of the manual labor and for help with research tasks and clinical duties. He kept his eyes on those students who excelled and showed the qualities necessary for making a difference in the demanding work of a veterinarian. Among early veterinary students at Auburn were a number of future stars, among them F. P. Woolf of the Class of 1910, who later taught many years at Auburn; B. H. Moon '10, who worked for the USDA in Alabama, Tennessee, and Iowa; and B. T. Simms '11, whose career reached perhaps the highest of any Auburn-trained veterinarian. Dr. Simms essentially started the veterinary program at Oregon State University and later (1938-45) headed the USDA's large animal disease laboratory at Auburn. He was tapped as director for the Bureau of Animal Industry in 1945, which organizationally put him over a 1,750-plus-member workforce. Dr. Simms also played a key role in the career of another Charles Allen Cary disciple and future Auburn dean, Dr. Redding Sugg.

After Dr. Simms left Auburn for an appointment at North Carolina State University's diagnostic laboratory, he met the young Sugg and, seeing his interest in a career in animal health, directed him to Auburn and Dr. Cary's program. Sugg, like Simms before him, served as one of Dr. Cary's student leaders while in school and went on to hold a prominent position in the life of the college. Dr. Sugg was named an instructor in bacteriology, histology, and pathology in 1920. Dr. Sugg later served as dean at Auburn from the occasion of Dr. I. S. McAdory's (the successor dean to Dr. Cary) resignation and return to teaching in 1940 until his own retirement in 1958.

Dr. Sugg served as state veterinarian 1940-51 and was lauded for strengthening the state diagnostic laboratory. He also spearheaded an effort to enable out-of-state students living where there was no veterinary school to enroll at Auburn, with their home states making up the financial difference between resident and non-resident tuition. For years, Auburn worked with students from Florida, Louisiana, Tennessee, Mississippi, North Carolina, and Kentucky on this enrollment plan. Ditto for Georgia during a period of suspension for the University of Georgia's veterinary school. This plan continues today under the Southern Regional Education Board. Presently, only the Commonwealth of Kentucky continues in this plan with Auburn, as most other Southern states years ago built veterinary colleges. South Carolina maintains a reciprocal arrangement with the University of Georgia, and Arkansas sends its veterinary students to LSU.

Dean Sugg, a member of the US Army Reserves, was called to duty during World War II and spent 1941-45 in service to his country. In his absence, Professor Everett S. Winters served as acting dean at Auburn. The College of Veterinary Medicine in 1960 named one of its research laboratories in Dean Sugg's memory; that facility, after a renovation or two, remains in use.

Another of Dr. Cary's hires at Auburn exemplified his eye for talent: veterinarian/cucumber farmer Dr. Mark Wirth Emmel (1895-1969), a Chillicothe, Ohio, native who had practiced veterinary medicine in Iowa, Arkansas, and Bushnell, Florida (where he also grew the cucumbers). He came to campus in the early 1930s as a professor of animal pathology and research. Dr. Emmel was a star scientist, having earned BS, MS, and DVM degrees at Michigan State University and, during his time at Auburn, pursued his PhD at Michigan State as well. The December 10, 1932, issue of the *Auburn Plainsman* noted that Dr. Emmel received international recognition because of his research work on poultry diseases. The International Review of Poultry Science, official organ of the World's Poultry Science Association, and published in Rotterdam, Holland, in a current issue, takes note of Dr. Emmel's work, and carries reports of three of his experiments which are considered as important contributions to the poultry industry. These publications deal with: (1) Bacteriology and Pathology of five hundred chicks affected with pullorum disease, and results, (2) The differentiation of pasteurella avicida and brucella infections in fowl, and (3) Epidermoid cancers on the feet of wild birds.[40]

The report described Dr. Emmel's work as focusing on an investigation of poultry paralysis, which to that point had not received much attention from researchers.

Dr. Emmel excelled at Auburn, and he, like the high-achieving Dr. Giltner, was a good one who got away. Toward the end of 1931, Dr. Emmel was appointed secretary of the AVMA's Section on Poultry for the coming year, evidence of his growing stature in the field. Earlier that year, in May 1931, Dr. Emmel was invited to speak on fowl cholera, typhoid fever, poultry sanitation, avian tuberculosis, and other poultry diseases at a three-day meeting of veterinarians at the University of Florida. While forty years before UF opened its College of Veterinary Medicine, the institution already was supporting an important and successful agricultural research program. Those in charge were impressed with the Auburn professor. Toward the end of 1933, UF apparently offered Dr. Emmel a visiting scientist role that eventually became a permanent appointment. Thus, by early 1934, Dr. Emmel had left Auburn for Gainesville.

In Dr. Emmel's absence, Dr. Cary turned to one of his own graduates, Dr. Fred D. Patterson, to continue work in pathology, parasitology, and in poultry diseases. Dr. Patterson, a native of Cuthbert, Georgia, had earned his DVM in 1921. He worked in private practice for a few years before joining the veterinary medicine research faculty at Iowa State University. He was establishing a name for himself by the time Dr. Cary contacted him, Dr. Patterson having earned an invitation to present a paper on poultry paralysis at the Twelfth International Congress of Veterinarians at their meeting in New York in August 1934. Dr. Cary, briefing the *Plainsman* on Dr. Patterson's appointment, said that invitation represented "an honor which comes to very few veterinarians."

Of Dr. Cary's early students, one other—Dr. Isaac Sadler McAdory—stands in Auburn lore as the most significant of Dr. Cary's lieutenants. McAdory came to Auburn from his prominent family's Pleasant Hill (Birmingham-area) home after his high school graduation in 1900. He played football at Auburn, completed his undergraduate agriculture degree in 1904, and stayed to work with Dr. Cary for a time in the veterinary science program before the degree-granting program was approved at Auburn. To prepare young McAdory for the work he had planned for him, Dr. Cary sent his protégé to McKillip Veterinary College in Chicago, from which Dr. McAdory graduated on Thursday, March 26, 1908, in the largest graduating class yet at McKillip—"122 gentlemen."[41]

Why did Dr. Cary send his prized pupil to Chicago for veterinary school? There were several schools available, but Dr. Cary's familiarity with the level of education available at that time most certainly played a role. Of the seven three-term programs then in existence, McKillip in Chicago was the nearest geographically to Auburn. The others were in New York City (two), Boston, Philadelphia, Montreal, and Kansas City. Dr. Cary would have deemed the two-term schools less sufficient.

McKillip Veterinary College was incorporated in 1892 by Drs. M. H. McKillip, J. M. Wright, and L. A. Merillat, with the first students enrolling in October 1894. M. H. McKillip was president of the first Illinois state veterinary examining board. The college was located in the heart of Chicago, a block west of Michigan Avenue and only a few blocks from the Lake Michigan waterfront where, in 1893, Chicago hosted the World's Fair. From its beginning, McKillip offered a course in veterinary training that took three years, with six months of study per year.

McKillip was held above some of the other contemporary private veterinary colleges because of the caliber of clinic associated with the school. As an example, for the fiscal year 1898-99, the clinic received 15,973 professional visits; logged 3,841 surgeries; boarded 8,937 patients; provided 1,320 dental surgeries; and treated an impressive total of 37,562 cases. Such volume as a training ground would have appealed to the practical-minded Dr. Cary. McKillip offered a thorough program, its faculty teaching courses in theory and practice, histology, pathology, helminthology, bacteriology, sanitary science, surgery, embryology, obstetrics, canine practice—one of only two colleges offering canine medicine as a specialty study at this time—anatomy, dental surgery, *materia medica* (a study of the therapeutic properties of any substance used for healing), natural history, chemistry, physics, and physiology.[42]

Researchers at McKillip proved their mettle by becoming the first in the US to make tetanus antitoxin in the school's bacteriological laboratory and veterinary hospital in 1894. This development might seem ho-hum today, but in the late nineteenth century, tetanus was an awful scourge to both people and horses. Only a decade before McKillip's opening did researchers discover the cause of tetanus, and the first tetanus antitoxins were not available until 1893. Having such a product for veterinarians within a year was no small achievement and would have reinforced to Dr. Cary the caliber of work performed at the school.[43]

McKillip Animal Hospital still operates a multi-doctor companion animal practice on North Clark Street in Chicago, only a few miles north of where the founding clinicians established their now-long-gone college.

After his graduation from McKillip in 1908, Dr. McAdory worked for a time with the USDA in Alabama in the tick eradication effort, but he soon returned to Auburn as a professor of anatomy and physiology under Dr. Cary. He earned a wonderful reputation as an instructor and clinician, served as Dr. Cary's right-hand man for the rest of Dean Cary's life, and succeeded him as the second dean of veterinary medicine at Auburn after Dr. Cary's death in 1935.

The close relationship that developed between the two prompted one of the enduring stories about Dr. Cary, coming from the days in which he was building the Cary Castle next door to his home. As reported by the *Orange and Blue* on October 1, 1910:

> While superintending the construction of his new house, Dr. Cary fell from the roof, sustaining injuries which will cause his absence from the class room for a few weeks. We are certainly glad to report that his injuries are not as serious as at first suspected. It is needless to say that his return to active duty again is anxiously awaited by both students and faculty of all departments.[44]

The distance Dr. Cary fell was not insignificant. He certainly could have died. He did break his leg. The rest of the story became a favorite tale among Auburn veterinary graduates down through the years. Dr. Cary insisted that Dr. McAdory set his leg. Perhaps college and town physician Dr. John Hodges Drake, III was out of town on this occasion or, perhaps, another reason led Dr. Cary to call for his trusted veterinary assistant. Dr. McAdory was summoned, and while Dr. Mac surely did a fine job, the story held that Dr. Cary walked with a limp for the rest of his life.

After Dr. Cary's death, Dr. McAdory led the school and remained at the forefront of state veterinary business, serving on the Alabama Board of Veterinary Examiners 1935-52, as assistant state veterinarian 1940-52, as secretary of the Alabama Veterinary Medical Association, and as second vice president of the Alabama Livestock Sanitary Association. He was involved in numerous other college and civic organizations: Masons, Shriners, Rotary Club, Alpha Psi veterinary fraternity, and Auburn United Methodist Church, where he taught Sunday school for many years. Significantly, though most of the credit for funding should go to President Luther Duncan, Dr. McAdory had a role in planning API's new veterinary building in the late 1930s, which in 1946 would officially be named Cary Hall.

Dr. McAdory died on July 5, 1952, and, like so many others prominent in the cadre of faculty and administrators that built the city and the educational institution, he was buried in Pine Hill Cemetery a few yards to the west of Dr. and Mrs. Cary. Auburn University in 1960 named its new Large Animal Clinic in Dr. McAdory's memory, and that building served the College well for more than a half-century until it was razed to make way for the present-day Bailey Small Animal Teaching Hospital. The primary hallway in that hospital is called "McAdory Hall," and includes a memorial tribute to its namesake on one wall.

Dr. McAdory may have deserved a special commendation for working with the demanding Dr. Cary for twenty-seven years. Certainly, they had a special relationship. The review of Dr. Cary's various lieutenants over the years bears out Dr. McAdory's many good qualities as the program's second dean stayed the course after many others left Auburn after rather short terms. The "revolving door" was recognized throughout the veterinary community. Writing to API President Luther Noble Duncan after Dr. Cary's death, in a letter in which he proposed a candidate for the position, AVMA Secretary Dr. H. Preston Hopkins described Dr. Cary as "one of my best friends," but reminded Duncan that Auburn under Dr. Cary "was regarded rather generally as a one-man affair. From time to time, Dr. Cary had a number of very good men associated with him, but, for one reason or another, these men left the institution rather regularly."[45]

Despite any lack of continuity among the faculty ranks, Dr. Cary served as the centerpiece of the assembled expertise of the program in the early 1900s. Auburn veterinary medicine under Dr. Cary increasingly made progress in attracting students, conducting research, and addressing many of the pressing public health problems that were costing millions of dollars in lost animals as well as proving deadly to people. With programmatic growth, new space was soon required, not only for the increasing student population and case load, but to provide adequate holdings for addressing serious economic and health threats.

One of the chief diseases, or families of disease, Dr. Cary targeted was hog cholera, a viral disease which plagued most of the United States through the nineteenth century and long into the twentieth century. Hog cholera—today more commonly called classical swine fever (CSF)—is a highly contagious swine disease that causes fever, skin lesions, and convulsions as it kills almost all its victims. The USDA holds that hog cholera was eradicated in the US by 1978, but before and during Dr. Cary's lifetime, it proved the most devastating disease affecting swine in the United States for more than a century. Outbreaks depleted or erased untold numbers of swine herds throughout the land. The USDA did not begin its hog cholera research until 1879, though symptoms and confirmation of the disease had been reported in herds as early as 1833 in Ohio. The USDA's Agricultural Research Service noted that outbreaks in 1886, 1887 and in 1896 each killed more than 13 percent of the hogs on America's farms, and a 1913 outbreak killed 10 percent. Losses were in the tens of millions of dollars most years, prompting the fervor with which Dr. Cary and his colleagues sought a solution.

Research efforts in Iowa, a collaboration of veterinarians from the Bureau of Animal Industry and Iowa State experts, led to development and use of a serum. This breakthrough led to Dr. Cary's efforts to build a serum plant to manufacture this product for farmers in Alabama and the region. When grassroots pleas from farmers got the attention of the legislature, Dr. Cary (by then the well-established state veterinarian) persuaded state leaders to make this investment for the common good. In 1915, API received $25,000 from the Alabama Legislature to construct a hog cholera serum production plant on the Auburn campus. This two-story, 4,200-square-foot brick and cement building—located a few hundred feet west of the original veterinary building—was adjoined by a brick and cement virus building, which measured

1,080 square feet, and a nearby 6,000-square-foot hog barn, with—advanced for the time—a cement floor. Efforts to improve the effectiveness of the serum continued for years, but the initial products offered some protection for those hogs inoculated, so the Auburn effort was appreciated by farmers and consumers alike.

Dr. Cary hired Dr. James Clifford Schoenlaub, a 1913 Ohio State University graduate, as the serum program's first director, though he only stayed two years. In 1919, Dr. Cary enlisted a new faculty member to lecture on the merits and fine points of anti-hog cholera serum and to assist with its production: twenty-five-year-old Dr. Everett Sompoyac Winters. Born in South Carolina in 1894, Dr. Winters was promoted to manager of the hog cholera serum plant in 1923, and he remained with the veterinary college until his retirement. Dr. Winters passed away on Christmas Day 1954. Among his many contributions during a solid career was his agreeing to serve as acting dean during World War II when Dean Sugg was away in military service. For his efforts during those years, and to ensure that the College does not forget Dr. Winters' contributions, an Auburn alumnus in the late 1990s permanently endowed a scholarship at the College in Dr. Winters' memory.

(A deeper look at Dr. Cary's efforts to combat hog cholera can be found in Chapter 15.)

One additional facility of note can be attributed to Dr. Cary's guidance of the veterinary program. the Physiology Building, built beginning in 1921 and opened in 1922 diagonally across from the serum plant. Apparently, a couple of false starts from the legislature had left unfulfilled a promise made to Dr. Cary for a new structure. Headed into the 1920s, campus veterinary facilities were wearing out. President Thach, who would soon be granted a leave of absence to address his failing health, had asked trustees for authorization to proceed with a more modern setting for the veterinary program; and, to reinforce the need, the president asked Dean Cary to spell out the matter. Dr. Cary wrote to the Board of Trustees to request a new building in May 1919, a request carried forth in President Thach's absence by acting president Dr. B. B. Ross:

To Members of The Board of Trustees of The Alabama Polytechnic Institute.

Dear Sirs:

At two different times an appropriation has been made by the Legislature of Alabama for buildings at the Alabama Polytechnic Institute. Each
time Pres. Thach has repeatedly stated that out of said appropriation a
Veterinary building would be constructed. The Veterinary College is not
decently housed and such as it has is not large enough for classes and
laboratory work. Students have complained of being compelled to work
without proper shelter from cold and rain. The American Veterinary
Medical Association has threatened to put this Veterinary College in
Class C because of lack of adequate buildings and equipment.

The Veterinary College and Department have been run under such
adverse conditions and upon such promises. Not less than $50,000.00
should at once be put into buildings and equipment for the College of
Veterinary Medicine.

Dr. Thach repeatedly stated that when the present appropriation bill
was up before the Legislature that the first building constructed would be
for the Veterinary College.

The Veterinary Alumni, in proportion to the total number of graduates, sent more graduates as officers and privates into the World War
than any department of the A.P.I. There is a great demand for veterinarians in practice, in the army and in official sanitary and inspection work.
No war can be [and] never will be run without horses and mules and
meat foods. No agricultural country will ever be run without horses,
mules, cattle, hogs, and poultry. I invite you to see what we have. Many
of you have never seen our present buildings. It is your duty to see them
and then act.

Very truly yours,
C. A. Cary
Dean

Trustees responded at their February 21, 1920, meeting by sending
word to Dr. Cary that "his communication concerning a building and
proper equipment for the College of Veterinary Medicine was received
and considered sympathetically by the Board and that Dean Cary be
assured that the Board will take action favorable to his department to
the very best of their ability when funds for buildings are available."[46]

Dean Cary got his new building: a 17,000-square-foot, two-level
brick structure used at first for basic science instruction and small ani-

mal clinical work. This structure served the college until relocation of its basic science program to Greene Hall on the Wire Road campus in 1970. The Physiology Building—it never got a more personalized name—was demolished in summer 2013, but not before also serving various programs of the College of Sciences and Mathematics for many years.

CHAPTER TEN

FARMERS' INSTITUTES

According to Joe Yeager and Gene Stephenson in their history, *Inside Ag Hill*, agriculturally focused meetings that came to be known as Farmers' Institutes originated in the 1870s. These gatherings apparently first were held in Alabama in 1889, emerging from the office of the Commissioner of Agriculture, with direction from the Alabama Legislature to get busy helping the struggling folks (and voters) back home. Gradually, the meetings took on more of a political rally theme than agricultural instruction and advice, as Agriculture Commissioner and A&M College Trustee Reuben F. Kolb sought the governor's office and used the sessions throughout the state for that purpose.

When Kolb lost the election in 1892, the legislature, in an effort to return the Farmers' Institutes to their intended purposes, directed the A&M College at Auburn, with its agricultural expertise, to take over this program. Whether a part of these Farmers' Institutes or some other outreach effort launched by President Broun, the A&M chief reported to the board of trustees in the summer of 1892 that "much interest now exists in educational circles in extending the benefits of the college by public lectures by the professors at suitable localities." He then noted that such lectures had been delivered by Auburn Professor Dr. George Petrie, the historian, in Montgomery; by Dr. Cary, who spoke on veterinary science in Opelika, LaFayette, and Girard (a community which would merge with adjoining Phenix City in 1923); and by Professor George Atkinson, the biologist, in Huntsville.

Dr. Cary apparently took part in some of these talks during his three-month temporary duty early in 1892; his appearances expanded after he returned from Germany and joined the staff permanently. President Broun's report a year later, in June 1893, noted that Dr. Cary, in the first half of that year, already had given twenty-one of these lectures "in different parts of the state on subjects related to veterinary science." The president continued in his report on the value of Dr. Cary's participation in the state-wide lecture plan: "Should it be made the duty of this professor to lecture in different functions of the state on subjects related to veterinary science it would be a direct effort of the college to promote the interest of the farmers, and thereby tend to fulfill the obligations of the law establishing the [Experiment] Station."[1]

Within a couple of years of his arrival in Auburn, Dr. Cary was traveling the state on a regular basis—always taking the train as he didn't buy his first car until 1926—making presentations related to diseases of farm animals and looking into disease outbreaks wherever they occurred. When he treated animals, he typically only charged for actual expenses and for any medicines he used.[2] When the time came for Experiment Station personnel to be involved in conducting Farmers' Institutes, he was a natural choice to participate. Dr. Cary's frequent travels to conduct Farmers' Institutes were, in part, a reason for President Broun in 1894 to call for the establishment of the office of state veterinarian, as Dr. Cary already was working in that role, at least to an extent, based on his professional activities.

The Auburn-directed Farmers' Institutes continued and grew during the next few years, and on June 13, 1898, President Broun reported to the trustees on the value of—and the mission of—Auburn hosting these gatherings "at such times and places as may be deemed advisable . . . I also recommend that Dr. Cary be made Director of the same, with an appropriation of $500 to pay the necessary expenses."[3] A&M College trustees approved the president's recommendation that afternoon, and Dr. Cary, as director, continued and expanded these programs. He involved other faculty members in this work as well, among them later a 1900 API graduate named Luther Noble Duncan. The concept of taking Auburn expertise throughout the state thus began within the Experiment Station, but this platform eventually gave birth to the Alabama

Cooperative Extension Service in 1920, which Dr. Duncan headed for years before he was named president of API in 1935.

Making his annual report to the Board on June 15, 1899, President Broun told trustees of the success of Dr. Cary's first full year as director of the program, and he used the occasion to remind them of the financial hardship the work caused the college:

> Farmers' Institutes were conducted by the officers of the Experiment Station under the direction of Dr. Cary, in different sections of the state, representing twelve counties. In some cases much interest was manifested. This practical educational extension of agricultural science will, if continued, excite in Alabama an interest similar to what it has in other states where Institutes receive a special appropriation, and thereby are enabled to command a number of special lecturers. I recommend their continuance, with the small means at our disposal, calling attention to the fact that we are notified by the Director of the Experiment Station in Washington that the money received from the U.S. Treasury cannot be used for this purpose.[4]

President Broun's report of June 10, 1901, noted that Dr. Cary, with assistance from others within the Experiment Station, conducted seventeen Farmers' Institutes in sixteen Alabama counties the previous year, and President Broun took the occasion once again to laud Dr. Cary and the overall effort:

> I regard these Farmers' Institutes as much value as a means of diffusing knowledge of scientific agriculture among the people, and recommend for your approval a renewal of the appropriation made for that purpose, and would recommend an increase were means available. The officers perform this work without remuneration, the appropriation being used only to pay the necessary expenses.[5]

A year later, President Broun had died, but Interim President Dr. O. D. Smith continued to update trustees on Dr. Cary's Farmers' Institutes, and like Dr. Broun before him, Interim President Smith also used the report to suggest enhancement of the veterinary science program. Dr. Smith told the Board in June 1902:

> The demand for Farmers' Institutes is constantly increasing. The enterprising and intelligent farmers regard them of much value in diffus-

ing a knowledge of scientific and practical agriculture. The demands upon Dr. Cary's time in holding institutes and meeting the numerous calls for his professional service as veterinary surgeon from stock raisers in different sections of the state, necessitate his absence from the college at frequent intervals. It is important that a competent assistant be provided to take charge of his classes in his absence and to further assist him in the increasing clinics and laboratory work of his department.[6]

During the 1902-03 school year, Dr. Cary and/or his fellow scientists in the Experiment Station conducted twenty-four Farmers' Institutes in twenty counties, with an average attendance of 109 farmers (totaling 2,613 people). The following year, Farmers' Institutes were held twenty-four times and spread over twenty-three counties, but the attendance had jumped to an average of 151 per event, or 3,639 attending in total.

These institutes were designed on many occasions to have morning, afternoon, and evening sessions. The format, of course, could be tailored to a location, depending on the speakers' travel schedules, the size and nature of local facilities, the availability of electric light, etc. A notice in the *Montgomery Daily Advertiser* on August 5, 1898, suggested how the Farmers' Institutes typically may have been planned. This announcement previewed a program planned in North Alabama:

> Dr. C.A. Cary, director of the Farmers' Institutes for the Agricultural and Mechanical College at Auburn, informs the Advertiser that an institute will be held at Cullman, Alabama, Monday, August 15, one in Florence, August 17, and one in Huntsville, August 20. Professors Ross, Baker, Earle and Duggar will lecture at these institutes. Professor Ross will discuss fertilizer. Professor Duggar will discuss Plants for Forage and Soil Improvements. Professor Earle will discuss Diseases of Plants and Practical Horticulture. Professor Baker will discuss How to Recognize and Destroy Injurious Insects.[7]

At the Cullman Farmers' Institute, as at most other such events, Dr. Cary discussed in depth with farmers the diseases their animals might contract and his advice for returning their animals to good health. Dr. Cary planned morning, afternoon, and evening sessions at this Cullman program; he was certainly of a mind to offer as much beneficial information as possible in each location. He told the newspaper, "These institutes are strictly for the benefit of farmers and every effort will be made to make them practical and interesting."[8]

In 1902, English Professor Dr. Charles Coleman Thach was named permanent president, succeeding the interim Dr. O. D. Smith and prompting presidential hopeful Dr. P. H. Mell to leave his API faculty position and accept the presidency at Clemson. Dr. Thach addressed the trustees on June 6, 1904, and reported on animal husbandry and veterinary science, noting that during the winter and spring, nearly a dozen head of pedigreed stock were added to the Experiment Station herd and a car load of steers purchased. Research involving four different feeds was conducted with these cattle; a bulletin outlining the results was in preparation. Dr. Thach further reported:

> During the session the college veterinary surgeon inoculated and treated a herd of Hereford cattle, the purpose being to render them immune from Texas fever, the dread cattle scourge of our Southern states. This herd was brought from Kentucky and considered of the finest specimens of animal raised in that state. A public sale was held at the college and attracted wide attention, representatives being present from six Southern states and from Cuba. The 60 head sold realized about $13,000. The possibilities of animal raising in Alabama are just on the threshold of development. The industry is of supreme importance to our state, and it seems that every encouragement for its development should be afforded by the college.⁹

A year later, at the 1904-05 academic session's concluding trustees meeting, President Thach made interesting comments about the student body, which had reached a record 515 this year, with thirty enrolled in veterinary science. His words reflected the entire body, but surely Dr. Cary and his veterinary students were at the forefront of President Thach's mind when he told the Board,

> The spirit of work pervades the entire institution to a degree that it would be difficult to surpass. It is not meant that there are no individual exceptions to diligent attention and study on the part of the students, but these exceptions are gradually eliminated, and altogether there is a spirit of serious, persistent study and a lively interest in the work at hand.

In that June 1905 report, President Thach specifically cited Dr. Cary's role in a cattle sale that, in the president's mind, reflected Auburn's role in early development of the cattle industry in Alabama. He spoke of a "winter cattle sale of two herds of Aberdeen Angus and

Short-horn [cattle]," which "attracted wide attention and favorable comment. These cattle were rendered immune against Texas fever by inoculation, the work being done by our veterinarian and his assistant," Thach said. "The purpose of the college in fostering these sales is to promote the introduction into our state of those breeds of cattle which will make beef production profitable."

Expansion of research efforts and of the number of farm animals on campus supplied Dr. Cary and other faculty additional subject matter to share with Alabamians. The president's report in June 1905 noted that Dr. Cary's twenty-eight Farmers' Institutes in twenty-eight counties attracted 4,611 attendees, an average of about 165 each time. A new program—a week-long educational "Summer School for Farmers" that brought the farmers to Auburn—had been introduced the previous year and tried twice by the time of this meeting. President Thach reported:

> A new and successful extension of this work has been the summer school for farmers at Auburn the last two years. Last year, 245 farmers attended from July 23-August 1. Besides members of our teaching staff, experts from other colleges and other states were secured for lectures on horticulture, truck gardening, corn judging, poultry raising, swine breeding, cattle judging, etc.[10]

As president, Dr. Thach had taken a personal role in helping Dr. Cary recruit attendees and market his summer school program. Auburn University Archives' Thach Presidential Papers collection preserves copies of several letters he sent to various officials in localities throughout Alabama, asking them to circulate the information about the Summer School for Farmers wherever they could. Included also is a letter from President Thach to the leadership of the railroad company whose train made the trips through Auburn, asking if they would schedule railroad transport into the town on the date the summer school opened.

During 1905, Dr. Cary's salary was $1,800 per year, putting him at the highest ranks of earners among faculty members at Auburn. He was vastly underpaid. The three leading faculty members at the Kansas City Veterinary College in 1910 were paid $6,000 each—for seven months' work.[11] Happily, President Thach saw in Dr. Cary the same qualities President Broun had noticed, and Thach did what he could to ensure Dr. Cary's continued appointment. President Thach also echoed President Broun of several years earlier, calling for Dr. Cary to be appointed as an official state veterinarian, a role he played in all but title:

> The professor of veterinary science and veterinarian of the [Experiment] Station is practically a State veterinarian. His services are at the command of the farmers, and much of his time is devoted to calls made from all quarters of the state in connection with the diseases of animals. This service to the state is highly valuable, and it is recommended that the Legislature be urged to make provision of the official recognition of the officer as State Veterinarian, and, as in other states, an adequate appropriation be made for extending the help of the department even more widely throughout the state.[12]

Dr. Cary, in 1905, again hosted a successful and expanded series of Farmers' Institutes, organizing thirty-five such programs which attracted 3,744 Alabamians throughout the state, an average of 107 each time. President Thach reminded trustees in his 1906 report that the Farmers' Institutes were "entirely at the expense of the institution" and were "under direction of the professor of veterinary science, and he is aided from time to time by all of the professors connected with the various departments pertaining to agriculture." Dr. Thach made the point to trustees that the legislatures of Mississippi, South Carolina, and Texas were all underwriting the same type programs in those states, and he suggested that a portion of the state tag tax be used toward supporting Alabama's Farmers' Institutes.

These institutes being under direction of the veterinary science professor guaranteed that they would be full of valuable content. A notice in the *Opelika Daily News* from July 1913, authored by Dr. Cary and promoting an upcoming Saturday Farmers' Institute in LaFayette, described the several subjects that would be covered and concluded with this exhortation from the man himself: "Every one should attend and assist in improving farming conditions. If possible, bring your dinner as there will be a morning and evening session."

During August 1905, Dr. Cary's summer farmers' school brought 239 registrants to Auburn for several days of instruction, the guests coming from twenty-nine Alabama counties and four other states.

The next school year, 1906-07, Dr. Cary organized two dozen Farmers' Institutes, which attracted 2,857 attendees, an average of 115 each.

The August 1906 Farmers' Summer School on campus brought 405 attendees.

The president's report in June 1907 noted that some of the veterinary science research under the leadership of Dr. Cary had focused on the poisonous influences of cotton seed meal fed to hogs, as well as the level and type of germs found in Alabama-produced milk. This meeting announced the veterinary program's elevation to a degree-granting school.

President Thach again noted the continually expanding role Dr. Cary was carrying throughout Alabama. "The services of the professor of Veterinary Science and of the professor of Animal Industry have been secured by the state as officers of the live stock sanitary board for the protection and development of stock raising in Alabama. The college receives no remuneration for their time, but the arrangement seems to subserve in a very substantial way important interests of the state."[13]

The September 7, 1908, issue of the *Orange and Blue* reviewed the benefits of Dr. Cary's Farmers' Summer Schools:

> For the last five or six years, there has been held at Auburn a summer school for farmers. This school consists of a course of lectures in the lecture room and upon the Experiment Station farm upon subjects of interest to all wide-awake farmers. The Institute, as it is called, is directed by Dr. C. A. Cary, who arranges the programs and selects lecturers. These lecturers are of the agriculture faculty of the college and prominent farmers from different sections of the country, in fact from all over the United States. The lectures are well attended by farmers from the surrounding neighborhood, all over the state and some from our sister states.
>
> The benefits derived from these meetings are three-fold. It is educative to the farmer, it brings them in touch with each other and in touch with our great college. Not a one of the lectures fails to bring out some point of interest. The farmers get acquainted with each other, discuss different methods, crops, plans for farming, etc., each giving the other some new thought perhaps. Again, they get to see the things going on about the college and conceive of the greatness of the Institution. Perhaps this will help to dispel the idea among farmers that a college is no good and a college education is no good, or, at any rate, an agricultural education is no good.
>
> Taken altogether, from start to finish, the Farmers' Institute is a good thing. If more attention is paid it, there will be more interest in the agricultural courses here and that is what is needed. We need educated farmers, we must have them, and we shall have them.[14]

The week-long Farmers' Summer School of August 1911 brought 1,100 farmers to Auburn, but campus authorities decided this school would be the last year of free barbecue provided for attendees. Thus, campus officials prepared for a decrease in numbers the following summer. When the "Dutch treat" version of the program of 1912 still attracted more than 900 farmers, President Thach once again credited the veterinary school dean. "Dr. Cary is director and deserves the credit for making it one of the most helpful agencies in the education of the Alabama farmer," President Thach said of the week.[15] He spoke as highly the following year, again lauding Dr. Cary and the Farmers' Institutes in his report to the Board of Trustees: "This work, under the supervision of Dr. C. A. Cary, is conducted entirely at the expense of the 'college fund.' Full recognition of the pioneer work of Dr. Cary in this field of agricultural extension is at all times due."[16]

One likely overlooked aspect of the Farmers' Summer Schools Dr. Cary hosted at Auburn was the variety of speakers he lined up. His program at the 1913 school, for example, included not only Dr. Cary's opening day lecture on "The Anatomy and Physiology of the Chicken," but an industry-focused lecture by University of Georgia Professor L. L. Jones on "The Poultry Industry in the South," and talks by laymen on various aspects of gaining success in the poultry business. He also included a laywoman: Mrs. P. T. Calloway of Washington, Georgia, spoke on "Poultry Profits in the South" and "Selection of Type, Mating and Feeding" of chickens.

In 1914, thirty-four Farmers' Institutes held across two dozen Alabama counties attracted 5,785 attendees. The Summer School for Farmers the first week of August that year brought 810 farmers, representing every Alabama county. For his work, Dr. Cary again received laudatory comments from President Thach, though the president seems to have relied, almost verbatim, on his notes from the previous year:

> This work, under the supervision of Doctor C.A. Cary, is conducted at the expense of the "College Fund." Full recognition to the pioneer work of Doctor Cary in the field of Agricultural Extension is at all times due.[17]

The key word in that comment by the president may be "Extension," for, in these years, a transition was taking place which brought to an end Dr. Cary's directing role with Farmers' Institutes and the Summer School for Farmers. In fact, those programs were changed with the advent of the Alabama Cooperative Extension Service after 1915.

County agents and farm and home demonstration specialists were hired throughout Alabama, and their work resulted in tremendous numbers of meetings and demonstrations, in effect taking over planning that Dr. Cary and others had been doing with the Farmers' Institutes and Summer Schools.

One cannot imagine Dr. Cary missed a beat. He had plenty of work to pursue, including ongoing fights against Texas fever, tuberculosis, and hog cholera. In addition to these actions and overseeing the growing College of Veterinary Medicine, Dr. Cary continued his work with the American Veterinary Medical Association, the Alabama VMA, and the Alabama Live Stock Association.

CHAPTER ELEVEN

DR. CARY AND THE ALABAMA
VETERINARY MEDICAL ASSOCIATION

In his late twenties, Charles Allen Cary began a forty-five-year membership in the American Veterinary Medical Association, attending almost every national meeting, serving on numerous committees of varying areas of focus, chairing committees several times, earning election as vice president and as president of the national organization. He was active for many years in the National Live Stock Sanitary Association. He helped to organize the Southern Cattlemen's Association and served multiple years as its president. He served during 1897 as president of the United States Experiment Station Veterinarians organization. He served as president of the Alabama Swine Breeders Association in the late 1890s.

In 1907, Dr. Cary brought to life the defunct Alabama Veterinary Medical Association, working to make it a state-wide force for good, and held the office of secretary-treasurer for the rest of his life so he could guide the Alabama VMA to his high level of expectations and use its platform to further his professional plans. He initiated a student Veterinary Medical Association at Auburn, which not only elevated the scholarship of his professional students but which introduced them at an early age to the value of organized veterinary medicine. He arranged and conducted free clinics almost every week on the Auburn campus for the benefit of area farmers and, as importantly, for training his students in animal handling, diagnosis, treatment, medicine, and client relations. He held Farmers' Institutes throughout the state, cooperative programs designed to educate Alabamians about animal diseases, diagnostic methods, and treatment planning. He used these occasions to bring in other specialists so he could build relationships with them, as well as help them, himself, and his Auburn program gain the trust of people at the grassroots level. He organized Farmers' Summer Schools at Auburn, with farmers from throughout Alabama staying a week or sometimes two weeks, attending demonstrations on all phases of agriculture.

He arranged for creation of—and a leading role on—the State Livestock Sanitary Board, so he could direct work done toward battling dairy and cattle diseases on Alabama farms. He cooperated with any number of county, state, and federal officials in various actions, most notably in efforts to rid the state and region of Texas fever, hog cholera, and tuberculosis. He served on the Auburn city school board for many years. He sat on the board of the first bank begun in Auburn from 1907 to 1935. He not only made time for church on Sundays, but served for two decades as superintendent of Sunday School at Auburn Presbyterian Church, either teaching Bible classes or arranging for someone else to teach. He was also an elder in Auburn Presbyterian. In short, under the word "collaboration" in the dictionary, one may well find his picture as its definition.

Many type-A geniuses with seemingly endless energy, unmatched work ethic, and an almost-superhuman focus on their chosen targets are unable to function in a team environment. Many such persons never learn to delegate and their efforts at collaboration result in frustration for all concerned. They prefer, and perhaps work best, as lone wolves. But Dr. Cary, whether via his mental makeup or from experience he gained early in life, was a man who understood the value of bringing people together to accomplish a goal.

A lengthy letter dated March 18, 1957, from Auburn Veterinary Dean Redding S. Sugg to W. H. Smith, a leading businessman and farmer in Prattville, Alabama—another of the items kept in the collection of Cary family memorabilia—details Dr. Cary's accomplishments through collaboration. Dean Sugg's letter is worth reading practically in its entirety:

Mr. Will Howard Smith
McQueen Smith Farms
Prattville, Alabama

Dear Mr. Smith:

Dr. Cary, while best known for his work in Alabama in eradicating ticks, was also a pioneer in public health work, and was particularly interested in seeing that Veterinarians were trained to carry out their responsibilities in the control and prevention of diseases in animals that were transmitted to man. Dr. Cary's education and experience, particularly in Germany, made him particularly well qualified to inaugurate and promote this phase of medicine. Dr. Cary's training in Germany was under some of the most noted scientists of the day including Dr. Robert Koch and students of Louis Pasteur, as well as some eminent German physicians and surgeons.

In 1896 Dr. Cary wrote an ordinance providing for meat inspection in the city of Montgomery. It is said that Montgomery was the first city in the South to adopt such an ordinance. The ordinance required that only qualified veterinarians would be employed by the state to do the inspection. Previous to this time, it had been customary for the chief of police or some of his assistants, or some other layman to do the inspection. Under the Federal meat inspection law, as well as all state ordinances, qualified veterinarians are the only ones authorized to do official meat inspection.

Dr. Cary was also interested in and promoted dairy farm and milk inspection. The cities of Birmingham, Montgomery and Mobile were the first to have full time dairy and milk inspectors. This work was inaugurated between 1900 and 1910.

Dr. Cary realized that if the livestock production was to be developed in Alabama, that there was a big job of educating farmers to be done. Early in his career he inaugurated a free clinic at the Alabama Polytechnic Institute, even before the School of Veterinary Medicine was established. Farmers were invited to attend this clinic every Saturday morning and present any animals suffering from disease that they might have, for diagnosis and treatment. Dr. Cary undertook to explain the cause of these diseases, not only methods of treatment, but to give the farmers information on proper methods of feeding and farm sanitation in order that losses from disease could be minimized or prevented. This work was not only carried on at the college in addition to his teaching duties, but Dr. Cary was officially designated as Director of the Farmers' Institute. Each summer Dr. Cary would hold these institutes in different parts of the state. These meetings lasted from a day to as long as a week. Dr. Cary was in charge of these institutes and invited noted scientists from other states to accompany him and to present lectures and demonstrations at these meetings. In addition to visiting lecturers, members of the staff of the School of Agriculture and Experiment Station also participated. Dr. B.B. Ross, Dr. Miller, Dr. J.M. Duggar, Dr. L.M. Duncan, Dr. Dan T. Gray and others were called on by Dr. Cary to give information at these farmers' meetings. Dr. Cary continued to direct Farmers' Institutes until the Alabama Agricultural Extension Service was developed in 1920 ...

In addition to conducting Farmers' Institutes, Dr. Cary took an active interest in promoting livestock production. He was particularly interested in cattle production and assisted in organizing the Southern Cattlemen's Association, which consisted of leading cattlemen, in all the Southern states. Dr. Cary served as President of this organization about 1910 to 1912.

Dr. Cary conducted a question and answer column in the Agriculture Press (Southern Ruralist) and contributed articles on causes and methods of control of diseases and parasites.

Dr. Cary was much impressed at the damage that fever ticks were doing to cattle in Alabama and had done considerable research work at the college on methods of control and eradication. At the same time the Federal Bureau of Animal Industry research workers were also working on the life history of the tick and also practical means of control.

Dr. Cary worked very closely with the Federal officials in developing this work. In 1907 Dr. Cary was made State Veterinarian of Alabama. Under a special act, the Livestock Sanitary Board, consisting of the Commissioner of Agriculture, one outstanding livestock producer, and the head of the Animal Husbandry Department of Auburn, with Dr. Cary as Executive Secretary, was organized. Under the law the Livestock Sanitary Board was authorized to promulgate such regulations as they deemed necessary for the control and prevention of livestock diseases. Dr. Cary of course, wrote the regulations, and in addition, such legislative acts as were needed to make the regulations conform to the constitution. Dr. Cary was fortunate in having intimate contact with the Governors and leading lawyers of the state, and due to Dr. Cary's training and expertise, his requests and opinions were accepted without questions.

Dr. Cary started tick eradication by working on a voluntary basis in various counties, but in 1919 a state-wide tick eradication law was adopted by the Alabama legislature. After this time progress in eradicating the tick was rapid. Previous to this time county politicians would discontinue tick eradication at periodical intervals and of course all ground gained would soon be lost as the ticks would again spread over all the beats or sections of the county which had been cleaned up. In 1929, all counties in Alabama were declared tick-free, however, dipping had to be continued on the borders as the adjoining states of Alabama had not as yet completed eradication.

In addition to work on ticks, Dr. Cary in cooperation with the Bureau of Animal Industry, began Tuberculosis testing in dairy herds in Alabama in 1917 on an individual herd basis. This work was continued on an accredited herd plan until 1929 at which time area testing by counties was undertaken. This work was continued until 1936 at which time the entire state was declared a county-wide Tuberculosis free area.

In spite of an extremely busy life, Dr. Cary found time to reorganize the defunct State Veterinary Medical Association. On December 20, 1908, Dr. Cary called veterinarians of the state of Alabama for a meeting in Auburn at which time the Alabama Veterinary Medical Association was reorganized, a new constitution adopted and a Code of Ethics adopted. Dr. Cary was elected the first Secretary-Treasurer of the Association and continued to serve in this capacity until his death in 1935. The state association held annual meetings at which time Dr. Cary was instrumental in arranging educational programs in order to keep the practitioners up-to-date on the developments of medical science. An important part of all the meetings was Polyclinic. At such clinics, Dr. Cary always took a leading part in demonstrating up-to-date procedures and methods of treatment.

Contagious abortion (now known as Brucellosis) was becoming a problem. Dr. Cary, again working in cooperation with the Bureau of Animal Industry, began testing selected herds with the Agglutination test. This work was carried out more or less on an experimental basis until 1933 at which time county area testing was started. This work was just getting under way at the time of Dr. Cary's death in 1935.

Hog cholera was another disease that Dr. Cary attacked with vigor as this disease caused enormous losses in hogs. In order to provide farmers with hog cholera serum at the lowest possible price, Dr. Cary wrote an act authorizing the establishment of a hog cholera serum plant at Auburn. This plant was completed [in] 1915 and was continued until serum could be bought commercially more cheaply than it could be manufactured in small quantities. Dr. Cary's success in inaugurating animal disease control programs and in promulgating laws and regulations governing the movement of animals was due primarily to the thoroughness with which he prepared and presented educational programs throughout the state and also to his reputation for sincerity and honesty,

which gave him influence with the political leaders of the state and county. In addition to the public services mentioned above, Dr. Cary was also
a teacher of outstanding ability and reputation. The School of Veterinary
Medicine was established in 1907 and Dr. Cary did practically all of the
teaching for the first 20 years; with only 4 assistants he was able to maintain an accredited college and graduate veterinarians that were so badly
needed in all the counties of Alabama. The School of Veterinary Medicine had a reputation of turning out graduates who were practical and
were capable of facing realities and solving the many problems that con-
fronted them without elaborate and expensive equipment.[1]

Perhaps only someone who knew Dr. Cary personally, who watched
him in action, and who followed in his footsteps as dean of the College
of Veterinary Medicine would have had the perspective to summarize
in one letter so many of the qualities and achievements which can be
attributed to Dr. Cary. Dean Sugg had come to Auburn in 1913 after
earning his BS at North Carolina State University, the result of academic guidance by another Auburn veterinarian, Dr. Bennett Thomas
Simms '11. Dr. Simms was teaching and conducting research at North
Carolina State's Agricultural Experiment Station when he encountered
the promising undergraduate and suggested he pursue the doctoral
course in veterinary medicine Dr. Cary had set out at Auburn. Redding
Sugg graduated a few years later and joined in the line of students Dr.
Cary personally selected for special assistance in his program. Dean
Sugg, who later served in the Veterinary Corps during World War II,
wrote this letter twenty-two years after the death of his mentor. With
an obvious sense of respect, he never referred to him as "Cary," but
always "Dr. Cary."

Dr. Cary got his start in collaborative efforts with the United States,
later the American, Veterinary Medical Association, and with his
membership in state veterinary medical associations of Iowa and then
South Dakota. Not many years after he arrived in Alabama, Dr. Cary
pursued involvement with the state and national Live Stock Sanitary
Associations, as well as the Alabama Swine Breeders and Stockmen's
Association.

The Alabama Swine Breeders, at some point, elected him its president, and in February 1899, the group met in Auburn. Despite what
the *Orange and Blue* described as "very bad weather," the group met in
the Veterinary Building on a Tuesday morning, with Dr. Cary lecturing
on scoring hogs. There was later a demonstration of scoring hogs, an

exhibition of Berkshire and Poland-China breed hogs, a talk by Experiment Station Director Dr. J. F. Duggar on "Food for Hogs," and additional talks by invited speakers through the next two evenings. Dr. Cary spoke on Wednesday on "the salient points of the Jersey cow for beef and for milk."[2]

Alabama's Swine Breeders met at Auburn's Veterinary Building again the following January, 1900, and among several lectures were Dr. Cary's talks on scoring hogs, "Acclimation of Northern Cattle," and "Profits on the Farm." Dr. Cary also arranged for his API colleague W. B. Fleming to report the latest on hog cholera. This meeting concluded with the election of Captain J. M. Thornton of Talladega as the Swine Breeders' new president, Dr. Cary most likely determining that his time was more valuable spent towards other priorities.

Of all the organizations he helped to establish and/or in which he took part—and many of these were central to his professional ambitions—one in particular was key to Charles Allen Cary's being in position to accomplish the monumental tasks before him: eradication of ticks that brought about Texas fever and decimated Alabama's cattle industry; freeing Alabama from deadly tuberculosis by setting up science-based and proven meat and milk inspection protocols; and producing and making available at affordable costs a hog cholera serum that would enable producers to thrive. Dr. Cary accomplished much else, but these three undertakings represented the brightest stars in his public health service crown. In each of these endeavors, he succeeded because of the consensus he fostered through his organizing and growing the Alabama Veterinary Medical Association.

Charles Allen Cary's involvement with organized veterinary medicine began in earnest with his joining the United States Veterinary Medical Association at that national convention in Chicago in 1890, only three years removed from having earned the DVM at Iowa State Agricultural College. His experiences were deepening during that time as he held the assistant state veterinarian position in Iowa for a couple of years after graduation and then served for a year as founding president of the South Dakota Veterinary Medical Association in 1891. During this same time, he served as South Dakota's resident secretary to the AVMA. He held this resident secretary position for Alabama, too, for a time, beginning with his full-time Auburn appointment in 1893. His involvement with several cattle associations—including the Alabama Cattlemen's Association and especially the United States Live Stock Sanitary Association—also played a role in his strong belief in the power of organizations.³ All of these early experiences taught him the importance of organizing the state's veterinarians in Alabama.

A fledgling Alabama Veterinary Medical Association existed before Dr. Cary's arrival in Auburn. Degree-holding veterinarians probably numbered only in the teens, certainly fewer than two dozen, in Alabama in 1891 when some of them had formed the first Alabama VMA in Montgomery. Interestingly, in the same issue of the *American Veterinary Review* in which a report details the Charles Allen Cary-led effort to establish the South Dakota Veterinary Medical Association in September 1891, there appeared notice of the Alabama VMA meeting in the parlors of the Exchange Hotel in Montgomery with Dr. A. H. French in the chair and serving as president.

"This meeting was called with the object of securing such necessary legislation for the practice of veterinary medicine in the State of Alabama as will maintain its proper place in medical science," the report noted.⁴ That organization "died from neglect after two or three annual meetings," Dr. Cary later reported to readers of the *American Veterinary Review*.

Like Dr. Cary and company afterwards, those first Alabama VMA members had organized for the purpose of persuading state lawmakers to enact legislation toward beneficial practices—practices they realized might not be immediately palatable to animal owners who were largely unenthusiastic about governmental authority. Their plans apparently did not work in 1891, but early Alabama veterinarians gave the effort another go in 1894. A report in the October 5, 1895, *Opelika Morning Post* recapped "the second annual meeting of the Alabama Veterinary Medical Association" in Montgomery on the previous day. The report noted Dr. Cary's having presented a paper on "Treatment of Tetanus," with the group discussing the devastation of tuberculosis. VMA members approved a resolution calling for "a thorough system of meat inspection under the personal supervision of a graduate veterinarian and system of daily inspection wherein constantly the general sanitary conditions of the dairy herds shall be inspected . . . ." At this meeting, Dr. Cary was elected president of the Alabama VMA, but apparently the organization soon phased out.⁵

While initial efforts never took off, Dr. Cary, after he had been at Auburn several more years, decided to resurrect the organization. This time, its headquarters would locate in Auburn, where the veterinary science program was evolving into a degree-granting school.

The original group's president was still around: Chicago Veterinary

College-trained Dr. Anderson H. French, a Confederate Army veteran who, at this time, operated a practice in Birmingham. According to his obituary in the *Journal of the AVMA*, Dr. French was born in Jackson, Ohio, November 28, 1840, and died in Birmingham at the T.C.I. Hospital in Fairfield on October 12, 1928. The report claimed he, at eighty-seven, was the oldest member of the AVMA at the time of his death. He came to Birmingham from Aberdeen, Mississippi, and during the Civil War served as a captain in General Nathan Bedford Forrest's cavalry. He finished veterinary school in 1891 and, when he died, was the dean of Alabama's few legitimately educated practitioners. He "doted on ethics in veterinary practice," the *Journal* article noted, and served as a member of the Alabama State Board of Veterinary Medical Examiners.[6]

In those early days, Dr. Cary contacted him, or met up with him—the details are not recorded—and discussed with Dr. French the re-launching of the Alabama VMA. The year was 1907, a pivotal year for Dr. Cary and for veterinary medicine in Alabama—the year API upgraded its veterinary science program into a school, with Dr. Cary appointed its first dean. Also that year, in March, the Alabama Legislature passed the law creating the Livestock Sanitary Board and the office of state veterinarian, finally following the advice of API Presidents Broun and Thach and legally naming Dr. Cary Alabama's first state veterinarian.

That fall of 1907, Dr. Cary organized his veterinary students into a student veterinary medical association in order to give future practitioners a taste of the benefits of organized veterinary medicine as well as to supplement their lecture and clinic experiences. (He may have copied this idea from others, or the concept of student academic organizations may have sprung from a campus-wide plan. API student associations formed about the same time in engineering, agriculture, and other programs.)

Also, in the late stages of 1907, Dr. Cary persuaded Dr. French to send a letter to each of the former Alabama VMA members, and perhaps to new veterinarians with whom he may have become familiar, inviting them to take part in the new organization. On Saturday, December 20, 1907, Dr. Cary and others at Auburn welcomed their guests to town for two days of strategizing toward a re-organized Alabama VMA. Among attendees were a few private practitioners, some veterinarians who worked in governmental service or industry, and some from other educational institutions. Included were several members of the Georgia Veterinary Medical Association, notably that group's first president and Georgia's first state veterinarian, Dr. Peter Frederick Bahnsen. A Dane who had been educated in Germany and who had come to the US in 1900, Dr. Bahnsen operated a top-quality dairy in Americus. He would be responsible for Georgia's initial veterinary practice act in 1908.

The meeting was not devoted exclusively to organizational matters, as the *Orange and Blue* student newspaper told of Dr. Bahnsen's giving Auburn students "demonstrations in handling a horse. With a single piece of half-inch rope and alone he casts the strongest horse and binds him so securely that an eight-year-old boy can manipulate him." This gathering in Auburn would begin many years of collaboration between Drs. Bahnsen and Cary. This December meeting also may be considered the first meeting of the excellent organization that exists today as the Alabama VMA.

Records show that eleven veterinarians from within Alabama traveled to Auburn by train or perhaps along the state's primitive, unpaved roads by horse-drawn carriages or coaches. Most likely, Dr. Cary preferred that he *not* be elected president, so the group voted Dr. French as the organization's first president—for the second time. Those listed in the record as present were: Dr. G. W. Browning, a graduate of New York College of Veterinary Surgeons; Dr. Clive Daly, a Kansas City College of Veterinary Medicine alum; Dr. Ward Giltner of Auburn, who was elected vice president; Dr. William B. Fleming, a University of Pennsylvania graduate; Dr. M. F. Jackson, a Toronto Veterinary College alumnus employed to care for the mules owned by Birmingham Steel and Mining Companies; Dr. F. C. McGuire, another University of Pennsylvania graduate; Dr. Joseph Piatt, a German graduate of the Kansas City College of Veterinary Medicine; Tennessean Dr. Samuel H. Saul, a Montgomery practitioner; and Dr. William D. Staples, like President French, a Chicago Veterinary College alumnus. Five of those attending—Drs. Browning, Fleming, Giltner, Jackson and Staples—would serve as Dr. Cary's first corps of assistant state veterinarians.

Three men at the meeting—Auburn's Dr. Giltner, Dr. Jackson, and Dr. Saul—were asked to draft the new organization's constitution and by-laws, which they modeled on the best document they could find for this purpose: the constitution and by-laws of the AVMA. Association members approved the trio's effort, and the Alabama VMA had its first ground rules.

Attendees at the chartering—or perhaps Dr. Cary—approved a $2 initiation fee and annual membership dues of $1 each, to start putting at least something in the bank account. With Dr. Cary serving as secretary/treasurer, he likely arranged to keep the money safe at the new Bank of Auburn, established by his friend and drug company owner, Sheldon Toomer, who that same year had persuaded Dr. Cary to join his bank's original board of directors. Dr. Cary would serve on the Bank of Auburn board as the bank's secretary/treasurer for the rest of his life.

That first Alabama VMA meeting—the organizational meeting with the horse-roping interlude—saw a majority take its first look at Dr. Cary's proposed code of ethics. The group wished for time to mull over the requirements laid out in that code of ethics, so they postponed voting on that document until the next meeting. Also at the first meeting, three committees were formed: an executive committee, a committee on diseases, and one on legislation. Dr. Cary was elected a member of the first and third of these, and he surely was pleased that his Auburn colleague, Dr. Ward Giltner, was voted a member of the diseases committee.

The Friday-Saturday meeting included talks by the Georgia guests plus tours of Auburn campus facilities. Discussions naturally gravitated to the real-life cases these practitioners had faced, or were facing, in their own clinics, as well as practical lectures and demonstrations of surgery by Dr. Cary, along with Dr. Bahnsen's horse handling.[7]

The re-igniting of the Alabama VMA was a success, and those present agreed to meet again in six months' time, with Birmingham the chosen location. Records show a meeting at the Birmingham City Hall June 16-17, 1908, with lectures and committee reports taking place there, and clinical demonstrations held at Dr. French's clinic (where he shared duties with Dr. Jackson, the mule veterinarian). Reporting on the meeting in the *American Veterinary Review* a short time later, Dr. Cary noted that "most of the members were royally entertained by Dr. A. H. French, and a very interesting clinic was held at the hospital of Drs. French and Jackson, Drs. Fleming, Jackson and Cary performing neurotomy, tenotomy and quitter operations, and all members participating in diagnosis of cases of lameness."[8]

Dr. Cary's report of that first substantive meeting in June 1908 confirmed papers presented by: E. M. Duncan, city milk and meat inspector, Birmingham, on "Sanitary Regulation of Municipal Milk Supply"; Dr. W. D. Staples, "Inflammation"; Dr. G. W. Browning, "How to Distinguish the Texas Fever Ticks from Other Ticks"; Dr. S. H. Saul,

"Tuberculosis in the Cow" and "Treatment of Colics in Horses"; Dr. A. H. French, "Shoeing"; Dr. C. Daly, "Tetanus"; Dr. M. F. Jackson, "Cases of Rheumatism, Bone Spavin and Periodic Ophthalmia"; Dr. C. A. Cary, "Epizootic Lymphangitis"; Dr. I. S. McAdory, "Gonitis"; and Dr. T. J. Jackson, "A Case of Rupture of the Stomach and a Quick Death Following a Draft of Cold Water."

One now-amusing aspect of this meeting was Dr. Cary's complaint that few if any members had made preparation to present results of any work to the group, despite Dr. Cary having written to the membership to request this input. The ever-ambitious Dr. Cary then made assignments and suggested the members step up their participation in sharing their findings with the others. The secretary/treasurer had big plans for the Alabama VMA and he was not about to let this organization die as the 1891 group had.

The Alabama VMA approved Dr. Cary's proposed code of ethics—modeled on those of the AVMA—at this Birmingham meeting; immediately, the document's regulations were brought into action against members who violated the terms. On this occasion, the group resolved to petition the Alabama Legislature to approve a law regulating veterinary education, the idea being to elevate the program at API and drive out any unqualified practitioners who were either at work or who might surface.

The group met again a little more than a year later, July 23-24, 1909, in Auburn, with seven visiting veterinarians and sixty farmers from various parts of Alabama attending. API President Thach welcomed the group. Papers were presented on a variety of subjects, first among them Dr. Cary's overview of the "applications of the State Live Stock Sanitary Law of Alabama." Dr. Cary also had right-hand man Dr. McAdory present his findings on "Chorea in Dogs," one of the earliest talks in Auburn veterinary medicine that did not deal directly with farm or food animals. Federal Veterinarian Dr. J. A. Kiernan, whose work related to tick eradication in Tennessee, Mississippi, and Alabama, spoke on "the progress and value of tick eradication in Alabama," calling tick eradication "the most important and valuable movement in the interest of agricultural improvement that had been undertaken by the Bureau of Animal Industry." Kiernan's presentation led to the group's calling for financial help in the tick battle on the local, state, and federal levels.

This meeting brought back to Auburn the Americus, Georgia, veterinarian Dr. Peter F. Bahnsen, whose discussion on "Differential Diagnosis of Colics" proved a hit with the crowd. Dr. Cary later would relate that this paper was the most discussed among those presented at the meeting. Dr. Bahnsen's presentation must have made a strong impression on Dr. Cary as the two would collaborate on a number of occasions from this point forward. To verify his significance to the meeting's proceedings, the Alabama VMA voted Dr. Bahnsen an honorary member. Seven out-of-state veterinarians attended the meeting, a strong indication of the early reputation the group and the program at Auburn already had achieved. They and the resident attendees were joined by several dozen local farmers, whom Dr. Cary had invited.

Determined to meet annually, the Alabama VMA convened again in Montgomery July 20-21, 1910. Despite a small turnout—reportedly, only eleven members came—the group received timely information on illnesses, injuries, and meat inspection. Alabama VMA members again heard from Dr. I. S. McAdory—who was serving as Alabama VMA president that year—on treating fistulous withers, which "led to a lively and long discussion." All but two of the veterinarians attending presented papers, with Dr. Cary lecturing on hernia surgery. The big news from this meeting, however, was Dr. Cary, assisted by Dr. William B. Fleming of Birmingham and Dr. G. W. Browning, drafting proposed legislation that, if enacted by the Alabama Legislature, would constitute the state's first practice act. "All the members were very much interested in having a law passed in order to stop extensive quackery in the state," Dr. Cary wrote in his later submission to the *American Veterinary Review*.[9]

Dr. Cary apparently returned the favor of attendance to his Georgia counterparts at some point during 1911. The Georgia VMA that year adopted a resolution "In Regard to the Suppression of Certain Form of Shipping Fever or Strangles in Horses and Mules," and a note in the *American Veterinary Review* gave credit for offering this resolution to "Drs. Jolly, Burson and Cary," suggesting he attended the Georgia meeting.

The Alabama group met in Birmingham Friday-Saturday, June 16-17, 1911, with thirteen members attending, but eleven new members were voted to the roll, and seven out-of-state guests also took part. Sixteen Friday presentations on all manner of animal health issues included talks by Dr. French on rabies, Dr. McAdory on milk production, Dr. J. E. Threadgill on a dozen cases of tetanus, and Dr. William M. Howell on tuberculosis among oxen. Perhaps most notably, with the Bureau of Animal Industry's tick eradication program in its fourth year, veterinarians discussed the new proposal making the rounds: using constructed dipping vats for treatment of cattle.

Saturday, attendees convened at Dr. French's Veterinary Hospital for a clinical experience. Drs. Piatt and Staples performed plantar neurectomy procedures, surgical removal of a deep-seated nerve to reduce hind limb pain. Drs. McAdory and Bahnsen teamed to amputate a pointer's penis. Dr. Cary operated on an umbilical and a ventral hernia. Dr. Bahnsen demonstrated his method of casting and restraining animals. Dr. French demonstrated safe use of the rabies virus.[10]

Auburn hosted the August 2, 1912, meeting at its veterinary building. Ten Alabama VMA members attended; eight came representing the Georgia VMA. In fact, this was a joint meeting, also serving as the annual convention of the GVMA.

One of the significant presentations was by the University of Georgia's chief veterinary science professor, Dr. William Burson, who spoke on hog cholera serum production at the recently constructed production facility in Athens. If Dr. Cary had not already been seeking to build a hog cholera serum plant on the API campus, Dr. Burson's presentation would have lit that fire. The General Assembly of Georgia had made an appropriation in 1911 for the Athens campus to construct its facility, where it would produce the Dorset-Niles brand of hog cholera serum. UGA's production was a part of its effort "that students may be better instructed concerning swine diseases and the manufacture and administration of the cholera serum," the university's 1915 bulletin assured. At UGA, as at Auburn later, the serum was provided at cost to hog farmers through the office of the state veterinarian. Dr. Cary clearly was pursuing this same setup for Alabama hog producers. Auburn's plant would open three years after Georgia's, the delay, of course, a result of waiting for funding.

An important resolution from this 1912 meeting focused on the growing need for veterinary preeminence in meat and milk inspection. The resolution, presented by Dr. M. F. Jackson of Birmingham and unanimously approved, read: "That it is for the best interests of the public and for efficient service that all meat and milk inspection in Alabama should be done by graduate veterinarians." This public safety best practice would become law, but not for a while.

The affiliated clinical event brought twenty-five cases for the veterinarians—and any veterinary students in town—to investigate. They worked from ten o'clock until five that afternoon on these cases, including one that arrived moments before closing time: a mule with a flatulent colic. Given that task, Dr. R. B. Nixon successfully treated this case, to the relief of all, chiefly the mule.[11]

The Alabama VMA group met next at the Birmingham Chamber of Commerce headquarters on June 6, 1913, and the following day at a local clinic for surgical demonstrations. Attendance was growing. This meeting attracted sixteen members, plus ten guests, and five veterinarians who were to be inducted into the association that night. The thirteen talks again covered a variety of subjects: meat and milk inspection practices and recommendations, colics, drug therapy, tuberculosis, wound management, influenza in horses and mules, and the use and abuse of vaccines. On June 7, the group met at Dr. Piatt's Birmingham hospital for a day of clinics. Among other actions, Dr. French demonstrated inoculation for rabies, and Dr. Cary operated on a roarer, a horse or mule suffering from paralysis of the laryngeal nerve, which results in reduced airflow and often a "roaring" sound.

The following year, the group was back at Auburn for its annual meeting. This gathering was earlier in the season than the others: March 5-7, 1914. Eleven members and ten guests were joined by sixty-seven API students. Dr. Cary again asked President Thach to welcome the group, and the president took the opportunity to review for the audience the impressive growth of the veterinary program under Dr. Cary. He also promised to work toward getting the program a new building as soon as the college could afford it. Another guest speaker, API football coach Mike Donahue, spoke on the value of athletics, the relation of play to work, and the spirit to be found on the API campus.

In addition to the roster of campus speakers, in 1914, Dr. Cary brought to Auburn an officer of the national organization. Dr. Nelson S. Mayo, a vice president of the American Veterinary Medical Association, spoke to students and Alabama VMA members on the breadth needed in an adequate veterinary education. Only later would those students likely realize what a heavy hitter Dr. Cary had brought to speak to them. Two years earlier at the AVMA convention in Indianapolis, Dr. Mayo had been appointed chair of an AVMA committee charged with assisting editors of farm journals to eliminate from their publications "fake and misleading advertisements concerning proprietary preparations put out for the use of veterinarians and the public." Dr. Cary had served as a member of this committee, likely the first time the two had worked together. Dr. Mayo served as secretary of the

AVMA 1913-15 and 1918-22, which overlapped Dr. Cary's term as president 1919-1920.

Dr. Mayo had served as a professor of physiology and veterinary science at Kansas State University and as the AVMA secretary from Kansas in the 1890s. He later served a lengthy spell as chief of the Department of Animal Industry of the Bureau of Animal Industry's Experiment Station at Santiago de las Vegas—located about twelve miles south of the center of Havana, Cuba. He held this appointment from the late 1890s through much of the first decade of the twentieth century.[12] He taught animal husbandry at Virginia Tech beginning in 1909. Dr. Mayo was credited with developing an efficient arsenic dip in the fight against Texas tick fever[13] as well as authoring works which explained veterinary medicine for agriculture students.[14] He also wrote on occasion for the popular press towards explaining veterinary medical activities to the lay reader.[15] He served in the 1920s as an officer in the Army Veterinary Reserve.[16] Dr. Mayo also was active in the United States Live Stock Sanitary Association. In many of these circumstances, his and Dr. Cary's paths crossed. He was active in AVMA for sixty years until his death in 1958.

Dr. Mayo was the first of an incredible list of visiting speakers Dr. Cary would bring to Auburn to benefit his students and graduates as they attended the school's annual conference/short course during the next several years. The roster of national-caliber speakers is amazing, especially given the time-consuming train travel of the day. Every appearance of a guest speaker at the Auburn conferences in this era can be credited to the sterling reputation Dr. Cary had earned as an energetic, forward-thinking leader in the AVMA and as a pioneering, crusading veterinarian in the poor South.

Dr. Cary's well-known leadership in the AVMA helped him make the connections key to these invitations. After joining the United States Veterinary Medical Association in 1890, Dr. Cary held his first office in 1898-99 when he was elected AVMA secretary. He was elected one of five vice presidents on the Executive Board for 1907-08, and secretary again for two terms, 1913-15, the period in which he brought Dr. Mayo to Auburn. Dr. Cary would serve as AVMA president in 1919-20, the first of six Auburn-affiliated veterinarians to hold the top post. Others have included Dr. B. T. Simms '11 in 1946-47; Dr. Walter L. "Ooogie" Martin, Jr. '53 in 1988-89; Dr. Shelton Pinkerton '54 in 1990-91; Dr. Henry E. Childers '54 in 2005-06; and Dr. James O. Cook '76 in 2008-09.

Papers presented at the 1914 state meeting addressed such subjects as emphysema, distemper, diseases common during animal transport and how to prevent their spread, meat inspection, and hog cholera. Of note this year, Dr. Cary directed two of his veterinary students to present to the group, beginning a trend that would run for several years as he constantly sought ways to prepare his students for their roles in the profession. As became the norm at these short courses, API veterinary students hosted their guests at a banquet on the evening of March 6 in the basement dining room of O. D. Smith Hall. The March 1914 *Auburn Alumnus* noted that "covers were laid [places were set] for 125. The hall was tastefully decorated in purple and white, the colors of the association, and very pleasing music was rendered by the API orchestra."[17]

The Alabama VMA met in Auburn again March 26-27, 1915—marking the first time the group met two consecutive years in Auburn. The thirteen members and sixty-five veterinary students attending celebrated the Alabama Legislature's having passed the veterinary practice act ten days earlier, on March 17. This act was designed "to regulate the practice of veterinary medicine and surgery in the State of Alabama and establish a veterinary medical examining board." To be licensed, a veterinarian must have earned a degree from an accredited veterinary school with at least a three-year program. There was also an examination component included in the licensure, with a $15 sitting fee. The act clearly defined "veterinarian" as a person who had gained the requisite credentials, not simply performing some animal health practices, as had been the case with some unschooled, "shade-tree" animal doctors of years past. There were financial penalties for violating this act, which protected the class of legitimate veterinarians and the animal-owning public, not to mention the degree-granting program at Auburn.

In addition to presentations by experienced veterinarians, J. L. Bonner, a senior student, read his paper on "Black Tongue, or Sore Mouth in Dogs."

The next day's clinic brought twenty-five cases. Nashville practitioner Dr. George R. White castrated two colts, standing, in less than a minute each. Soon, Dr. White was on a roll, castrating a mule, spaying one or more pigs, all the while "demonstrating various kinds of harness for these purposes." Dr. Cary joined in the surgical demonstrations, doing one solo and one in collaboration with Dr. White.

In only a few years, Dr. Cary as state veterinarian and secretary of the Alabama VMA, had built the annual state meeting into a special event, attended by a regular corps of practitioners and beneficial to his veterinary students. The organization's next annual meeting was held at Auburn during February 18-19, 1916, with twenty-five veterinarians—one-sixth of those then practicing in Alabama—and seventy veterinary students taking part. They were joined by other students from the college's agriculture programs and by a few area farmers. Dr. Cary, enthusiastic about educating people, welcomed all.

That 1916 meeting's first day consisted of a dozen or so scientific papers and organizational talks. That night the API veterinary students hosted a banquet for all attendees. They fed more than 150 people in the dining room of O. D. Smith Hall, a dormitory built across College Street from API's Main Building in 1908 and named for President Thach's father-in-law who taught English at Auburn, then math, and who then served for several months as acting president upon the death of President Broun in 1902.

The second day of the meeting was given to a "polyclinic," with about twenty animal cases seen, treated, and discussed. Attendees witnessed several surgeries performed by the man from Nashville, Dr. George White, who in Dr. Cary's words "was chief operator, doing more operating than any other veterinarian present." Dr. Cary performed a tenotomy—a dividing or lengthening of the deep flexor tendon—in a four-year-old stallion.[18] Guest speaker Dr. White and Dr. Cary met as early as 1901 when they each presented papers on meat and milk inspection at that year's AVMA convention in Atlantic City.[19] Dr. Cary would have been impressed with the Tennessean during the 1904 AVMA meeting in St. Louis when, in a surgical laboratory, Dr. White demonstrated "the passing of the stomach tube . . . something which undoubtedly most of those present had not seen done . . . ." For good measure, Dr. White repeated this stomach tube routine during the following year's convention in Cleveland.[20] (This was apparently an ancient practice used for either administering medicine to cattle or horses or for relieving the animal's bloat, a practice that had been abandoned or forgotten by veterinarians until a few such as Dr. White resurrected the procedure.)[21]

The Alabama VMA's next annual meeting also was held at API during February 23-24, 1917—forty days before the US would join Britain, France, Russia, and Italy in the Great War. The first day of the veterinary meeting featured a dozen medical papers and a discussion led by Dr. Cary on contagious abortion. A special guest was Dr. I. R. Bremer of the *American Journal of Veterinary Medicine*. Again, the students hosted a banquet on opening night. This time, the dean (or, more likely, Mrs. Cary) arranged for women of the Auburn Presbyterian Church to voluntarily staff the serving line. While there is no record of it, they may well have done the cooking, too.

The next day, attendees inspected Auburn's still-new serum plant and affiliated slaughterhouse. After the tours, the afternoon of the second day again featured a dozen or so clinical cases. A description of one of the cases offers insight into Dr. Cary's use of these events to teach his students:

> The first case was a two-year-old colt with congenital contraction or shortening of the perforans tendon in each front limb. The heels were high and the toes short and the deviation from the normal axis occurred at the distal phalanx. The veterinarians present differed some as to method of treatment. Some advised tetonomy, others cutting down the heels and applying toe clips. The owner decided in favor of toe clips and Mr. Schimmel, a senior veterinary student, trimmed the foot and applied the tip shoes.[22]

The Alabama VMA met next in Auburn the first two days of March 1918, and Dr. Cary's report of this meeting in a subsequent issue of the *Journal of the American Veterinary Medical Association* noted that Dr. H. C. Wilson, federal veterinarian in charge of hog cholera work in Alabama, discussed the use of serum and virus and advised veterinarians who used these products. Papers also were presented by two senior veterinary students—A. R. Gissendanner ("Shoeing Draft Horses in the South") and J. R. Sullivan ("Shoeing the Light Horse in the South").

Dr. Cary described that night's gathering as a "War Banquet," which he said was "one where they were short on food and long on talk. There was a flow of language and a feast of reason, minus logic." Perhaps the hard times of the First World War reduced the amount of food available. The gravity of the situation surely was felt as the students read out the names and ranks of their API veterinary predecessors who were serving in the US Army at that time. Poignantly, Dr. Cary noted that "while the banquet was one of the very best, some speakers that have been nearly always present were missed." That night, the Alabama VMA members voted to send $25 from their treasury to the Relief Fund of the American Army Veterinarians, a program run by the AVMA.

The next day, more than a dozen clinical cases from local farms were on offer for the consideration of those attending.[23]

The next year, the Alabama VMA met in Birmingham February 20-22, 1919, in connection with the third annual meeting of the Southeastern States Veterinary Medical Association, another of the organizations in which Dr. Cary held membership. In fact, at that meeting, he gave the welcoming speech.[24] Two weeks earlier—on February 7—the Alabama Legislature had approved legislation requiring compliance with the Texas fever eradication program begun twelve years earlier by the Bureau of Animal Industry. This action was cause for celebration among the veterinarians, as they and tick inspectors finally had authority to require all cattle in Alabama be dipped. Once again, Dr. Cary's work toward organizing the veterinarians for the common good—and for lobbying the Legislature—had proven successful.

The Alabama VMA's 1920 annual meeting was back in Auburn at the end of February—coinciding with Dr. Cary serving as president of the AVMA—and the state meeting focused on two of the critical animal health issues of the day: tuberculosis and abortion. Eleven veterinarians spoke on the first day, as well as two senior veterinary students. Again, the program featured an opening night banquet in O. D. Smith Hall and a second-day clinic "with various operations and diagnoses."[25]

The next annual meeting of the Alabama VMA was held at API February 23-26, 1921. Varied scientific paper presentations supplemented a demonstration of tuberculosis testing on a dozen cows and ten hogs. This year's banquet was held at the long-gone Varsity Café in Auburn, and 150 veterinarians and students attended. Dr. Cary and staff also arranged for a testing period in which practitioners could practice for the federal exam which authorized readiness for testing cattle and hogs for tuberculosis. Dr. Cary's report, published in the *AVMA Journal,* served as a warning, or perhaps a scolding, for some:

> On Saturday morning 30 veterinarians worked on the Federal and State examination from 9 a.m. until 12 noon, so as to be given the right to test accredited herds. It appears that some veterinarians look upon tuberculin testing as easy work. But the profession must know that it is difficult and that the art of applying and interpreting the reaction requires skill, study and close and careful scrutiny. Make it accurate and then it will mean something and be accredited in fact.[26]

The Alabama VMA next met at Auburn in late February 1922, with presentations made by a mix of college, private, military, and federal veterinarians. One of the campus speakers Dr. Cary lined up was Dr. E. R. Miller, API chemist, who spoke on "some peculiar cases of chemical poisons." Emerson R. Miller (1860-1929) was hired to Auburn in 1895 by President Broun as the college's first professor of pharmacy. A University of Michigan graduate, Miller—like Dr. Cary—studied for a while abroad, at Marburg University in Germany, earning his master's degree there. Miller Hall, adjacent to Cary Hall on the Auburn campus today, is named in his memory.

Dr. Cary's description of that meeting's Saturday clinic offers insight into the nature of the gruesome side of veterinary work in those days:

> A grade Holstein heifer that had been given tuberculin reaction was killed at the Serum plant slaughterhouse and postmortem was held for the benefit of the students and veterinarians present. This was a case of generalized tuberculosis in which a large number of body and visceral glands were infected, but there was very slight infection in the lungs and no apparent infection in the kidney. This heifer was only two years old and came from a tuberculous herd.[27]

New construction awaited the Alabama VMA members when they met at Auburn in February 1923, as the college had opened late in the previous year its latest facility, which for decades afterward would be known as the Physiology Building. This two-story, rectangular structure sat across from the later location of Cary Hall. As the topography was elevated in comparison with the location of the serum plant and the previous veterinary building, it launched what became known as "Vet Hill." In an article published in the College of Veterinary Medicine's *Quarterly* magazine in summer/fall 2004, Redding S. Sugg, Jr., son of the former dean, wrote about his father and his experiences in the early days of the twentieth century. The later dean told his son "about standing with Dr. Cary on what was about to become Vet Hill while Dr. Cary sketched the plan of that building on the back of an envelope." Redding Sugg, Jr., described going into his father's laboratory in that now-demolished building and his remembrance of events of that location in his day:

> My memories of Vet Hill start in the late 1920s. I have snapshot recollections of going with Daddy [Dean Sugg] to his office at night. This opened

off the lab. I was allowed to peer into the microscopes and was mesmerized by whatever specimens were floating in glass jars and demijohns in half-light about the deserted lab. Downstairs in what must have been the anatomy lab, I was intrigued by mounted skeletons of animals large and small. The building had a limey odor emanating from whitewashed terra cotta tile walls. The children of the West Magnolia neighborhood used Vet Hill as a playground. There was always something to watch.[28]

In addition to the new Physiology Building, another innovation took place at the college the following year: continuing professional education. The state association's annual conference of February 4-9, 1924, represented, in Dr. Cary's words, "the first time in the history of the college [that a] practitioner's course has been given at the College of Veterinary Medicine." Talks related the latest information on treating diseases of dogs, cats, poultry, cattle, mules, horses, and swine, and the array of speakers was impressive for this era. Dr. Cary brought in some of his most esteemed colleagues from around the country, notably J. C. Flynn, B. F. Kaupp, and Peter Bahnsen.

Dr. Flynn, a canine specialist from Kansas City, Missouri, would later serve as both a vice president and as president of the AVMA.

Dr. Kaupp, a poultry specialist from Raleigh, North Carolina, for years edited poultry-related articles for the *Journal of the AVMA*. He was by this time a world authority on poultry diseases and had addressed the first World's Poultry Congress in September 1921 in The Hague, Netherlands.[29]

Dr. Bahnsen, the state veterinarian of Georgia, demonstrated practical methods for restraining horses and mules. Also at the meeting, Dr. Elmer E. Lash of Washington, DC, reviewed federal success in tuberculosis eradication. Auburn's future dean Redding Sugg spoke on and demonstrated the method for taking blood from various animals in conducting the agglutination test. Dr. Cary spoke and gave demonstration related to infectious abortion, ovarian cysts, retained corpus luteum in cows, sterility, and udder diseases in cows. Not to be outdone by the Tennessean Dr. White from the 1916 meeting, Dr. Cary demonstrated the "Iowa method" for passing a stomach-tube in swine. By special request, he also performed "a roaring operation on a mule."

Dr. Cary's feats aside, the meeting highlight surely was Dr. Flynn's film presentation, which brought new levels of instruction for students and practitioners alike. He showed three moving pictures: "Clean Hearts and Herds," "Exit Ascarsis," and his own movie of "Furious

Rabies in Dogs." After Dr. Flynn's lecture on rabies and the related film, a rabid animal was brought before the audience and exhibited.

Dr. Flynn was accustomed to making the rounds. Prominent practitioner and prolific author Dr. John Victor Lacroix said of him:

> Dr. J.C. Flynn gave the better part of two years of his time, without compensation, in criss-crossing the country by automobile accompanied by Mrs. Flynn, in response to invitations extended by the secretaries of veterinary organizations, small and large. Doctor Flynn was a successful practitioner in the treatment and hospitalization of small animals at Kansas City, Mo. He was a capable and versatile exponent of demonstrational methods, and whenever he gave clinical demonstrations, attendance was good and interest high. His sutureless technic [sic] for spaying puppies, created of economic necessity in his practice, was something of a sensation as he executed this operation . . . With an unusual background of experience in small animal practice, a good speaking voice, and a ready wit, Doctor Flynn quite naturally encouraged hundreds of veterinarians to engage in small-animal practice.[30]

Dr. Flynn's popularity and the high regard his fellow veterinarians had for him earned him election as AVMA president in 1935.

Dr. Cary must have been pleased with the level of programming he arranged for that 1924 meeting as he wrote in the *AVMA Journal's* recap of the meeting. "Thirty-three attended the short course. Every man went away feeling that he had been repaid with knowledge and pleasure, declaring he would come back for a like course next year."[31]

The next year, the first week of February 1925, the Alabama VMA again met at Auburn, but Dr. Cary, sensing that his programming had taken a turn in emphasis the previous year, billed it as "the second annual short course for graduate veterinarians" held at the College of Veterinary Medicine. Visiting veterinarian Dr. Albert Thomas Kinsley reported on the meeting for the *Journal of the AVMA*—rather than Dr. Cary, most likely for convenience sake, as Kinsley already had ties to the publication. Dr. Kinsley noted that

> veterinarians from practically all the Southeastern states grasped the opportunity and were in attendance. Many more veterinarians would have attended the short course but for the fact that there was a steady down-pour of rain during the first day or two and many of the highways were almost impassable.

Dr. Cary gave the program's opening address, then the lectures lasted until nine o'clock the first evening, with breaks only for lunch and dinner. Dr. J. C. Flynn from Kansas City—who that year chaired the AVMA's Committee on Small Animal Practice—was back to lecture on diseases of dogs and cats and to show another moving picture, this one featuring the work of his own hospital. Drs. Kaupp, Bahnsen, and Kinsley headlined the other speakers, and Dr. Cary again took attendees on a short field trip to the campus slaughterhouse to "demonstrate a modern city abattoir." Dr. Cary also spoke on the efficient municipal meat inspection program.

Dr. A. T. Kinsley (1877-1941) was a particularly noteworthy guest speaker for this meeting. The runner-up to Dr. Cary in the election for AVMA presidency in 1919, he would win that office two years later. He was well known in AVMA circles, speaking regularly on a variety of subjects at the annual conventions and holding the presidency during 1921-22. Dr. Kinsley, an Iowa native, earned BS (1899) and MS (1901) degrees at Kansas State, studied at the University of Chicago, and earned a veterinary degree from the Kansas City Veterinary College in 1904. He invested in the college in 1912, taught pathology, bacteriology, and parasitology there, and served as president of the Kansas City Veterinary College from 1913 until the school closed in 1918. He presided over the school's move from a three-year to a four-year course of instruction in 1916. He founded Kinsley Laboratories in Kansas City, which, according to advertisements, made the first bacterins—vaccines made from killed bacteria—for use by veterinarians. He served as editor of swine articles in the *Journal of the AVMA* for a time, so his presentations to Auburn students likely dealt with hog cholera. Dr. Kinsley authored three important veterinary texts in those early years: *Textbook of Veterinary Pathology* (1910), *Swine Diseases* (1914), and *Swine Practice* (1921). His 1933 sweeping essay on "A Century of Hog Cholera" was held as the standard on that subject.[32]

Dr. Kinsley's report to the *AVMA Journal* from Auburn noted that the "College of Veterinary Medicine at Alabama Polytechnic Institute is well arranged and equipped not only to educate young men in veterinary science, but also to give graduate veterinarians a splendid short course, and the short course in February 1925 was a success and a credit not only to Dr. Cary and his co-workers, but also to the profession."[33]

Dr. Cary's and Auburn's third annual short course, which doubled as the 1926 annual meeting of the Alabama VMA, was held the first week of February and again brought to Auburn a number of distinguished veterinarians, thanks to the continued personal connections Dr. Cary maintained in his professional work.

Dr. Charles Murray came from Iowa State College and performed autopsies on chickens and surgeries on dogs. An Ohio native, Murray grew up in Iowa and pursued veterinary studies about two decades after Dr. Cary. He taught bacteriology at the Iowa State College after graduation and eventually was named head of the college's Department of Veterinary Research, an appointment he held at the time of his Auburn visit.

Dr. John W. Adams (1862-1926) was the AVMA president when he visited Auburn for this meeting. He began his career as an English teacher at a military school and was an All-America center for the University of Minnesota Gophers football team while he pursued a degree in classical studies. He changed course after graduation, pursuing veterinary studies at the University of Pennsylvania, graduating in 1892. He then studied in Germany—at institutes in Berlin and in Dresden—before joining the Penn faculty. At the time of his visit to Auburn, he was in his thirty-third year as a Penn faculty member. At Auburn, Dr. Adams "gave complete word-and-drawing lectures and performed operations," according to Dr. Cary's meeting recap. "He worked and worked and never wearies in his well-doings," Dr. Cary said of his friend, Dr. Adams, in words that could well describe the Auburn dean. Dr. Adams would die suddenly in Pennsylvania eight months later, soon after completing his term as AVMA president.

Another special guest was Dr. W. E. Cotton of the Bureau of Animal Industry in Washington, DC, who lectured on foot-and-mouth disease and who brought along his moving pictures to illustrate the California and Texas outbreaks of that disease in 1924 and 1925. Dr. Cotton would receive a significant honor at the 1946 convention: the AVMA's Borden Award—an annual award for excellence in cattle research—in recognition of his research on brucellosis.

While getting Drs. Murray, Cotton, and AVMA President Adams to Auburn was tribute enough to Dr. Cary's place in the AVMA, his bringing to east Alabama Dr. E. L. Quitman from Chicago was perhaps even more of a coup. E. L. Quitman (1870-1937) visited Auburn in the midst of almost a half-century of work in veterinary medicine, lecturing his Auburn audiences on various diseases of dogs and cats. His obituary in the April 1937 *JAVMA* said of him, in words that easily also would have described his Auburn host: "Living as he did during the building of a veterinary profession in the American Republic, where none existed before, his tireless labors in behalf of scientific progress under strictly ethical standards of application, place his name among the architects of our undertaking . . . ."

Dr. Quitman's career included owning a private practice in Chicago and appointment to the teaching faculty of the Chicago Veterinary College from after his graduation in 1891 until it closed its doors in 1920. He served as dean of Chicago Veterinary College from 1914 until 1920. He was active on all levels of organized veterinary medicine and served on a host of AVMA committees during his forty-plus years of membership.[34] He also served during 1921 as editor of an important journal of the day, *Veterinary Medicine.*

After the Saturday clinics, some of the attendees rode to Tuskegee for the afternoon and "visited the Booker T. Washington Negro School" there.[35] Again, the level of expertise and influence Dean Cary brought into the lives of his students and graduate attendees through such conference experiences and guest speakers was of incalculable value.

Neither the *Journal of the AVMA* nor the *Auburn Plainsman* included any references to the 1927 meeting of the Alabama VMA, but apparently there was a short course during 1927. While the *Plainsman* of that era often covered non-academic subjects with far greater enthusiasm than events of the academic programs, there simply may not have been a report filed for the 1927 meeting.

The College hosted its next annual Short Course for Graduate Veterinarians in February 1928, and Dr. Cary again brought nationally prominent veterinarians to Auburn. This year, he welcomed Dr. W. L. Boyd of the University of Minnesota and, again, Dr. Charles Murray of Iowa State University. Dr. Boyd spoke on sterility in cows among other subjects, and Dr. Murray "gave very profitable talks on hog cholera, hemorrhagic septicemia, infectious enteritis and swine flu." Three other speakers—Drs. F. D. Patterson, E. D. Everett, and J. M. Bryan—comprised much of the other programming. One evening of this week's affair was devoted to "educational moving-pictures," including Dr. B. T. Simms' "excellent and famous film on salmon poisoning, in which the action, life history and anatomy of the salmon fluke were vividly and accurately presented." In an interesting description in his attribution, Dr. Cary noted that Dr. Simms was "one of the investigators and producers of the film . . . a native of Alabama and an Auburn graduate." Not an API graduate, but an Auburn graduate.[36]

On at least three occasions—beginning in 1928—the Alabama VMA held what it billed as a "Mid-Year Special Meeting." These were one-day affairs, the first of which was held on Saturday, July 7, 1928, at the Birmingham Chamber of Commerce office. After being welcomed by Birmingham Mayor James M. Jones, Jr., those gathered heard remarks by Dr. J. S. Andrade and Alabama VMA President Dr. J. M. Bryan and the secretary's report by Dr. Cary. Two discussions followed, related to issues facing livestock producers and general veterinary practitioners.

After lunch, the group discussed the status of meat and milk inspections in Alabama and heard Dr. F. D. Patterson's thoughts on the relationship between the association and the veterinary college. The program also included reports from whatever committees were active at the time.

Meat and milk inspection practices were apparently unsatisfactory to veterinarians in the summer of 1928. Those attending this meeting approved a resolution which Dr. Cary, as secretary, had likely authored. He then forwarded the resolution to appropriate state officials. The resolution informed that the "Alabama Veterinary Medical Association respectfully request the State Health Office of Alabama to employ only graduate veterinarians as heads of the meat and milk inspection departments."[37]

The Alabama VMA met again, and API held its annual Short Course for Graduate Veterinarians, during February 4-9, 1929, in Auburn. This meeting brought forty-five veterinarians from eight states for lectures, clinical diagnostic demonstrations, and surgical instruction. Again, a lineup of national caliber speakers was present. Ontario Veterinary College graduate Dr. T. H. Ferguson headlined the gathering, coming from Lake Geneva, Wisconsin, to operate on a mule and to lecture. He was a frequent speaker at AVMA conventions and internationally recognized for his surgical expertise. J. F. Smithcors wrote of Dr. Ferguson that "for many years no AVMA clinic was considered complete without a demonstration by him."[38] Dr. Ferguson (1873-1957) practiced in Lake Geneva for more than sixty years and, in 1929, served as the fiftieth president of the AVMA.

The famous Dr. E. L. Quitman came once again from Chicago and "was given all the clinical cases in dogs and cats that he could handle," Dr. Cary wrote in his recap. Dr. W. E. Cotton of the Bureau of Animal Industry Experiment Station in Bethesda, Maryland, lectured on foot-and-mouth disease. Dr. Cotton would be elected to a vice presidential post with the AVMA four years later. Dr. Cary "operated on a roarer, a mule weighing 1,200 pounds."[39] Dr. Cary performed a laryngoplasty, an attempt to restore some of the animal's airflow.

Auburn's next annual short course was held February 3-8, 1930, and again Dr. Cary persuaded Dr. T. H. Ferguson—who the previous summer had been elected AVMA president—to attend. Dr. Ferguson spoke on diseases of cattle and gave a series of demonstration surgeries, operating on cattle, horses, mules, and sheep, "so many," Dr. Cary wrote later, "that it would take too much space to write of each one." Also on the speaking lineup that year was Dr. D. A. Eastman of Cedar Rapids, Iowa, who discussed diseases of dogs and performed multiple surgeries. Dr. Eastman would, in 1933, serve as the American Animal Hospital Association's founding vice president and, in 1940, as president of AAHA. Those gathered in the evening were treated to more moving-pictures on animal diseases. The work of the Alabama VMA, taking place largely at its meeting on February 7 during the Auburn event, resulted in the following resolutions being approved, the meaning of which should make clear the political battles simmering at that time:

1. That the head or director of milk inspection of the State Health Department should be a licensed graduate veterinarian.
2. That the director of meat inspection of the State Health Department should be a licensed graduate veterinarian.
3. That all veterinarians employed in meat and milk inspection shall be graduate licensed veterinarians.
4. That all meat and milk inspection done in Alabama shall be done by licensed graduate veterinarians.
5. That agricultural extension demonstrators, vocational teachers of animal industry in schools and colleges shall confine their work to (a) first aid work for farm or domesticated animals, (b) to teaching or instruction in hygiene and sanitation, and (c) to physiology, and exterior and gross anatomy.
6. That extension and vocational agricultural teachers shall not practice veterinary medicine and surgery.
7. That all tests for diseases of animals, including poultry, shall be done by graduate licensed veterinarians or under their supervision.
8. That all research work in animal diseases shall be directly under the supervision of, or shall be done by, graduate licensed veterinarians.[40]

The Alabama VMA held another one-day, mid-year meeting on Tuesday, July 1, 1930, at Montgomery's Gay-Teague Hotel, at the corner of Commerce and Bibb Streets downtown, at the time the tallest building in the capital city. Lodging cost $1.50 for those staying overnight. Long-time Mayor William Gunter, Jr., welcomed the group, and VMA President Dr. C. Thigpen spoke. The rest of the morning was given to issues weighing on the minds of veterinarians during this era: meat and milk inspection, controlling parasites, infectious abortion. The group heard and discussed presentations on "How [to] Make Meat and Milk Inspection possible in Small Towns," by Dr. D. J. Meador; "Who are qualified to do Meat and Milk Inspection," by Dr. P. F. Bahnsen; "Control and Eradication of Animal Parasites," by Dr. E. M. Neighbert, who would head tick eradication in Georgia; and "Infectious Abortion," by Dr. Ed Everett. After lunch, the assembly took a short walk to inspect Swift and Company's new packing house—where livestock were slaughtered and butchered, and the meat packaged and prepared for distribution—and the nearby Montgomery Union Stock Yards. In each of these places, veterinarians performed meat inspection demonstrations.

Apparently, the state's handling of meat and milk inspection was still not to the satisfaction of the veterinary community. Dr. Cary and others may have seen state officials increasingly depending on inspectors the veterinarians felt were not qualified to do this work, perhaps even veterinarians who had ventured off the approved path. The Alabama VMA during this July 1, 1930, meeting again took opportunity to draft and approve a resolution in which the organization called on the state to authorize meat and milk inspections be "done by licensed graduate veterinarians who are in good standing in the Alabama Veterinary Medical Association."[41]

Auburn hosted its next Short Course for Graduate Veterinarians during February 2-7, 1931, and, for the third straight year, Dr. Cary persuaded his friend and AVMA compatriot Dr. T. H. Ferguson of Wisconsin to travel south and take the stage. Dr. Ferguson "talked and operated on horses, mules, cattle and hogs every day," Dr. Cary later wrote.

Another VIP speaker that week, and yet another example of Dr. Cary's influence in bringing excellent, high-profile speakers to Auburn, was Dr. D. M. Campbell (1880-1952), who lectured once or twice each day. Dr. Campbell was a 1907 graduate of the Kansas City Veterinary College. Three years after his graduation and after working for a time in general practice and in meat and milk inspection, he founded, published, and edited the *American Journal of Veterinary Medicine*, later called *Veterinary Medicine*. He was serving as editor of this publication at the time of his Auburn visit, which meant he was one of the best-known visiting speakers Dr. Cary ever brought to Auburn. He also taught at the KCVC: chemistry, pharmacy, and medical language. He later taught chemistry, physics, and veterinary jurisprudence at the Chicago Veterinary College. He operated a private practice for some years, and between 1910 and 1913, headed Abbott Laboratories' veterinary department and the company's work in municipal food inspection. Like Dr. Cary and many other speakers who came to Auburn's short course during these years, Dr. Campbell was active in the AVMA, serving on numerous committees. Dr. Campbell would achieve a deserved level of lasting fame in 1935 when he co-authored with Dr. Louis A. Merillat a sweeping, two-volume book on *Veterinary Military History of the United States*.[42] Both men were lieutenant colonels in the Army Reserve at the time they wrote their 1,172-page history. Later promoted to the rank of colonel, Dr. Campbell was buried with full military honors in Arlington National Cemetery.

One night during the 1931 meeting was devoted to instruction and discussion of meat inspection, and another night to talks, moving pictures, and discussions on milk inspection. These evenings were coordinated "to bring before the veterinarians that federal, state, county and municipal meat inspection was work that belongs exclusively to the graduate veterinarian and that it was time for the veterinarians to take the field and do their duty to the public and the profession." Chiefly, those two nights' presentations were designed to remind state attendees of the resolutions they had approved previously and to keep momentum progressing toward these precepts being made into law. Dr. Cary had summoned to Auburn Dr. A. H. Williamson, milk inspector of Charlotte, North Carolina, to present a "moving picture of his local inspection system." Dr. E. D. King, an early Auburn graduate and at this time the meat and milk inspector of Valdosta, Georgia, returned to lecture on the system at work in that city.[43]

On Monday, July 6, 1931, the Alabama VMA held another one-day, mid-year meeting, this gathering back in Birmingham at the Tutwiler Hotel, a thirteen-story, 425-room edifice located at Fifth Avenue North and Twentieth Street. The agenda for this meeting revealed a changing time in veterinary medicine, at least in terms of a broadening focus for practitioners. Presentations included several talks related to poultry, one devoted to rabies, one on mange in dogs, as well as an address on infectious abortion in cattle.[44]

The following February 1-6, 1932, Auburn again hosted its Annual Short Course for Graduate Veterinarians. One keynote speaker was

Dr. Walter Long Williams (1856-1945), an 1875 graduate of the Montreal Veterinary College and at this time—at age seventy-six—a professor of veterinary surgery, obstetrics, zootechnics, and jurisprudence at Cornell University. He lectured on breeding problems of cows and horses. Dr. Cary would have met Dr. Williams at his first national meeting in Chicago in 1890, two years before Dr. Williams served a term as president of the USVMA. Dr. Williams, who also served stints as president of the state VMAs of both Illinois and New York, proved a prolific writer on a variety of veterinary medical subjects, authoring two noted texts: *Veterinary Obstetrics* (1909) and *Diseases of the Genital Organs of Domestic Animals* (1921). J. F. Smithcors credited Dr. Williams with recognizing dourine in horses in Illinois and for creating "much of our knowledge of this disease." Dr. Smithcors called him "a man of many facets"[45] and listed him among "an even dozen of the men who played major roles in establishing the veterinary profession as a vital force prior to 1900."[46]

Veterinary Medicine Editor Dr. D. M. Campbell made his second consecutive trip to Auburn and discussed Army veterinary problems as well as particular feeds and the general feeding of dogs. Colonel B. A. Seeley of the US Army in Fort Benning, Georgia, discussed foot disease and shoeing of Army horses and mules. Dr. Mack Hays and Dr. M. W. Emmel of Auburn spoke on dogs and chickens, respectively. Dr. Cary, "assisted by a number of veterinarians engaged in tuberculosis eradication work, gave a demonstration of the intradermal injection of tuberculin in the caudal fold and in the labiae of the vulva in cattle." In the midst of this week's activities, the Alabama VMA met and conducted its yearly business, including appropriating $150 toward that summer's AVMA convention in Atlanta.[47]

Auburn and Dr. Cary again hosted an annual Short Course for Graduate Veterinarians during the second week of February 1933. Dr. T. A. Sigler of Green Castle, Illinois, was a guest speaker, and Dr. D. M. Campbell returned to review some of the outstanding advancements in veterinary science of the previous year.[48]

The 1934 meeting at Auburn, held during February 6-10 that year, brought back Dr. D. A. Eastman, at this time from Moline, Illinois, to speak on issues related to dogs. Dr. F. D. Patterson spoke on poultry, and Dr. H. W. Sawyer presented a paper on heartworms in dogs. Dr. H. M. O'Rear of the Tuberculosis Eradication Division of the Bureau of Animal Industry in Washington, DC, spoke. The students' banquet fed more than one hundred attendees, and in keeping with recent trends,

Dr. Cary planned the program to feature a Tuesday night session entirely on meat inspection and Wednesday night exclusively about milk inspection. Dr. Cary's colleague from Auburn, Dr. Everett S. Winters, was featured speaker on the milk inspection program.

The Alabama VMA's meeting that week was on Friday evening, February 9, and the body voted to affiliate formally with the American Veterinary Medical Association, which gave it the right to send a delegate and an alternate to represent the state at the next AVMA convention, scheduled for August 1934 in New York City. This legislative action signaled another, and one of the final, state political victories for Dr. Cary, as he in essence saw the teaming of both "his" state and national organizations.[49] Dr. Cary would attend that August 1934 AVMA meeting as the Alabama VMA's first delegate to the AVMA. It would be the last AVMA convention he would attend.

The Alabama VMA met in Auburn for the 1935 short course during February 6-9. For the final time, the Alabama VMA re-elected Dean Cary as its secretary/treasurer. The *Auburn Plainsman* student newspaper suggested in its February 13, 1935, issue that "according to many of the 80 practicing veterinarians who came to Auburn from five states to attend the short course, the one just held was the best ever conducted at Auburn." The report noted that nearly one hundred surgical procedures and lectures were offered. The meeting marked the return to Auburn of former AVMA President Dr. T. H. Ferguson of Lake Geneva, Wisconsin, whom the paper called "one of the outstanding practitioners in the entire country." The number of clinical cases handled during the meeting was "the greatest ever assembled at an Auburn short course," the *Plainsman* noted.[50]

A month before Dr. Cary's death, during the third week of March 1935, the student chapter of the AVMA welcomed Dr. P. F. Bahnsen as the principal speaker for its mid-week meeting. Dr. Bahnsen, at this time no longer serving as Georgia's state veterinarian but affiliated with the Albany-based Haver-Glover Factories, spoke on the present-day problems of the veterinarian, including building one's reputation and convincing the public for the need of professional veterinary services. According to the *Plainsman* issue of March 23, 1935, Dr. Bahnsen was in Auburn "for the past several days for conferences with Dr. C.A. Cary, dean of the School of Veterinary Medicine and one of the leading veterinarians in the United States."[51]

CHAPTER TWELVE

ANNUAL REPORTS OF THE STATE VETERINARIAN

The signal event of Dr. Cary's tenure at Auburn, if one moment can be isolated within the forty-three bountiful years he was at the helm, came in the spring of 1907. After some time spent lobbying, pleading, explaining, selling, and whatever else he needed to do, to the API leadership and agricultural and political leaders he knew, Charles Allen Cary won the victory that set him on the path to achieve many of his goals.

On March 12, 1907, the Alabama Legislature passed a bill establishing the State Livestock Sanitary Board and creating the office of state veterinarian. Dr. Cary's chief lieutenant of the time, Dr. Ward Giltner, wrote a letter to the *American Veterinary Review* that same week, published in the next issue, which spelled out the happy story for their colleagues throughout the land:

Auburn, Ala., March 13, 1907

Editors, American Veterinary Review:

Dear Sirs:—I send you under separate cover a copy of a state live-stock sanitary bill just enacted by the Alabama Legislature, thinking that the Review would be interested in a triumph for veterinary medicine in the

South. This measure is the culmination of years of untiring effort on the part of Dr. C.A. Cary, to whom all the credit and much praise are due for framing the act and successfully piloting it through the Legislature. Alabama is to be congratulated upon having, at last, a live-stock law, and, moreover, one that is pronounced by experts on sanitary law and by those highest in authority in the veterinary profession, the most efficient measure of its kind in the States. At least one of the "quarantined states" can cooperate with the Federal government, and has hopes of seeing the finish of the *Boophilus annulatus* [the Texas cattle fever tick], besides having at its command a means of controlling infectious diseases.

Trusting that you may deem this bill worthy of the consideration of the Review readers, I am

Yours respectfully,

Ward Giltner, D.V.M.

As Dr. Giltner's letter reveals, Dr. Cary spent years working toward this piece of legislation, reading relevant, similar documents from elsewhere in the country, drafting his preferred version, perhaps re-writing sections based on input from legal sources, thinking this bill through in the same manner with which he approached a complicated diagnosis. The bill itself specified that the commissioner of agriculture and industries in Alabama; the state health officer; and the professor of animal industry and the professor of veterinary science—both based at the Alabama Polytechnic Institute—would constitute the State Livestock Sanitary Board.

The bill made clear that the professor of veterinary science would serve as state veterinarian, and, in this role, had specific authority for establishing quarantines and for making and enacting regulations related to transport of farm animals as he saw fit. The law gave the state veterinarian authority in these matters over the various transportation companies at work in the state. The law spelled out all manner of slaughterhouse protocols, including issues related to sanitation.

Dr. Cary worked into this bill a number of elements related to the work then in progress of eradicating the cattle tick in Alabama, and the legislation provided for fines and imprisonment for those working counter to the law. The bill also required the state veterinarian to submit an annual report to the governor of Alabama related to the previous year's animal health activities in the state. With this legislation in place, Dr. Cary largely held the authority to pursue actions that he believed were in the best interests of enhanced public health practices in his adopted state.[1]

His achieving this goal was anything but clear sailing. The work had begun years earlier—as early as Dr. Cary's January 1892 arrival at Auburn as visiting lecturer in veterinary science, and continuing upon his return from Germany as he assumed the professorship of veterinary science in January 1893. His body of work earned high praise from Presidents Broun and Thach, as recorded in the president's reports to the board of trustees. As early as 1893, President Broun suggested to the board that their new man should be named Alabama's first state veterinarian, since he was qualified and already was fulfilling many duties this office required.

There may have been a general consensus in the state, at least in some quarters, that Dr. Cary by the last years of the nineteenth century *was* the state veterinarian. An article published in the December 20, 1898, *Birmingham Weekly Age Herald* newspaper carried a story about a meeting of the Jefferson County Dairymen and Live Stock Association the day before, with Dr. Cary attending and lobbying the group for its support of legislation he apparently wanted to bring before the Alabama Legislature early the next year.[2]

Dr. Cary received approval for his proposal by those gathered that day; but, apparently, plenty of the organization's members were *not* in attendance. When the *Age Herald* reported on this proposed legislation the day after the meeting, with the idea of a license requirement for dairy owners built into the plan, the membership demanded a reconsideration. In a few days, the group stood opposed to Dr. Cary's plan. The newspaper referred to the API visitor as "State Veterinarian Cary of the Polytechnic Institute at Auburn," though the newspaper's use of that title was premature. Dr. Cary's official appointment as state veterinarian would come nine years later in 1907.

But Dr. Cary certainly acted the part long before it was official. Dr. Calvin Schwabe noted in his 1992 talk at the College that Dr. Cary began making political inroads from his earliest Auburn days. "For as much as he was an educator and innovator," Schwabe said, "Cary was a consummate politician." Within three years of his arrival in Auburn, according to Schwabe, Dr. Cary was able to establish a presence among the state's political leaders "by writing and securing prompt adoption by Alabama's capital city of the first meat inspection legislation in the South."[3] Montgomery's adoption of Dr. Cary's meat inspection protocols were followed, of course, by the city also enacting his plan for dairy and milk inspection in 1896, practices that eventually spread throughout Alabama and the nation.

When, finally, in 1907, he achieved the appointment as state veterinarian, Dr. Cary melded his personal high standards, eminent capabilities, and visions for public health into an array of laws and statutes approved by the Alabama Legislature. With credentials and both federal and state law on their side, Dr. Cary and his compatriots were enabled to make their lasting marks on public health and veterinary medicine. Dr. Cary's lofty goals required more time and presence in Montgomery and an adjustment of his day-to-day management of the veterinary school. An article published in *The Birmingham News* on November 7, 1971, marking the day Auburn University officials dedicated the Wire Road veterinary complex, took a look back at Dr. Cary's time and summarized what his routine by 1907 likely entailed:

> A typical day for him would be to leave at daybreak for his nearby farm, return home for breakfast, drive the two-wheel cart to campus for his eight o'clock class and then leave it at the depot where he caught the 9:18 train to Montgomery. The remainder of the day would be spent performing his duties as state veterinarian.
>
> He would return home on the 8 p.m. train, dispose of his day's mail, with the help of a student who served as his secretary, and then go home for supper.[4]

Once he became state veterinarian, through resolute determination and a relentless work ethic, Dr. Cary elevated his profession in the state and beyond, accomplishing much of the agenda he had envisioned when he first came to East Alabama. He also had to make a few changes around the Auburn campus. With his duties now expanded to include working several days each month in Montgomery and throughout Alabama, Dr. Cary delegated some of his School of Veterinary Medicine caretaking to trusted colleagues, the most trusted of whom would be Dr. I. S. McAdory when Dr. McAdory returned in 1908 after earning his DVM in Chicago. Dr. Cary would select a veterinary student to serve as his "secretary," and he would meet with that individual either before leaving for Montgomery or after he returned, or both, to check on the day's events at API and make the following day's assignments.

As the 1971 newspaper report suggested, he likely began many of his typical days with a visit to his farm in what is today the Cary Woods subdivision of Auburn. After breakfast at home, he would either venture to campus to teach an early class or proceed directly to the Auburn depot. He took the Western Railway of Alabama train to Montgomery on those days, arriving at Union Station on Water Street, downtown along the Alabama River. From the train station, he undoubtedly took a streetcar a few blocks to his office, whether in the state capitol or at another nearby location. From Union Station, he could reach many of his destinations in Alabama or beyond. He held the role of state veterinarian for his remaining twenty-eight years, so he became accustomed to this routine, however many days each week or month he repeated it.

Dr. Cary's role and successes can be understood better through examination of the Annual Reports of the State Veterinarian he authored and submitted to the governors of Alabama—as required by Alabama law—beginning in 1908 until he submitted his last only weeks before his death in April 1935.[5] Reading through these annual reports, one gains an appreciation for the unpaved-street, farm animals-in-the-yard kind of world in which Dr. Cary operated in early twentieth-century Alabama. His reports detailed the various diseases that befell animals and herds of that time. As well, these documents suggested his constant and pervasive involvement in all aspects of animal and public health: conducting examinations and inspecting facilities; hiring qualified assistants; and overseeing both the politics and medicine involved in eradicating cattle ticks, controlling hog cholera, eliminating tuberculosis, and establishing milk and meat inspection. The reports suggested his role as collector of data for those various efforts; his lobbying legislators and others having influence; and his writing proposed legislation.

These annual reports reflected his working life outside of the already-busy role of professor and dean of veterinary medicine at Auburn. No diary has been discovered which would show in any level of detail Dr. Cary's day-to-day activities, but these annual reports—considered alongside the records of his AVMA duties, the veterinary science program at Auburn, and the Farmers' Institutes he held—enable readers a century later to appreciate and marvel at the breadth and depth of this man, his ambitions, drive and work ethic, the miles he traveled, and the lasting influence he had on so many people and communities.

Report for 1907

Dr. Cary's first *Report of the State Veterinarian of Alabama* was dated January 30, 1908, and was addressed to Governor Braxton Bragg

Comer (1848-1927), for whom Auburn University's primary agriculture building has been named since the 1920s. This report covered the time from March 12, 1907—the date of the Legislature's acting to establish the office—through the end of the year. This first submission listed the barebones staff of assistant state veterinarians Dr. Cary appointed to help him in the work: G. W. Browning and W. B. Fleming of Montgomery; Ward Giltner of Auburn; M. F. Jackson of Birmingham; and W. D. Staples of Anniston.

The report opened with a special notice to all who might read it, directing that "all reports of contagious, infectious or spreading diseases of animals should be reported to the State Veterinarian," with those reports to include the age, sex, and breed of the animal involved, plus a full history and description of the following diseases, if applicable: glanders in horses and mules; tuberculosis in cattle and hogs or other animals; black-leg or black-quarter in cattle; hog cholera and swine plague; anthrax or charbon in cattle, horses, mules, or any animal; rabies in dogs or any animal or in man; Texas or tick fever in cattle; sore mouth and sore feet in cattle or sheep; sheep scab in sheep; and parasitic skin diseases in horses, mules, cattle, or swine. All of his Annual Reports included such direction related to keeping the state veterinarian in the animal disease loop.

Dr. Cary's first report also explained to the veterinarian and lay person how to send a tissue sample to him at Auburn:

> When diseased organs or abnormal parts are found in animals on post mortem or after death examinations, wrap some or all of the abnormal part in a clean cloth saturated in 5 or 10 percent carbolic acid, pack in ice and express to the State Veterinarian. *Prepay express.* Or parasites and parts of abnormal organs may be put into a clean fruit jar (wrapped as above directed or covered with alcohol) carefully packed and expressed to
>
> C.A. CARY
> *Auburn, Ala.,*
> State Veterinarian.

State Veterinarian Cary's first report revealed that some Alabamians had worked to enact compromises in the public laws Dr. Cary and others had persuaded legislators to approve. The 1907 law which established the position of state veterinarian—the Live Stock Sanitary Law—held that the approved work in tick eradication "could be taken up in any county in Alabama," and that the work was to commence in all the counties north of the Tennessee River and in Baldwin County in southwest Alabama. But in April, after farmers in Baldwin County—by area, the state's largest—convened, a push had been made to exempt from the tick eradication work those Alabama counties where cattle had free range. Thus, Dr. Cary noted in his report that "the people decided that it would not be best to attempt tick eradication under existing range conditions. The State and Federal inspectors were then withdrawn and it was agreed that tick eradication work would not be taken up in that country until the people were ready for it."

The next month, farmers fought back again, this time in North Alabama. Work had begun in two counties of North Alabama immediately, and Dr. Cary noted in his report that "work progressed in such a manner that the two counties would have been cleaned of cattle ticks by December 1, 1907. But the legislature passed an amendment to the law and it distinctly prohibits cattle tick eradication in a county that does not have a majority of its area under a stock law which prevents cattle running at large." That amendment was passed on August 6, 1907, and ten federal and state tick inspectors in those counties were withdrawn.

One senses the frustration those on the public health side must have felt. "Three months more of work would have cleaned these counties and then the quarantine line could have been removed below the counties to the Tennessee River," Dr. Cary wrote in his initial annual report.

That August 6 amendment specifically prohibited the state veterinarian or any assistant state veterinarians from pursuing their tick eradication work as well as from inspecting horses and mules for glanders, and from inspecting any animals for infectious or contagious diseases in the non-stock law counties. The amendment did allow continued inspections in all counties of animals in dairies or for any animals shipped into the state, as to whether these animals had entered with the requisite health certificates as per guidelines of the Live Stock Sanitary Board. At the time, twenty-eight Alabama counties were either "non-stock law" counties or had less than half of their areas under stock law. That left Dr. Cary and the inspectors thirty-nine counties in which to work.

The report detailed that Dr. Cary and his assistant state veterinarians inspected fifty horses and sixty-three mules for possible cases of glanders in 1907 in five counties. Dr. Cary personally inspected forty-one of these animals during four days in Demopolis, Cusseta, Evergreen, and Dosterville. Thirteen total were found positive for glanders from all these inspections, and most of the afflicted animals were destroyed. But because of the farmers' lobbying to gain their August amendment, many more horses and mules in the state that should have been tested were not; undoubtedly, disease spread. The farmers either did not know, or acted despite knowing, that a twenty-five-year-old Alabama farmer suffered horribly for a month before dying a painful death the previous August from contracting glanders from an accident related to a horse he had purchased without inspection. Dr. Cary repeated the gory details of the poor man's death as written by Carrolton physician Dr. H. W. Hill in this first report to the governor.

Black leg disease was found in several Alabama counties in the previous five years, and Dr. Cary's report fully described for the governor what this disease entailed for animals and owners. He commented on rabies having occurred in some counties; but, as no rabies records had been collected, the scope of this disease in Alabama was not known. Dr. Cary reported that a few outbreaks of hog cholera and swine plague had been confirmed and that there were confirmed tuberculous cattle in Alabama.

The first report itemized the expenses for work related to the Live Stock Sanitary Board from March through the end of that year, including salary and expenses for Dr. Cary and the assistant state veterinarians, a few purchases, land rent, and services such as typing and printing. The total for the ten months was $2,579.81.

Report for 1908

State Veterinarian Cary's second *Annual Report*—covering 1908—was dated January 30, 1909, and reflected that Dr. Giltner had left for Michigan, where he would go on to a stellar career in academic and organized veterinary medicine. He was succeeded in his work in Auburn by Dr. I. S. McAdory, newly graduated from the McKillip Veterinary College in Chicago. The other four—Drs. Browning, Fleming, Jackson, and Staples—remained as assistant state veterinarians. This report reflected an adjustment to those Alabama counties under a stock law preventing cattle from running at large. This list of forty-two counties showed that behind-the-scenes work by State Veterinarian Cary and those supporting him had served to move Lawrence, Marion, and St. Clair counties to the list of counties with stock laws—some modest progress.

In this second report, Dr. Cary informed the governor that tick eradication work in 1908 progressed "under some unfavorable conditions," due chiefly to a delay in the arrival of federal inspectors, who had been expected in early spring. He noted that three-quarters of cattle land in Montgomery County had been "cleaned of cattle ticks," which he attributed to added numbers of inspectors and "good roads and pastures." Notably, Dr. Cary lauded the role public education played in the progress there and in other places. He wrote:

> . . . educational instruction given will materially assist in the eradication work this year. In fact, the greater number of cattle owners in the four counties know how and what to do in order to eliminate the cattle ticks from their pastures and cattle. This intelligence and instruction has [sic] not been limited to the counties in which active work has been done. The people of the surrounding counties have learned by coming into contact with inspectors and by complying with quarantine regulations, that there are simple and practical methods of eradicating the cattle tick. Moreover, people have learned that it pays to get rid of the cattle tick.

No doubt, Dr. Cary's and others' presentations at the Farmers' Institutes offered instruction on the dipping methods and benefits of cattle tick eradication.

State Veterinarian Cary suggested to the governor that, if counties would invest $500 to $2,000 toward this work, additional inspectors could be hired and "prevent a loss of many thousands of dollars to the farmers of the county." He included detailed reports made to him by the veterinarians in charge of tick eradication work in Montgomery, Wilcox, Lowndes, and Dallas Counties. The reports—limited to those four counties—revealed the inspectors' multiple visits to every farmer, inspections of more than 4,000 locations where cattle were kept, and inspections of more than 125,000 cattle, the majority of which were infected with ticks.

Dr. Cary's second report detailed also the city meat and milk inspection work during 1908 in the five Alabama cities that offered at least some levels of inspection at the time: Montgomery, Birmingham, Ensley, Mobile, and Selma. Dr. Cary reminded the governor that Montgomery had been the first city in the South to enforce milk and meat inspection. Those inspections in 1908—at least in Birmingham, Ensley, and Montgomery—included almost 5,000 dairy cattle, more than 31,000 cattle that were to be slaughtered for beef consumption, more than 17,000 hogs that were slaughtered, almost 11,000 sheep, and hundreds of goats. Disease findings were minimal, but Dr. Cary used the report to remind the governor that insufficient funding (and the resulting insufficient number of trained and qualified inspectors) left a vast amount of inspection undone:

> The milk inspection force is too small. The inspection of 800 cows, 20 to 30 dairies in different localities and milk depots, restaurants, etc., will require more than one man. Montgomery should have one man for the milk laboratory testing work and one for inspection of cows, dairy barns, houses, collecting milk samples, etc.
>
> In Birmingham there are nearly 4,000 dairy cattle and over 100 dairies, and the law says that the cows should be tested annually for tuberculosis with tuberculin. They are not tested because the milk inspection force is too small. The inspectors are efficient and are doing all they can with the present force; but every dairy should be inspected once a week at least.
>
> The meat inspection force in Birmingham is short one man. No microbial examination is made for trichina in hogs. This should be done. Birmingham should have another milk and another meat inspector.
>
> Mobile is greatly in need of a union slaughter house and an efficient force of meat inspectors.

Dr. Cary wrote again of tuberculosis, reporting that the incidence of the dreaded disease was somewhat contained in Alabama, limited to dairy herds here and there and in some cities where "5 to 20 percent of the cows are tuberculous." But he urged the governor to get behind efforts to "eliminate tuberculosis from Alabama dairy cattle. Let the cities of Alabama do their duty and at once begin a vigorous campaign against the use of tuberculous cows in dairies." Dr. Cary's call served as a plea for the governor to take a bit of political risk and more openly and actively oppose farmers' efforts at avoiding federal and state inspectors.

This second report noted an increase in the incurable glanders disease found among horses and mules, with Dr. Cary reasoning that an increased number of inspectors found cases that would have slipped through the cracks the previous year. Also, he noted, twenty-four of the fifty-four cases found in the state were within a single shipment of horses into Alabama from a state out west, making clear the importance of Dr. Cary's insistence of a trained inspector seeing every shipment of imported farm animals.

Dr. Cary reported that 1908 brought "heavy losses from hog cholera" in Alabama. He made reference to a "new serum method of producing immunity to hog cholera . . . being quite extensively tested in Iowa, Missouri, Michigan and other states." In those early days of 1909, he suggested to the governor that

> with sufficient money we could establish a hog cholera immunizing plant sufficient to supply the demands for serum treatment in Alabama. But at present our funds are largely devoted to tick eradication work. It would require not less than one thousand dollars a year to maintain such a plant. The good results obtained for the farmer would mean many dollars saved for every dollar expended.

Dr. Cary would see that serum plant built on the Auburn campus in 1915, and its results yielded exactly as he predicted.

The second annual report also noted "the great prevalence of rabies in dogs in Alabama," and the state veterinarian called for a state dog law to check the spread of this deadly disease. The plain-speaking, politically incorrect, but forward-thinking Dr. Cary wrote that such a law would "permit Alabama farmers to raise sheep and force more . . . people . . . to raise hogs and sheep instead of worthless, sheep eating and dangerous dogs. Good dogs are useful and should be rated as property and taxed to help make free schools."

To remind the governor of regulations by which public health measures related to animals were to be conducted, Dr. Cary included in this second report the full text of regulations adopted by the Live Stock Sanitary Board of Alabama. He followed the three pages of those regulations with a reprint of the Code of Alabama's 1907 act—in its 1908 amended form—related to the formation of the State Live Stock Sanitary Board, the members of which (including Dr. Cary) had

> full power to make or enact such rules and regulations as they may deem necessary for governing the movement, transportation or disposition of live stock that may be quarantined . . . affected with, or exposed to, a contagious or communicable disease, or on account of being infected or infested with the carrier or carriers of the cause or causes of a contagious, infectious, or communicable disease of live stock.

One assumes Dr. Cary penned those words, carefully designing the authority he knew those in his position would need in order to ensure the public health in an environment where competing interests often butted heads. In addition to establishing the Live Stock Sanitary Board, the act established the professor of veterinary science at API as the state veterinarian, with the authority to "nominate as many assistant State Veterinarians and State Live Stock Inspectors as they may deem necessary and as the funds at their disposal shall permit." This act also established authority for putting into quarantine such lots and stalls as the state veterinarian deemed necessary; authorized official inspection of animals taken to any transportation place for export; and authorized the inspection of livestock brought into the state. Regulations also addressed cleaning and disinfecting places where animals were kept. As important as any of the actions, the act authorized the state veterinarian or any assistant state veterinarians to "enter upon the premises or into any barns or other buildings where live stock are temporarily or permanently kept in the State of Alabama in the discharge of their duties . . . ."

Dr. Cary, aware of financial problems that had plagued the state, also wrote into the act an annual appropriation of $5,000 to offset the state veterinarian's travel and work expenses, plus another $500 annually as salary for the state veterinarian. This came to $46.66 monthly, on top of his salary as professor at Auburn. His assistant state veterinarians sometimes made more than him, sometimes less, depending on the number of hours they worked.

Report for 1909

Dr. Cary's third *Annual Report of the State Veterinarian of Alabama*, dated January 31, 1910, was again addressed to Governor Comer. This report once more showed a change in the ranks of assistant state veterinarians. Gone now was Dr. Jackson from Birmingham. Added were O. R. Eatman of Gadsden, W. M. Howell of Dothan and P. W. Hudson of Mobile.

The list of counties subject to the stock law was unchanged—remaining at forty-two counties during 1909. But there was some progress in tick eradication work, undoubtedly due to Dr. Cary and supporters working behind the scenes politically. House bill ninety, passed on August 20, 1909, gave county commissioners in any no-stock-law county the authority to "enter an order providing for tick eradication work in a no stock law county." That legislation did not exactly throw open all doors to Dr. Cary and other cattle tick inspectors, but it offered some potential access where none was guaranteed before.

This report provided an overview of the tick eradication efforts for 1909 in eight counties, with more than forty different inspectors involved. Dr. Cary lobbied the governor for additional resources and, with an eye to the future, explained the urgency of their making headway in this program. He wrote:

> . . . tick eradication in Alabama is seriously handicapped for want of sufficient State funds to push this much needed work. Upon the eradication of the cattle tick depends the prosperity or profit in the cattle business in Alabama. The boll weevil is coming and Alabama must then practice diversified farming. The cattle business is one of the lines of live stock that will form a prominent and profitable link at home and make more home fertilizer for soil improvement; it will add humus to poor lands; it will help bring prosperity. Cattle will always bring good prices in the future; beef will be high because the great cattle growing countries can not produce beef as fast as the population of the meat eating world increases. In other words the supply can not catch up with the demand. Hence cattle and beef will be high. Alabama farmers must get their share in the profits of cattle raising. Mississippi has just appropriated $40,000 for this work, and other states are also eradicating the tick.

In this third report, Dr. Cary noted that, during 1909, tuberculosis was found among oxen of logging teams. Out of ninety-three head of oxen in a logging operation in South Alabama, he reported as an example, sixty reacted to the tuberculin test. One of the problems, he told the governor, was that many of these animals were never inspected. Twenty-six oxen were driven illegally into Alabama and then transported to the National Stock Yards in Chicago, and twenty turned out tuberculous. Sixteen others were shipped from South Alabama to Oklahoma before making their way to Chicago, and ten of these tested positive. In three other herds totaling 135 oxen, he wrote, ninety were tuberculous. Dr. Cary pointed to the speed of the disease spreading in these populations, suggested measures to contain the disease in logging settings, and reminded the governor that Alabama law prohibited tuberculous cattle from being brought into the state as well as authorized inspection of all such transported animals.

Dr. Cary also addressed the numerous hog cholera outbreaks he and other inspectors faced during 1909. He reminded the governor that he had received several calls for hog cholera serum, but that

> the State Veterinarian had no funds at his disposal for making and distributing the serum. Since the hog industry in Alabama is rapidly becom-

ing commercially profitable and likewise interesting to Alabama farmers, it is quite necessary that the next Legislature appropriate $2000 to $3000 for the establishment and maintaining [of] a hog cholera serum laboratory and plant.

He would see the results of this request in five years' time.

Report for 1910

Dr. Cary's fourth *Annual Report of the State Veterinarian of Alabama* was dated January 31, 1911, and was addressed to the new governor, Florence native Emmett O'Neal (1853-1922). The cast of characters had undergone another change as reflected in this report, with P. W. Hudson no longer listed among assistant state veterinarians, replaced in Mobile by C. C. Middleton. Also added to the ranks was 1910 API graduate and future Auburn veterinary medicine faculty member Dr. F. P. Woolf, working out of Montgomery.

This report noted that demand for tick eradication work was increasing, which meant the modest budget allocated for this statewide effort was again short. Dr. Cary reminded the new governor that the inevitable coming of the boll weevil would heighten the need for tick eradication to strengthen the cattle industry. The federal government had provided $22,000 toward tick eradication efforts in Alabama in 1910, with Alabama's counties ponying up a total of $14,000 and the state government another $4,000. "The legislature has been asked to give funds for the extension of this work and the appropriation was not made," Dr. Cary reminded Governor O'Neal, noting that tick eradication was an economic plus for the state.

This report also detailed that Dallas County had between eighty and one hundred dipping vats throughout its various communities, serving 603 separate herds. When the Dallas County inspecting was done, 12,275 cattle had been quarantined. This county led the state in terms of federal money spent on tick eradication, totaling $3,974.12 in 1910, along with $3,518 from the county. Twenty-three federal and state inspectors had worked for varying lengths of service during the year. Dr. Cary predicted that Dallas County would be tick-free by the end of 1911 "unless some unforeseen event prevents."

A note in this section of the report, related to work in Elmore County, revealed the ongoing nature of tick eradication at this time. Dr. Cary wrote that Elmore County had a few dipping vats but needed many more. "Most of the disinfecting of cattle is done by hand and this is very unsatisfactory," he reported. "The method above all others is the vat containing the arsenate of soda dip." Another note in the report, relating to Madison County, showed further progress in the overall effort, as county commissioners there voted to request and authorize tick eradication work despite that North Alabama county being on the "no-stock-law" list. Madison County political leaders could have skirted tick eradication efforts due to the open range laws of the county at the time, but, in the view of the veterinary forces, they chose wisely in taking part in the tick eradication program.

The section of Dr. Cary's report related to Montgomery County noted that "there were very few vats in the county and all were not in use. A few were using oil or oil emulsion which was not as cheap as the arsenate of soda dip." But encouraging to veterinary officials, Montgomery County leaders decided to construct ten additional dipping vats later that year and to employ the arsenic dip. Dr. Cary expressed hope that the new approach and a doubling of the inspector force to ten would lead to this county being "nearly, if not entirely, clean by the end of 1911."

Sumter County—Dr. Cary spelled it "Sumpter" in his report—had constructed and was using one hundred dipping vats throughout its various communities in 1910 and, despite this county having "more cattle in it than any other Alabama county," there was good cooperation among the farmers. Dr. Cary predicted this county also would be tick-free by the end of 1911. Cooperation in Sumter County contrasted with a lack of cooperation in the no-stock-law Wilcox County, where county commissioners refused to sign a memorandum of agreement with authorities of the Bureau of Animal Industry. As a result, county and BAI inspectors left their work in early summer. Dr. Cary expressed optimism about the future, despite the 1910 setback:

> There are a number of vats in the county and quite a number are keeping up the work of tick eradication so far as their individual farms are concerned. This county has some fine herds of purebred Devons, Herefords, etc., and it is a good cattle county. In time it will and must take up the work and exterminate the ticks in order to raise cattle with profit and compete with tick-free counties.

As this report was submitted to a new governor, Dr. Cary repeated some of the information about tuberculosis, hog cholera, and other diseases, and about the laws related to inspection. He mentioned again the need for anti-hog cholera serum, which at that time cost "from 30 to 60 cents a dose," suggesting "the state should furnish the serum free to all farmers of Alabama." Many states at this time were providing serum free to their farmers, Dr. Cary wrote, as could Alabama for $5,000 each year, a request already made by the Alabama Live Stock Association and other farmers' organizations.

One detail in the fourth report that demonstrated Dr. Cary's uncompromising demand for attention to details came following a four-page listing of animals shipped into Alabama during 1910, with the names of all inspectors in the various states who inspected these animals. After the list, Dr. Cary included a special notice to buyers and inspectors, identifying sixty-one of the 175 inspectors as having

> failed in some manner in filling out health certificates, failed to give his address, his degree or his qualifications, or to give the address of the shipper, or the buyer, or to describe the animals, etc. etc. All of these parties will be held as disqualified to give health certificates until they make satisfactory explanation to the State Veterinarian of Alabama. Buyers must take due notice and never employ any disqualified party or any one else who fails to fill out a certificate (original and duplicate) in full. Certificates are void unless filled out in full.

Fifty-five of the identified, non-compliant inspectors were from thirteen states and the District of Columbia. Six other inspectors were so non-compliant as to not list the state in which they inspected animals in transit.

Report for 1911

Dr. Cary's fifth *Annual Report of the State Veterinarian* for 1911, again submitted to Governor O'Neal early in 1912, listed a dozen assistant state veterinarians as Dr. Cary continued spreading this professional representation around the state: O. R. Eatman in Gadsden, W. B. Fleming in Montgomery, F. R. Harsh in Mobile, W. M. Howell in Auburn, W. L. Ingram in Florence, D. J. Meador in Selma, I. S. McAdory of Auburn, R. B. Nixon of Demopolis, J. T. Prickett of Talladega, W. D. Staples of Anniston, J. E. Threadgilll of Troy, and E. D. Yerion of Huntsville.

Dr. Cary noted a problem in September and October in Dallas County "when the big cotton crop so completely employed all the time of the overseers and laborers on the farms that they neglected the cattle dipping. The long continued hot season of fall favored the rapid reproduction of ticks. Hence the cattle ticks were not completely eradicated from Dallas County."

This development was countered with success stories in Elmore, Madison, and Sumter Counties, all of which Dr. Cary predicted were on the way toward release from the cattle quarantine. Of Sumter County, Dr. Cary wrote, "There was a distinct decrease in the number of infected herds and premises and it appears to be a question of whether Sumter or Madison will be the first Alabama county to obtain release from Federal quarantine."

To reinforce the economic point with his gubernatorial audience, Dr. Cary spelled out the importance of tick eradication in words even a politician could understand:

> If the State and Bureau of Animal Industry had more funds to lead the way in all of these and other counties in Alabama the work of tick eradication would soon become as extensive as it now is in the State of Mississippi. Tick eradication has passed the experimental and doubtful stage. It is growing, extending and becoming more and more interesting and popular because it pays and it can be done at a reasonable expense.
>
> Over 160,000 square miles of tick infested territory have been cleaned of ticks and the United States quarantine has been raised. The cattle in this territory are now for a world market. One of the southern counties in Mississippi that was cleaned of ticks in 1911 has shipped beef cattle to the five northern markets. All the tick free counties in all the different States are proud of the fact that they are tick free and are ready and willing to defend their free territory by vigorously opposing re-infestation. And all tick free counties unanimously acclaim that it pays to eradicate the tick and then keep free. Moreover, the people of all tick free counties say that the live stock industry grows and develops faster and better when the ticks are gone.

Dr. Cary's report revealed the continued but slow progress of milk and meat inspection work in several Alabama cities, with fifteen inspectors at that time on the job in Birmingham, Montgomery, Mobile, Selma, Bessemer, and Troy. He wrote at length on the causes and nature of hog cholera and on the use, availability, and affordability of serum—"Anti-Hog Cholera Serum is furnished free by several states (not by Alabama) to farmers . . . "

With "I-told-you-so" frankness, Dr. Cary reported that 1911 saw

"more outbreaks of cholera in Alabama than occurred in the state during the previous twenty years. Actual reports of outbreaks came directly and indirectly to this office [state veterinarian] from 50 out of 67
counties in Alabama . . . in every month during the entire year." Dr.
Cary predicted the losses associated with these outbreaks, and their
associated farm animal deaths, would cost Alabama farmers and producers between $100,000 and $150,000. He noted that practically all of
the losses "could have been prevented by timely and proper use of
anti-hog cholera serum."

A similar report on animals entering Alabama during 1911, and the
inspectors who inspected them before or as they arrived, revealed substantial improvement from the calling out Dr. Cary had made in the
previous year's report. For 1911, only twenty-one of 160-plus inspectors had failed to supply the fully required information. The offenders
were directed to "make satisfactory explanation to the State Veterinarian of Alabama."

Report for 1912

Dr. Cary's sixth *Annual Report of the State Veterinarian* was
addressed again to Governor O'Neal and listed a dozen assistant state
veterinarians. Drs. J. S. Andrade in Huntsville and F. P. Woolf in
Auburn had replaced W. M. Howell and E. D. Yerion from the previous year.

Dr. Cary predicted that Madison County, with fifty-seven active dipping vats, would become the first tick-free county in Alabama and told
the governor that "the sentiment for tick eradication in other parts of
Alabama is growing rapidly." He detailed progress in Dallas, Madison,
Montgomery, and Sumter Counties, which he described as the most
active in tick eradication.

Through 1912, Dr. Cary reported, 185,000 square miles in the South
had been made tick free and released from federal quarantine. This
represented one-quarter of the territory infected at the beginning of
the tick eradication effort.

Dr. Cary reported on dairy and meat inspections in Birmingham,
Bessemer, Montgomery, and Troy, noting that no reports had been
given by those responsible in Mobile and Selma. He told the governor
that he was "frequently called on to furnish outlines of laws or . . . ordinances for city or town inspection." He suggested the importance of
having a graduate veterinarian and a central slaughterhouse in each
community.

"As a rule, the slaughter houses used by butchers of the average towns and some of the cities where no inspection has been required are inadequate, unsanitary and poorly equipped."

Dr. Cary described in cold detail the ideal slaughterhouse:

> The slaughter house should be constructed as far as possible of brick, cement, stone and iron or steel. A small slaughter house should contain a killing room on the second floor. An incline cleated drive way will permit animals to be driven to the killing floor. On this floor should be the scalding vats and scraping tables and killing beds for cattle, sheep, etc. Here also should be the gutter for conveying the blood, and also the rendering tank should open on this floor so that all materials to be conveyed to it can be easily dumped into it. On the second floor there should also be an office, a cooling room, and a cold storage room if possible. On the lower floor should be the rendering tank, boilers, the engine and other such apparatus as is required for taking care of fats, offal and fertilizer products. Every floor should be made of the best reinforced concrete.

Dr. Cary listed for the governor a model milk inspection ordinance similar to legislation he had authored for the City of Montgomery. He included a multi-page review of the nature and problems caused by hog cholera as well as a section on "How to Use Anti-Hog Cholera Serum," reminding the governor that "Anti-hog cholera serum is furnished free by several states (not by Alabama) to farmers and is sold by private companies at from 2 cents to 3 cents per cubic centimeter." He listed ten places selling the serum, including the A&M College in Manhattan, Kansas, and the Veterinary Department of the University of Minnesota.

Dr. Cary reviewed glanders inspection for the year, although this disease was not a pervasive problem in Alabama in 1912. He reported on tuberculosis testing for incoming animals, and he estimated that hog cholera cost Alabama $1 million in 1912, a small percentage of the $66 million lost nationwide to this disease, but a massive hit to Alabama producers.

He also reminded the governor of a decision by the Alabama Supreme Court that upheld the very existence of the State Live Stock Association. The Court overturned an earlier decision from Sumter County denying the "constitutionality of the act of the Legislature establishing a State Live Stock Sanitary Board." The Supreme Court's decision firmly established the constitutionality of the Livestock Sanitary Law of Alabama after a Sumter County farmer had refused to cooperate with the law's section on keeping clean and disinfected areas where livestock were kept "when requested or directed by the State Live Stock board, the State Veterinarian or his assistants to do so."

Report for 1913

Dr. Cary's seventh *Annual Report of the State Veterinarian* opened with a report on tick fever and the progress made to date in various counties, noting which counties were building dipping vats. He reported on meat and milk inspection efforts in Birmingham, Mobile, Montgomery, and Selma, and on not receiving reports from inspectors in Bessemer, Greenville, and Troy, which clearly frustrated him.

Perhaps as a way of lobbying for funding to build a campus serum production facility, he wrote several pages on "the hog industry in Alabama," noting that "raising hogs in Alabama is as profitable as in any state or country," basing this conclusion on results from work at the Alabama Agricultural Experiment Station. He warned, however, that "that which stands in the way of a profitable Hog Industry in Alabama is Hog Cholera." He suggested that the state in 1913 lost $1 million to this disease, with national losses totaling $73 million.

Some hog operations had closed due to hog cholera's impact on their swine populations, creating not only an economic problem but contributing to a food shortage. "We need more meat, especially pork, for home consumption," Dr. Cary wrote, "to save the large sum of money sent out of state for fat salt pork, bacon, for hams, and for lard."

Report for 1914

Dr. Cary's eighth *Annual Report of the State Veterinarian* listed as new assistant state veterinarians Drs. L. E. Beckham of Tuscaloosa; J. S. Cook of Union Springs; C. W. Ferguson of Auburn; R. I. Kearley of Andalusia; W. W. Webb of Auburn; and F. B. Whitfield of Dothan. Dr. Harsh, by this time, had left the team.

This report, addressed to Governor Charles Henderson, opened with a glowing review of progress made in tick eradication over the previous year. "Some work is being done in nearly every county in the State," Dr. Cary wrote. "Educational work is making the sentiment for tick eradication grow rapidly. The dipping vat educates by doing the work so cheaply, simply and effectively as to convince everyone that the tick can be eradicated."

By this time, nine Alabama communities had some form of milk and meat inspection, but Dr. Cary assured the governor that progress was being hampered by the insufficient number of inspectors at work. Two of his assistant state veterinarians—Woolf and Beckham—were conducting these inspections part-time.

This subject was clearly a pet peeve. Dr. Cary wrote:

> In some towns, the officials seem to think that a city marshal, or a policeman, or a butcher are qualified to inspect meat and milk. This is a serious mistake. In many States the law specifically states that a meat or milk inspector must be a graduate of a legally recognized veterinary college. The time has come when such should be the case in Alabama, since Alabama has the only legally recognized and qualified veterinary college in the South.

Report for 1915

Dr. Cary's ninth *Annual Report of the State Veterinarian* was addressed to Governor Henderson and began with his discussing the appearance of hemorrhagic septicemia in Alabama in the past year, the first time he had written about this disease in any of these reports. Dr. Cary would reiterate the importance of a well-trained militia of veterinarians by including this disease in his next several annual reports. The disease occurred chiefly among cattle, he reported, though it could affect deer, wild hogs, horses, sheep, buffalo, and other animals. Dr. Cary gave an overview of its transmission and symptoms and how difficult it was to distinguish from anthrax. It was, he wrote, almost always fatal in cattle.

Dr. Cary followed with a section on hog cholera serum, concluding with his understated note that "serum can be ordered from the Hog Cholera Serum Laboratory at Auburn, Ala." Dr. Cary, by this year, finally had triumphed in securing state funding for the serum plant. He noted that serum could be ordered by wire "and unless check is sent in advance it will be sent c.o.d. by express or by parcel post. We send out virus only to parties whom we know are qualified to use it." He informed readers that graduate veterinarians, county farm demonstrators, and "some others who have received personal instruction can use virus safely."

He noted that tick eradication in Alabama in 1915 had made "more progress than any previous year." He credited the cooperative attitude fostered by Farmers' Institutes, campaigns by state and county livestock associations, by the farmers' summer school at Auburn, farm demonstrators, the work of Bureau of Animal Industry veterinary inspectors, counties building dipping vats, and even by the encouragement of school teachers and newspapers writing positively on the subject.

But Dr. Cary called attention to a lackadaisical attitude he had noticed among some tuberculosis inspectors:

> . . . Montgomery tested, in 1915, 540 dairy cattle out of 2,300. This is not what the city law requires. Every animal should have been tested . . . . Mobile failed to test or have tested 500 out of 2,000 dairy cows. The parties responsible for this neglect should remember that human life is at stake and little children or infants suffer and many of them die. Tuberculosis is a disease of concentrated populations and the larger cities of Alabama cannot afford to trifle with this most insidious and dangerous disease. Let the medical men and official authorities and people of these cities awake and meet the demands for pure and safe milk supply. Money or cost is not to stand in the way of public health.

Report for 1916

Dr. Cary's tenth *Annual Report of the State Veterinarian* noted that 1916 had been a record year in Alabama for tick eradication. Sixteen counties had been cleaned of cattle ticks and as a result had been released from the federal quarantine by year's end.

He noted in this report that cattle reacting to the tuberculosis test were largely confined to dairy cows and to oxen in lumber camps.

Report for 1917

Dr. Cary's eleventh *Annual Report of the State Veterinarian* added D. L. Allen of Auburn as an assistant state veterinarian. Before the end of 1916, Drs. Eatman and Webb had left the work.

This report opened with several pages overviewing slaughterhouse construction suitable for small cities and towns, and the report included photos of the slaughterhouse at Auburn. Dr. Cary advised on the design of such a structure: ". . . the wall is to be 12 inches thick . . . the floor should be 6 inches thick." He even listed the materials needed for building the basic slaughterhouse costing between $2,000 and $10,000. He then printed the city ordinance in effect in Auburn, which he undoubtedly authored.

During 1917, Dr. Cary reported, eleven additional counties had been released from the federal tick fever quarantine. In November, the Live Stock Sanitary Board passed a regulation to take effect on January 1,

1918, requiring all cattle to be free of visible ticks for shipment out of tick-infested counties in the state. At the end of 1917, thirty-nine Alabama counties were considered tick-free.

According to this report, in 1917, Alabama's hog population increased by 50 percent with "a great movement of breeding hogs from without the state and within the state. So hog cholera was spread somewhat extensively in Alabama." He noted that the Serum Plant at Auburn, under his direction, supplied farmers with serum "at the lowest possible cost to them." In 1917, Dr. Cary reported, farmers obtained more than four million cubic centimeters of anti-hog cholera serum at a penny per cc. Still, he lobbied for additional resources to fight this disease:

> When the State Veterinarian is given sufficient funds, a law is enacted that will control the movement of all hogs and enforce disinfection of hogs, premises, etc., and control the use and distribution of hog cholera virus and serum—then this very destructive hog disease can be controlled and eliminated.

Report for 1918

Dr. Cary's twelfth *Annual Report of the State Veterinarian*, covering 1918, revealed that four Alabama counties had been released from federal cattle tick quarantine, making forty-three in the clear, with twenty-four still working toward that goal. Dr. Cary pointed out that Mississippi, Louisiana, Arkansas, Texas, and Georgia each had state-wide tick eradication laws on the books, and Mississippi by this time had seen all of its counties released from the federal quarantine. Focusing on the two dozen unreleased Alabama counties, Dr. Cary noted that those counties had 800 dipping vats in place, about a quarter of the number of vats he recommended. At this time, two-thirds of the state of Alabama, nearly 70 percent of its land area, had done enough to be released from the quarantine.

The progress the inspectors made, thanks to increasing cooperation from farmers and politicians, had been the result of hard work all around. Data supplied to Dr. Cary reflected in the report showed 3,561,399 cattle had been dipped in Alabama's 6,638 vats during 1918. By the end of 1918, there were 18,392 head of cattle still in quarantine.

In this twelfth report, Dr. Cary brought before the governor the text of Auburn's—his—new city ordinance (summarized below) related to meat inspection. This local statute held that:

1. Every animal killed for meat production and consumption in Auburn was to be slaughtered at the Serum Plant Slaughter House under supervision of veterinary inspectors affiliated with the college;

2. Every animal was to be inspected before slaughter according to BAI regulations;

3. Meat carcasses were to be removed from the Slaughter House on the day of slaughter, with fees for owners who left their meats there overnight;

4. Charges for slaughter meats were listed by species and weight, with most being $.25 or $.50, depending on the animal and its weight;

5. Inspection fees were also either $.15 or $.25, depending on animal type;

6. All carcasses or parts were to be stamped or tagged as appropriate until sold in a butcher shop or meat market;

7. All meat carcasses brought "into the town of Auburn from the country" were to be presented for inspection at the Veterinary Department, at the Slaughter House, or Serum Plant, with lungs, heart, liver and kidneys attached;

8. No carcasses or parts were to be sold or given away in Auburn unless the animals had been inspected, passed, stamped, or tagged by an official inspector;

9. All hotels, restaurants, public eating houses, and boarding houses in Auburn were prohibited from feeding boarders, guests, or the traveling public uninspected meats;

10. All meats not inspected that were offered for sale or as a gift were subject to being condemned and seized by the town marshal or the town meat inspector;

11. Meat markets were to be kept clean, sanitary, and screened, with any spoiled or inedible meat sent immediately to the rendering tank at the Serum Plan Slaughter House;

12. The meat inspector or his assistant was given authority to enter all meat markets, hotels, restaurants, or boarding and eating houses to inspect meats and fish, with authority to close the establishment if he deemed necessary;

13. All condemned meats were to be put into the rendering tank at the Serum Plant and were considered property of the Serum Plant;

14. The State Veterinarian or the Dean of the Veterinary College was to serve as the chief meat inspector and the veterinary supervisor of the Serum Plant, and given authority for final arbitration in all appeals over inspection decisions; and

15. Violators of these statutes were subject to fines of from $1 to $50 or imprisonment of from one to 50 days, plus the guilty party would pay all costs.

The report also gave an update on tuberculosis in Alabama, with Dr. Cary noting the decreasing incidences of the disease, thanks to continued and increasing numbers of inspections. During 1918, federal, state, and municipal authorities tuberculin-tested 15,139 cattle in Alabama, with only 1.3 percent reacting positively. Dr. Cary mentioned a new cooperative agreement between the BAI and the State Live Stock Sanitary Board to offer accreditation to tuberculosis-free herds. He explained the accrediting process in this report and directed that applications for this status be made to the State Veterinarian or to the BAI's office in Birmingham.

Dr. Cary also presented results from tests of hog cholera remedies conducted at Purdue University in Indiana the previous year. One example: the "Bourbon Remedy" made by the Bourbon Remedy Company of Lexington, Kentucky, proved "neither a curative nor preventive for hog cholera." In fact, all twenty-two products tested at Purdue proved to hold no value as a cure or preventive of hog cholera. Dr. Cary's point was likely that his tried and true methods of sanitary conditions and appropriate inoculation with proven anti-hog cholera vaccine were the *only* methods to prevent the disease among these valuable food animals, and the sooner all hog farmers took care of business the right way, the sooner the disease would be eradicated. Dr. Cary noted that the State Anti-Hog Cholera Serum Plant at Auburn sold to the state's farmers more than five million cc of serum during 1918, with an effort made to hold "the price of serum down to a reasonable basis for the farmers of Alabama."

Report for 1919

Dr. Cary's thirteenth *Annual Report of the State Veterinarian*, covering 1919, was addressed to Governor Thomas E. Kilby (1865-1943) and listed eighteen assistant state veterinarians: Drs. J. S. Andrade of Huntsville, D. L. Allen of Prattville, L. E. Beckham of Tuscaloosa, J. S. Cook of Union Springs, O. R. Eatman of Gadsden, C. W. Ferguson of Auburn, W. B. Fleming of Montgomery, W. L. Ingram of Marvyn, R. I. Kearley of Andalusia, E. D. King of Mobile, I. S. McAdory of Auburn, D. J. Meador of Selma, R. B. Nixon of Demopolis, J. T. Prickett of Talladega, W. D. Staples of Anniston, J. R. Sullivan of Auburn, F. B. Whitfield of Dothan and F. P. Woolf of Mobile.

Dr. Cary got his state-wide Tick Eradication Law passed in the Alabama Legislature in February 1919, and almost overnight he and the BAI and state inspectors—including his now-expanded roster of assistant state veterinarians—launched or re-started tick eradication work in twenty-two of the state's twenty-four quarantined counties. By the end of 1919, most of those counties were released from the quarantine. Parts of Bibb, Shelby, Cherokee, Calhoun, Cleburne, and all of Washington counties remained under quarantine at year's end. Side-by-side counties in west Alabama—Fayette and Lamar—were kept under strict quarantine "because they failed to supply the funds to do active work." In those two counties, any cattle movement was forbidden by law. Dr. Cary also noted that Houston and Choctaw counties were returned to quarantine status because "they became re-infested by the failure of the county authorities in preventing re-infestation from the infested herds that were left in the county at the time the quarantine was raised."

Overall, fantastic progress had been made in tick eradication in Alabama, and Dr. Cary pointedly noted the role of citizen and politician cooperation: "In every county where the State law was enforced without fear or favor the ticks were eradicated and the quarantine raised."

As 1919 closed, 91 percent of Alabama was released from the years-long federal cattle quarantine. Dr. Cary reported 7,110,215 cattle either inspected or dipped in Alabama's 8,438 vats during 1919. By the end of 1918, there were 14,704 head of cattle still in quarantine—3,687 fewer than the previous year.

His report for 1919 also showed tuberculosis holding steady, with city, state, and federal authorities testing 18,368 cattle. Only 300—less than two percent—reacted positively.

While Dr. Cary's report noted that 1919 saw numerous "losses of cattle from black leg, septicemias, and stomach and intestinal parasites," in Alabama, many cattle also died during the winter and early spring from lack of proper feed, with the downturned economy taking its toll. The year, though, saw a decrease in hog cholera cases because, as Dr. Cary reported, "hog raisers have been taking better care of their hogs and have been more judiciously using serum, and serum and virus."

Report for 1920

Dr. Cary's fourteenth *Annual Report of the State Veterinarian*, addressed to Governor Kilby and covering 1920, listed twenty assistant state veterinarians, with W. L. Ingram, E. D. King and J. R. Sullivan from the previous year's roster having taken other jobs, and five new appointments: Dr. N. G. Covington in Auburn, Dr. D. F. McCarthy in West Blocton, Dr. R. A. Roberts in Auburn, Dr. J. M. Smith in Greenville, and Dr. R. S. Sugg—a future dean at the school—in Auburn.

As was the case for most of Dr. Cary's first several reports, he opened with a recap of tick eradication efforts from the previous year, noting improved record-keeping by Dr. C. J. Becker of the BAI. Progress had come in the government's releasing Lamar, Fayette, and Washington counties from quarantine during 1920, though parts of Mobile and Jefferson counties, plus all of Escambia County, were put back under quarantine "because they became re-infested, and refused to co-operate or failed to enforce the law." There were still plenty of isolated areas infected with cattle ticks, but by the end of 1920, 94 percent of the state had been freed from the federal quarantine. Again, progress came through relentless effort on the part of inspectors. They collectively oversaw 3,138,490 cattle dippings statewide during 1920, with 8,014 different vats in use. By the year's end, only 9,911 individual cattle were under quarantine in Alabama.

Dr. Cary also lauded the inspectors and the cooperating farmers for only one case of glanders being found in Alabama during 1920, though the focus of providing horses for the Army during the World War brought about more attention to such screening. This success represented a welcome break from tradition, as Dr. Cary described "the only war that has occurred which has not been followed by great and costly outbreaks of glanders."

Tuberculosis, too, remained under control: of 22,214 animals tested with tuberculin during 1920, 572, or about 2.5 percent, showed a positive reaction. Dr. Cary urged vigilance in imported animals, however, as Alabama's incidence of TB was far less than what he noted in Northern states. "Our tests show that most of the tuberculous reactors in pure bred herds have been brought into Alabama or have become infected by contact with infected cattle brought largely for dairy and breeding purposes," he wrote, suggesting the danger of buying uninspected cattle or buying cattle by mail.

The practice of municipal meat inspection also was picking up. During 1920, the cities/communities of Auburn, Anniston, Birmingham, Gadsden, Huntsville, Montgomery, Mobile, Opelika, Union Springs, and Selma employed one or more meat inspectors for this work, with Tuscaloosa and Uniontown preparing to bring inspectors on board. Still, Dr. Cary's report bemoaned the modest budgets several of these communities provided in meat inspection. "Some of our cities are not up to the requirements with their inspector," he wrote. "One city . . . has a layman for an inspector. A very common mistake is . . . a butcher or a layman can inspect meat animals and meat and meat products. Every meat inspector should be a graduate veterinarian who has been given theoretical and practical instructions in meat inspection."

This report for 1920 again noted the decline of hog cholera, with Dr. Cary stating that fewer hogs had been "bred and fed in Alabama" in 1920 than in 1919. He mentioned, for the first time, a BAI inspector named Dr. H. C. Wilson, a specialist in hogs and hog cholera who would work with Dr. Cary for years. Dr. Cary's notes in this section hinted at the workload and the focus of the assistant state veterinarians under his authority:

> The State and assistant State veterinarians have been teaching prevention, cleanliness, inoculation and judicious feeding and sanitation. The State serum plant has helped to stabilize and keep down the price of serum. The State and Federal inspectors have made frequent diagnosis and regulated and controlled as far as possible the inter- and intra-state movements of swine.

While the number of hogs may have been down in 1920, numbers of other animals brought into Alabama were escalating. More than 18,500 mules, 8,570 horses, 3,200 cattle, 733 hogs and ninety other (goats, sheep, dogs) had been inspected as they arrived in Alabama. Holding to his exacting standards, Dr. Cary was not slack in assigning some blame for those animals whose inadequate inspections allowed in disease:

> As a rule, the animals shipped into this State were inspected but that did not keep out all diseases, because some diseased animals escaped detection by the inspectors (in some cases from neglect and inefficient attention of the inspector and in other cases from lack of development of the various diseases).

He warned that "numerous northern dealers and breeders . . . advertise grade and registered calves and try to ship them to Alabama without tuberculin testing." He also contended that "some state authorities permit the shipment of any and all hogs without inoculation and without inspection. Some state officials do not regard all railroad pens and

Cary

Above: Cary family crest

Top right: Charles Allen Cary,
about age four

Right: Charles Allen Cary
about the time he entered
Iowa Agricultural College

(Photos courtesy Cary Family)

Charles Allen Cary, back
row at left, about the time
of his graduation from
Iowa Agricultural College

Left: Emma Heck, soon to be married
Right: Charles Allen Cary early in his career
Below: Marriage certificate of Emma Heck and Charles Allen Cary
(Photos courtesy Cary Family)

Veterinarians meeting at the University of Pennsylvania for 1894 US Veterinary Medical Association convention. Dr. Cary is in the back row, fourth from left. (Reprinted from Journal of American Veterinary Medical Association*)*

Dr. Cary's
certificate of
membership
in the
United States
Veterinary
Medical
Association,
1890

*(Courtesy
Cary Family)*

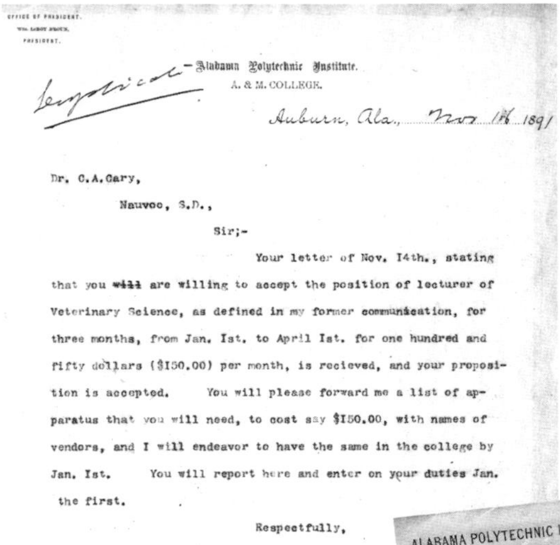

OFFICE OF PRESIDENT.
Wm. LeROY BROUN,
PRESIDENT.

Alabama Polytechnic Institute.
A. & M. COLLEGE.

Auburn, Ala., Nov 18 1891

Dr. C.A.Cary,

Nauvoo, S.D.,

Sir;-

Your letter of Nov. 14th., stating that you ~~will~~ are willing to accept the position of lecturer of Veterinary Science, as defined in my former communication, for three months, from Jan. 1st. to April 1st. for one hundred and fifty dollars ($150.00) per month, is recieved, and your proposition is accepted. You will please forward me a list of apparatus that you will need, to cost say $150.00, with names of vendors, and I will endeavor to have the same in the college by Jan. 1st. You will report here and enter on your duties Jan. the first.

Respectfully,

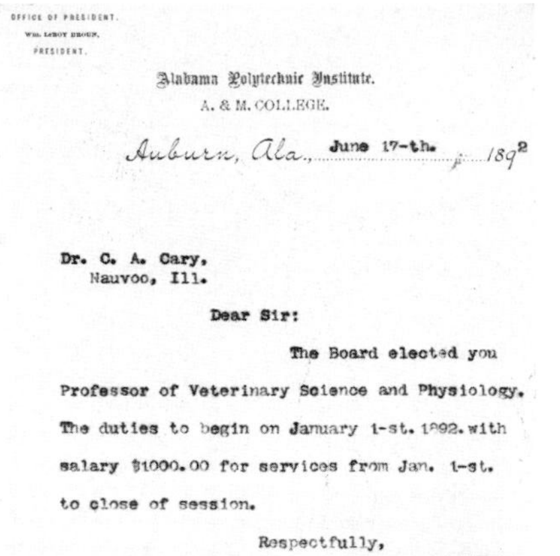

OFFICE OF PRESIDENT.
Wm. LeROY BROUN,
PRESIDENT.

Alabama Polytechnic Institute.
A. & M. COLLEGE.

Auburn, Ala., June 17-th. 1892

Dr. C. A. Cary,
Nauvoo, Ill.

Dear Sir:

The Board elected you Professor of Veterinary Science and Physiology. The duties to begin on January 1-st. 1892. with salary $1000.00 for services from Jan. 1-st. to close of session.

Respectfully,

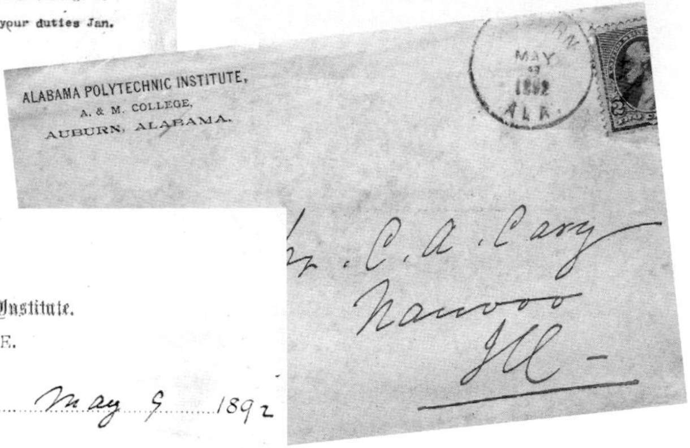

ALABAMA POLYTECHNIC INSTITUTE,
A. & M. COLLEGE,
AUBURN, ALABAMA.

MAY 1892 ALA.

Dr. C. A. Cary
Nauvoo
Ill -

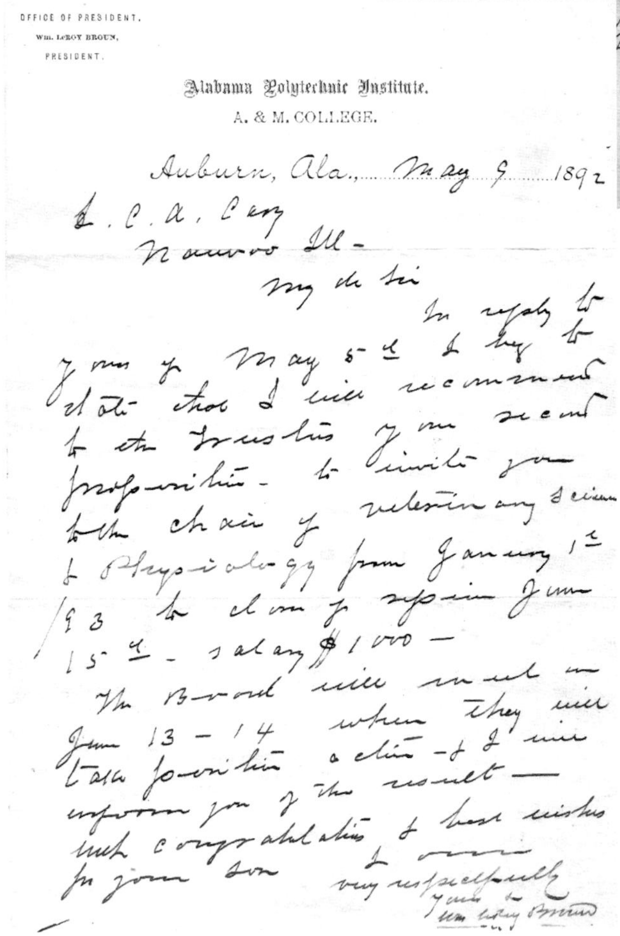

OFFICE OF PRESIDENT.
Wm. LeROY BROUN,
PRESIDENT.

Alabama Polytechnic Institute.
A. & M. COLLEGE.

Auburn, Ala., May 9 1892

Dr. C. A. Cary
Nauvoo Ill -

My dr Sir

In reply to yours of May 5th I beg to state that I will recommend to the Trustees your second proposition - to invite you to the chair of Veterinary Science & Physiology from January 1st 93 to close of session June 15th - salary $1000 -

The Board will meet on June 13 - 14 when they will take favorable action - & I will inform you of the result -

With congratulations & best wishes for your son I am

very respectfully
Yours &c
Wm LeRoy Broun

Above, left: 1891 letter from API/Alabama Agricultural and Mechanical College President William LeRoy Broun to Charles Allen Cary, with details of Dr. Cary's initial appointment as a visiting lecturer at Auburn. Left: Handwritten 1892 note from President Broun outlining his plan to recommend Dr. Cary as chair of veterinary science and physiology beginning January 1, 1893. Above right: President Broun's 1892 letter confirming the trustees' appointment of Dr. Cary. Note body of letter has wrong start year.

(Photos courtesy, top: AU Archives and, left: Cary Family)

Cary family photo from about 1894. Dr. Cary stands on back row, second from left, with his wife, Emma, seated in front of him holding baby Phoebe. Son Elwyn is seen in middle looking at his baby sister. Others are not identified. This image is rare as the only one found of Charles and Emma together in a photo.

The Cary family moved into this house at 360 N. College St. after Dr. Cary purchased it and four acres at auction in 1897 for $1625. Now known as the Halliday-Cary-Pick House, it is home to the Cary Center for the Advancement of Philanthropy & Nonprofit Studies, a program of AU College of Human Sciences.

The Auburn Dr. Cary found . . . Toomer's Corner around 1900, as seen from campus (Courtesy Auburn University Archives)

Dr. Cary, like many adults of his generation, learned penmanship and had a beautiful, flowing signature.

Mch 20. 1905

C A Cary

Auburn Ala

Two men—B.B. Ross, left, and Charles Allen Cary—walk across the dirt intersection of College Street/Main Street and Magnolia Avenue, Toomer's Corner, in turn-of-the-century Auburn. Figure at left unidentified. (Courtesy Auburn University Archives)

Chief faculty of the Alabama Agricultural and Mechanical College in the early 1890s, assembled by the back steps of the new Main Building (later Samford Hall) are, front row from left, Charles Coleman Thach, General James Henry Lane, O. D. Smith, President William LeRoy Broun, Patrick Hues Mell, Col. A. J. Bondurant, and Charles Allen Cary; center row from left, J. M. Stedman, John Jenkins Wilmore, Charles Ross, and George Petrie. Back row from left, A. F. McKissick, Bennett Battle Ross, and Col. John Wills.

The lecture room/museum Dr. Cary assembled to teach his earliest students in a third-floor room of the Main Building. (Photos courtesy AU Archives)

This split-level structure, built in 1894 about where Ramsay Hall now sits on the Auburn University campus, served as Dr. Cary's first veterinary building at Auburn. Students are wearing cadet uniforms and are joined by locals, who have brought horses and cattle. Dr. Cary is dressed in all-white, dirt marks on both knees, and wearing a derby about one-quarter in from the left of the photo.

(Photos courtesy Auburn University Archives)

The photographer may have been standing on a building at the southeast corner of College and Magnolia to take this photo of the veterinary building and its surrounding paddock area a few years into the twentieth century ... a vantage point from about the top of today's Ware Jewelers in downtown Auburn.

Auburn's second veterinary building, circa 1908, was actually the first building after a makeover and expansion. (Courtesy Auburn University Archives)

Dr. Cary in his horse-and-buggy, which he used locally until he bought his first car in 1926. He is shown at the front door of the veterinary building.

(Courtesy Auburn University Archives)

Top: Dr. Cary, foreground center, clothed in white with black hat, overseeing mule handling during a teaching exercise on the grounds outside the original veterinary building. Students are dressed in their cadet uniforms. Circa 1915 by George Ingram '16.

Bottom: This photo may have been taken at one of Dr. Cary's Saturday clinics, where locals brought their ailing farm animals for diagnosis and treatment. Taken in the paddock area adjacent to the original veterinary building, about where Auburn University's Aerospace Engineering Building now sits.

(Photos courtesy Auburn University Archives)

Top: Dr. Cary, back row, far right, with students who would graduate in 1909 in the first class of the School of Veterinary Medicine. This photo taken on the lawn outside Langdon Hall. Notice picket fence in rear, which lined College Street.

Center: Dr. Cary, at left, with some of his earliest veterinary science students attired in their "Sunday best." Photo taken around 1907, about the time the degree-granting program was approved.

(Courtesy Auburn University Archives)

Dr. Cary, seated below human skeleton at left of photo, poses with his growing corps of veterinary students outside the veterinary building in the early 1900s.
(Courtesy Auburn University Archives)

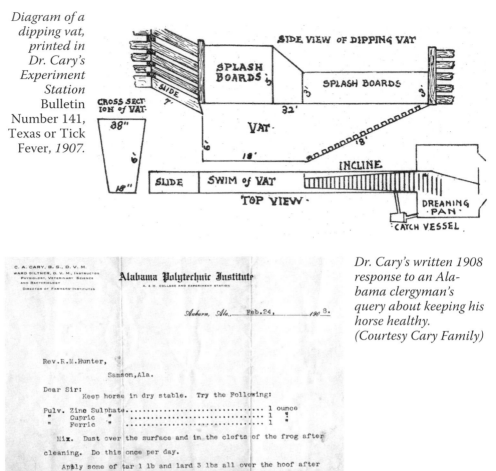

Diagram of a dipping vat, printed in Dr. Cary's Experiment Station *Bulletin Number 141,* Texas or Tick Fever, *1907.*

Dr. Cary's written 1908 response to an Alabama clergyman's query about keeping his horse healthy. (Courtesy Cary Family)

C. A. CARY, B. S., D. V. M.
WARD GILTNER, D. V. M., INSTRUCTOR
PHYSIOLOGY, VETERINARY SCIENCE
AND BACTERIOLOGY
DIRECTOR OF FARMERS' INSTITUTES

Alabama Polytechnic Institute
A. & M. COLLEGE AND EXPERIMENT STATION

Auburn, Ala., Feb.24, 190 8.

Rev.R.M.Hunter,

Samson,Ala.

Dear Sir:
Keep horse in dry stable. Try the Following:

Pulv. Zinc Sulphate...................................... 1 ounce
"   Cupric   "   .... 1 "
"   Ferric   "   .... 1 "

Mix. Dust over the surface and in the clefts of the frog after cleaning. Do this once per day.

Apply some of tar 1 lb and lard 3 lbs all over the hoof after applying the above.

Yours truly,

Dr. Cary, right, at the top of his game (Courtesy Cary Family) and, left, the father of veterinary medicine in the South, late career (Courtesy AU Archives).

Dr. Cary, center with sleeve rolled up, conducts a hog cholera inoculation demonstration for a group of county agents, probably about the time he succeeded in getting a hog cholera serum plant built at Auburn in 1915.
(Courtesy Auburn University Archives)

Right photo: Dr. Cary, left, late in his life, with an unidentified man. (Courtesy Auburn University Archives)

Dr. Cary, right, and one of his students, pictured probably in the first decade of the twentieth century. His dirty coveralls suggest an intense teaching demonstration of some type.

(Courtesy AU Archives)

Looking east on Thach Avenue through what is today the heart of campus. This photo, from the early 1920s, shows the hog cholera serum plant at left, with its barn/slaughterhouse in the rear. In the distance sits the Main Building, which would be named Samford Hall a few years after this picture was taken. Notice a couple of horses and buggies at the plant, with another making its way either toward or away from the plant on the dirt street.

(Courtesy Auburn University Archives)

Some of the eminent faculty members of API, pictured in the early 1930s. From left, George Petrie, John Jenkins Wilmore, Miss Allie Glenn, Bolling Crenshaw, and Charles Allen Cary. (Courtesy Cary Family)

This photo from the 1927 Glomerata *shows Dean Cary, about age 65, at his roll-top desk, typewriter at his right. Notice the ink containers on the desk.*
(Courtesy Auburn University Archives)

Above: Probably within his last year of life, Dr. Cary, left, poses with his chief lieutenant, Dr. Isaac Sadler McAdory, outside the Physiology Building on old Vet Hill. Right: Dr. Cary shares a laugh with an unidentified man outside the Physiology Building in 1934. Photos by veterinary student Silvio Fittipaldi, Class of 1937; provided by his son, Joe Fittipaldi.

Right, top: The Physiology Building, shown from the 1950s, was built near the Serum Plant in 1922, under Dr. Cary's direction, to house basic sciences and small animal work. Right, architectural drawing: The Veterinary Building across from Physiology was in the minds of API leadership at the time Dr. Cary died in 1935. The building was constructed in 1940 and in 1946 named for Dr. Cary. Physiology was razed in 2015; Cary Hall remains in use. (Courtesy AU Archives)

Today's Auburn College of Veterinary Medicine stands as legacy to Dr. Charles Allen Cary. From far left: J.T. Vaughan Large Animal Teaching Hospital and Bartlett Lameness Arena; Wilford and Kate Bailey Small Animal Teaching Hospital; Veterinary Education Center; and Greene Hall. (Courtesy Tajuan Sellars)

Dr. and Mrs. Cary and son Elwyn are buried in Auburn's Pine Hill Cemetery in sight of Samford Hall.

The three living deans of the College of Veterinary Medicine in Greene Hall in front of portraits of their four predecessors. From left, retired AU Provost Timothy Boosinger, Dean Emeritus John Thomas Vaughan, and Dean Calvin Johnson. Portraits, from left, are Charles Allen Cary, Isaac Sadler McAdory, Redding S. Sugg, and James E. Greene. (Courtesy AU Photo Services)

yards that receive hogs for shipment as cholera infected." These practices violated the law, and the vigilant Dr. Cary would not compro-
mise: "All calves coming in Alabama must be tuberculin tested by an
approved Federal or State veterinary inspector . . . Calves that have
suckled tuberculous mothers can not be shipped into Alabama," he
wrote. And regarding the lackadaisical attitude toward hog movement:
"This is a serious mistake and spreads cholera."

Report for 1921

Dr. Cary's fifteenth *Annual Report of the State Veterinarian*,
addressed to Governor Kilby and covering 1921, noted the departures of
Assistant State Veterinarians D. L. Allen, D. F. McCarthy and J. M.
Smith, and the addition of Dr. T. M. Dennis of Montgomery to the
team.

His introductory remarks about tick eradication work made clear the
political battle he and other inspectors faced when noncompliant farmers and others defied the law or established protocols. As for the work
during 1921, Dr. Cary noted that most Alabama counties had continued
to make good progress in eliminating cattle ticks, but—and the reader
can sense the steam coming from under his collar—he continued:

some have failed to work and some county authorities have stopped at
critical times and refused to go on with the work. During this time ticks
multiply and a great deal of territory and many cattle become infested and
therefore must be carried through another long period of active work.

Take the example of Shelby County: a large part of the county worked
and became tick free, and the range along the borders of Chilton, of Bibb,
of St. Clair, and of Jefferson, did not clean up, and the County Board of
Revenue of Shelby failed to continue the work. Consequently, the entire
county was placed under state and federal quarantine and ticky cattle have
been run into surrounding counties and re-infested them.

A case is now pending in court to compel Shelby County officials to do
active tick eradication. In another instance Mobile County Board of Revenue refused to continue tick eradication work when the State law makes
it mandatory. This county quit work on October 15, when it was very
nearly through with eradication. The County Board was served with a
writ of mandamus and ordered to work by the circuit judge and the case
was appealed to the Supreme Court and the lower court's order was sustained. The Supreme Court's decision makes it mandatory for all infested
counties to clean up ticks.

He noted another problem Alabama's tick inspectors and compliant cattlemen faced: counties that bordered other states where infection was allowed to go unchecked were at risk from re-infestation. In Florida especially, he wrote, "there are people who will run the risk of running cheap, tick infested cattle over the state line."

Alabama, which had been 94 percent free from quarantine the previous year, was back to 90 percent free of cattle ticks in 1920, according to Dr. Cary's estimate. The lack of drive to finish this effort and the lack of compliance among some Alabamians and some in bordering states was clearly exasperating for Dr. Cary and his co-inspectors. "The dairy and beef cattle industry have come to stay and the tick must go," he concluded.

For the year, Dr. Cary reported, 3,313,868 cattle were inspected or dipped in the fight against ticks—174,378 more than the previous year. These dippings took place in 7,353 vats. More than 8,000 vats had been used in the state in previous years. At the end of 1921, almost 16,000 cattle were in quarantine in Alabama—about 6,000 more than the previous year. While the veterinary inspectors were gaining control on a number of animal diseases, tick fever was proving difficult to finish off.

One other problem Dr. Cary noted in his report for 1921 was the lack of response from those charged with overseeing milk and meat inspection in the various communities where this work was being done. Perplexing the state veterinarian, Dr. Cary took the opportunity not only to call out those failing their duties, but to suggest that additional resources were needed for this life-saving work, especially when tick eradication and other activities took up so much of his time. He wrote:

> Mobile . . . should report, but for some unknown reason no records could be obtained by this office. In some other towns and cities no records are kept and no qualified veterinary inspectors are employed. Hence no authentic record of inspections could be made. We have often stated that it is not possible to obtain correct or efficient meat or milk inspection by laymen or non-qualified inspectors.

Dr. Cary's report reflected a significant increase in testing cattle for tuberculosis in Alabama in 1921. He reported 37,905 animals tested during the year, with 499 reacting positively. Whether from his lighting a fire under the assistants for some having missed diseased animals the previous year or for some other reason, the number of inspections in 1921 was up by 15,691 over the 22,214 inspections made during 1920. Again, happily, the incidence of TB was less than 2 percent.

Reports for 1922 and 1923

Dr. Cary's *Annual Reports* for these years in his role as the state veterinarian—which would represent his sixteenth and seventeenth such reports—are not found among the others, collections of which are maintained in both the Auburn University Archives and the Alabama Department of Archives and History in Montgomery. Further, while some copies of these annual reports may be found online, digitized by various libraries around the country, searches have not yielded the reports for 1922 and 1923. It seems more than a routine coincidence that the two places most likely to have preserved these reports—Auburn and the State Archives—should have printed copies of all but these two on their shelves. Perhaps, in an effort to keep publishing costs down, Dr. Cary's reports for these two years were not reproduced beyond a few copies, and none of those were forwarded to the archives.

Report for 1924

Dr. Cary's eighteenth *Annual Report of the State Veterinarian*, in a departure from precedent, was addressed to the State Board of Agriculture and served also as his annual report of the Live Stock Sanitary Department.

This report began with an overview of the "great progress" made in cattle tick eradication, with only Choctaw, Clarke, and Washington counties having "failed to do any work." These counties remained under federal quarantine, with cattle owners prohibited from moving any cattle for slaughter or other purposes. "Every one of these counties could have been made to do active tick eradication in co-operation with the State and Federal authorities had it been possible to get the state laws enforced," Dr. Cary wrote.

As 1924 ended, he listed twenty-two counties with a few infested or exposed herds, but he acknowledged that most county authorities were cooperating toward the common goal of tick eradication. Dr. Cary listed forty-two Alabama counties deemed free from cattle ticks. Threats remained to those counties which bordered other states, especially Florida and Southern Mississippi.

The year-end totals for this work included 3,590,313 cattle inspected or dipped during 1924; 7,204 dipping vats in use statewide; and 17,713 cattle quarantined as of December 31, 1924.

At the same time, tuberculosis testing of cattle took a substantial amount of the veterinarians' attention in 1924. Of the 31,200 cattle tested between October 1, 1923, and October 1, 1924—primarily dairy cattle, pure-bred cattle, and oxen—veterinarians killed or authorized killing 171 which tested positively for tuberculosis. Dr. Cary noted more requests for tuberculosis eradication work than the state and county budgets could bear, but that "in a few years, tick eradication will have been completed and then tuberculosis eradication area work can be done."

A new development at this time was the increasing incidence of tuberculosis in chickens, "a problem since there is now a movement on the part of extension workers to increase poultry in Alabama," he wrote. Again, the state veterinarian's advice was to buy breeding birds only from those sources that were able to provide a legitimate tuberculosis-free certificate. The beginning ascension of the poultry industry in Alabama may have coincided with a decline in the state's hog industry; and Dr. Cary used this report to recommend "a general regulation concerning the movement of poultry into Alabama." Whether he had authored such a regulation for the Live Stock Sanitary Board's or the Legislature's review at this time was not clear.

Also on the state veterinarian's radar during 1924 was "a disastrous scare" of anthrax appearing in Mississippi, Louisiana, Arkansas, Texas, and Tennessee. Fortunately, this disease did not erupt in Alabama, but Dr. Cary assured his audience that he and other inspectors were keeping careful watch of events in the exposed states and were taking measures to keep anthrax out of the state. A threat of quarantine against those states was a possibility, he assured.

Alarmingly, this report also described foot-and-mouth disease outbreaks in both California and Texas during 1924. Dr. Cary credited state and federal authorities working in those locations with taking appropriate measures to control the threat. He acknowledged that Alabama at this time was "poorly prepared to handle such an emergency disease." He suggested a wise move would be to prepare in advance for such an event by legislative action authorizing an emergency force which could be summoned to stamp out any unexpected outbreaks of foot-and-mouth disease at the least cost to the state.

Report for 1925-1926

The following year, Dr. Cary's reports changed to fiscal year rather than calendar year. Thus, the next report is the *Annual Report of the State Veterinarian of Alabama* for the fiscal year ending September 30, 1926. The cover of this publication noted that the same material appeared in the third annual report of the Alabama Board of Agriculture and Industries.

Dr. Cary reported that, as of October 1, 1926, fifty-one Alabama counties were entirely free of cattle ticks, with another half dozen counties having "very few infested and some exposed herds." Significant exposure and infestation were recorded in eight counties, with three counties—Choctaw, Clarke, and Washington—still inactive. Clarke County's board was called before the circuit court, and the judge ruled that the county board was not able financially to take up tick eradication as required by law. Dr. Cary's report noted, however, that the members of the board stated that they had made no effort to save or secure funds for tick eradication. This case was appealed to the Alabama Supreme Court, with Dr. Cary expecting a ruling not long after his report submission.

Happily, he reported progress for those counties bordering Florida, anticipating that "all the contiguous counties along the Alabama-Florida line will become entirely free of ticks and quarantine exposure in 1927."

The timing of the report may have had a bearing on the numbers reflected in his report, but Dr. Cary confirmed 1,967,485 animals inspected or dipped through the fiscal year ending September 1926; as October rolled in, 25,350 cattle were quarantined in Alabama.

This report noted that 50,571 cattle had been tested for tuberculosis during the previous fiscal year, with 134 testing positive. A new addition to Dr. Cary's report was the estimated 26,000 chickens inspected for avian tuberculosis. Only one bird was found to be tuberculous.

Again, reduced numbers for hog cholera suggested both the decline of the state hog industry and the effectiveness of serum applications widely available for a decade by this point.

Report for 1927

Dr. Cary's twentieth *Annual Report of the State Veterinarian* noted that, by the end of 1927, Alabama was tick-free in fifty-nine of her counties, with ten having received certification during the year. In 1927, records showed 1,868,450 cattle dipped in 7,190 vats. As if to remind the governor and others not to rest on any laurels, Dr. Cary's report included sections on incidents of stomach worms in sheep, round worms in swine, nodular disease in sheep, and tularemia in rabbits.

Report for 1928

Dr. Cary's twenty-first *Annual Report of the State Veterinarian* carried the happy news that, by the end of that year, all Alabama counties—minus Clarke—had been released from federal quarantine. More good news: all of Southern Mississippi was on schedule to be tick-free by the end of 1930, making, according to Dr. Cary, the Alabama border less of a problem.

Typical of his style, he wrote, ". . . when cattle speculation and politicians stop interfering with state and federal tick eradication, there will be no delay in the public economy of rapidly exterminating the last tick in the United States."

He reported that, in 1928, some 1,564,500 cattle had been dipped in Alabama's 8,178 vats, suggesting that nearly 1,000 new vats had been constructed in the preceding year.

Tuberculosis work had also shown wonderful progress: 59,776 animals were tested in Alabama during 1928, with only ninety-seven—or .016 percent—reacting positively.

For the first time, Dr. Cary included a rundown of rabies in Alabama. There were fifty-eight rabid dogs reported, two rabid mules, and three rabid cats. Alarmingly, eleven citizens had been bitten by rabid animals in the state that year. Dr. Cary noted that many veterinarians and other officials were not aware of a new regulation requiring records and reports of rabid animals, so the reported numbers were surely insufficient. Still, the public needed to know of rabies' presence in the state, and Alabamians needed to learn steps to prevent it spreading to their animals.

Report for 1929

Dr. Cary's twenty-second *Annual Report of the State Veterinarian* brought the news many had awaited: the close of the year had seen "Alabama on the federal tick eradication maps in the white released area." Inspectors had overseen 1,666,735 dippings in 7,893 vats during 1929. Progress in tick eradication was great news to cattle farmers, and it meant veterinarians could begin spending more time fighting other deadly diseases, chiefly tuberculosis.

Dr. Cary noted that the first step taken to prevent and control animal tuberculosis in Alabama had come in 1912 when all breeding cattle being shipped into the state had been required to pass the tuberculosis test before their arrival. The next step had been launching milk inspection in additional locations.

"Now we are just starting area tuberculosis eradication in cattle," Dr. Cary wrote. This effort would be collaborative among counties, the state, and the federal government, he noted, and would require a tuberculosis test of all cattle in a given county as well as all swine and poultry where the disease had been found or where it was suspected. "Tuberculosis eradication will be continued until the disease is eradicated in . . . Alabama," he promised.

Likewise, milk and meat inspections were being done in coordination with the State Health Department. Still, Dr. Cary wrote:

> . . . in some respects it is inefficient because the head men of the work are not qualified. All meat and milk inspection should be directed and supervised by a graduate licensed and trained veterinarian. I do not know a doctor of human medicine or a sanitary engineer who is qualified to do or superintend meat or milk inspection.

Milk and meat inspection had been established in Alabama in 1896—thirty-three years earlier—in Montgomery by Dr. Cary. Thanks to a number of veterinarians who had trained at Auburn under him in the twenty years since degrees were first awarded in 1909, inspection practices were under way in 1929 in Birmingham, Mobile, Selma, Anniston, Opelika, Auburn, Atmore, Brewton, Greenville, Lanett, Florence, Gadsden, Bessemer, Dothan, and Tuscaloosa. Each of those locations had full-time inspectors on the job in 1929. Also, efforts through part-time inspectors were being made at this time in Sheffield, Huntsville, Andalusia, Decatur, Union Springs, Troy, and Enterprise.

Report for 1930

Dr. Cary's twenty-third *Annual Report of the State Veterinarian* reported that tick eradication work had continued in 1930, with 949,771 cattle dipped in 7,953 vats. Similar to the previous year's report, with tick eradication under control, he turned his readers' attention to tuberculosis work. Until 1930, tick eradication had been the chief focus of the Live Stock Sanitary Department. Beginning in February 1930, Dr. Cary wrote, tuberculosis eradication became the leading work of the federal and state livestock sanitary forces in Alabama.

Tuberculosis testing had been underway for years in dairy and beef cattle, ensuring that milk sold to the public was unquestionably free of deadly tuberculosis. Increased testing, he reasoned, meant "in a few more years there will be no bovine or cattle tuberculosis in Alabama."

Dr. Cary's report on rabid animals for 1930 noted positive tests involving fifty dogs, one hog, two cats, and five cows—at least from reports made to the state veterinarian. Rabid dogs had bitten twenty Alabamians during 1930.

Dr. Cary referenced two new livestock sanitary regulations. First, an avian tuberculosis requirement adopted on July 8, 1930, mandated that all chickens four months of age or older pass the Standard Intradermal Tuberculosis test within thirty days of being brought into Alabama. Each tested chicken was to carry a leg band for identification. The tests, of course, were to be conducted by graduate veterinarians.

The second regulation, adopted by the Sanitary Board on January 2, 1931, held that

> All biological manufacturers, houses, dealers, agents and handlers of animal vaccines, within or without the State of Alabama, shall apply to the State Veterinarian for a permit to handle or sell or use vaccines in Alabama. No animal vaccine can be brought into or given away or sold in Alabama without a permit from the State Veterinarian.

Report for 1931

Dr. Cary's twenty-fourth *Annual Report of the State Veterinarian* noted that illegal movements of cattle from other, infected states had caused some re-infestations of tick fever. The ticks were on cattle brought in by truck, not by railroad, Dr. Cary determined. He noted that the overall cause had been helped because, by this year, states bordering Alabama were all free of fever ticks. Alabama saw 550,795 cattle dippings in 1931, making use of 7,972 vats. Most of these dippings took place in Baldwin, Clarke, Escambia, Jefferson, Mobile, Monroe, Sumter, and Washington counties.

By September of 1931, nine Alabama counties had completed tuberculosis eradication, and three others were making significant progress. Veterinarians had inspected more than 90,000 birds—mostly chickens—and found no incidence of avian tuberculosis in the state.

The rabid animal report listed thirty-five dogs, two hogs, and a cat, and noted that ten people had been bitten by rabid animals during 1931.

Fortunately, he reminded readers, hog cholera was decreasing in its presence "in spite of the fact that there were a large number of hogs and pigs moved without inoculation into and within Alabama by truck peddlers during the year."

Report for 1932

Dr. Cary's twenty-fifth *Annual Report of the State Veterinarian* noted that "tick work during 1932 was directed along the lines of prevention," the thousands and thousands of cattle dippings over recent years finally having paid off. He reported that 271,607 cattle had been dipped in Alabama in 1932, in 2,661 active vats.

Dr. Cary again complained that dairy inspection too frequently was performed

by many lay inspectors and the man in charge is a layman who depends mainly upon paper reports of bacterial counts which are made so infrequently that they do not give sufficient tests to make a reasonable average. A number of towns and cities have made no reports to us because they do not keep records or do not do sufficient work to make records.

The end of 1932 saw fourteen Alabama counties certified as tuberculosis-free, with two others "nearly free."

Someone or something got the attention of those who made rabies reports, because the 1932 tally jumped significantly. Rabies reports included 779 dogs, three horses, three mules, a dozen swine, nineteen cats, forty-four cattle, and two chickens. Twenty Alabamians were reported bitten by rabid animals during the year.

Report for 1933

Dr. Cary's twenty-sixth *Annual Report of the State Veterinarian* noted "a serious re-infestation of fever ticks in Mobile County" due to movement of four ponies from Louisiana by boat in the fall of 1932. The ticks on those ponies had not been discovered until the spring of 1933.

Dr. Cary confirmed 176,551 cattle dipped during the year in Alabama, with 1,709 vats used.

Dr. Cary clearly was fed up with the state of meat and milk inspection, and he used this report to rant on these subjects. His comments on meat inspection:

During the year there were employed, by selection and approval of the lay milk inspector in charge of State meat and milk inspection, two non-graduate permit veterinarians to do both meat and milk inspection in their respective towns or small cities. One of these men was called into court to show his qualifications and it was brought out in the evidence that the State health officials selected and endorsed this non-qualified lay inspector and that expert witnesses clearly proved that said inspector was incompetent to do the work of meat and milk inspector. And also it was established that the State inspector in charge of the State health office of meat and milk inspection was not a graduate in human or veterinary medicine. This case has been held up in the court on account of some technical legal question. What seems or appears most serious is that the State health officers should select and employ an incompetent man to protect the health of people of a city and State.

Several city inspectors have failed to make an annual report of their work. It is surprising how cities permit local influences to determine the selection and work of a local meat and milk inspector. In one instance a city meat inspector (a graduate veterinarian) was employed and kept on the work for more than one or two years; and there were periods when this inspector did not go to the slaughter house to do actual inspection more than once a week. This work appeared to satisfy the city officials.

Let it be clearly understood that the only qualified man who can do efficient meat inspection is a competent graduate veterinarian who attends strictly to his inspection work and is always present at the slaughtering of all animals and actually makes a thorough inspection of the living animal before slaughter, and the meat carcasses during and after the slaughter.

Dr. Cary's take on the state of milk inspection:

One of the most important factors or essentials is that all milk must be kept safe from the time it comes from the udder of the cow until it is used by the consumers. Taking small samples once a week is just chance shot and may score the milk producer but rarely keeps all milk in safe, clean and pure condition. Some of the attempts at milk inspection are just uncertain bluffs to scare the producer. In other words some officials hold a weekly or monthly bluff club over the consumer by taking and analyzing periodic samples of milk. Again the famous and much advertised bacterial count may be used to scare the producer in order to make said producer do certain things that may have more to do with politics than producing clean and safe milk. What the milk inspection system needs most is an honest, frequent and efficient inspection that will make the public or the consumers have confidence in it. The most serious factor in our present system as employed in nearly all state and city milk inspection work is the fact that politics never make milk for public consumption. All milk inspection should be entirely separated from politics: and then employ only good, competent inspectors and the very best methods.

He concluded this report with news that 610 rabid dogs had been reported in Alabama in 1933, and six citizens had been bitten by a few of them.

Report for 1934

Dr. Cary's twenty-seventh *Annual Report of the State Veterinarian* would be his last. He noted that tick eradication work had continued in 1934 with 210,896 cattle dipped in 2,076 vats.

Again, Dr. Cary's frustration with the milk and meat inspection efforts was clear from comments he made on that subject:

> Several City inspectors have failed to send in their records. Some town or city inspectors reports are so inaccurate that they can not be published. It appears to be very unwise for the State Health Department to employ incompetent laymen or quacks to inspect meat or milk.

Yet as he neared the end of his life, Dr. Cary expressed optimism about the potential of solid veterinary medicine and live stock sanitary work. A new menace had surfaced: the screw worm. Dr. Cary concluded this, his final report, with words reflecting the "can do" spirit that had characterized him all his life.

> Many doubt the possibility of eradicating the screw worm flies. When we started to eradicate fever ticks some said it could not and would not be done. But it was done and it paid the South and the North to do it. Now it is said that the screw worm fly moves faster and farther than the fever ticks. Also it is said that the screw worm has more hosts upon which to deposit its eggs and in which the screw worm lives. But the screw worm fly does not lay or deposit as many eggs (200-1200) as the old female tick lays (4000-5000). Moreover, it is said that we do not know as much about the life history of the screw worm fly as we know about the life history of the fever tick.
>
> If all flies and screw worms are killed they will be eradicated. The screw worm lives in wounds, carcasses and in the ground. The worms can be killed in living animals if all of them are treated correctly. If all carcasses are burned or deeply buried the screw worms will be prevented from developing into flies. If all the screw worm flies are trapped and destroyed the production of screw worm fly eggs may be stopped. In other words we must get after the screw worm fly in all parts of its life history as we did in eradicating the fever tick.

If all the screw worm infected states will work under direction of the Federal Government, this pest can be eradicated. In fact, the time will come when this pest will be eradicated.

CHAPTER THIRTEEN

STATE BOARD OF VETERINARY
MEDICAL EXAMINERS

In the early years of the twenty-first century, Auburn veterinary graduate Dr. Arthur David Hayes, Class of '68, researched and wrote "A Brief History of the Alabama State Board of Veterinary Medical Examiners," which he generously provided for use in this manuscript.

Dr. Hayes held membership on this board, and his history of the Alabama State Board of Veterinary Medicine, later known as the Alabama State Board of Veterinary Medical Examiners, covers the organization's work from its establishment in 1915 through the early 2000s. The first quarter or so of that document overviews the initial era that involved Dr. Cary. Following is a slightly revised and excerpted version of Dr. Hayes' compilation.[1]

Upon arriving in Auburn in the early 1890s, and subsequently as he had opportunity to travel the state in his work, Dr. Cary encountered time and again a problem he had known since his boyhood in Iowa: the untrained, minimally successful "horse doctor" who would be at work in almost every community. One can hardly blame these entrepreneurs for attempting to earn a living in this way at that time. There were few trained veterinarians in Alabama in the late nineteenth century, and animals were continually falling ill or getting injured. Animal owners needed *somebody* to do *something*. Opportunity always brings someone ready to take advantage of a situation, qualified or not.

After Dr. Cary had launched the South's first School of Veterinary Medicine in 1907—building on his teaching veterinary science for more than a decade prior to that date—and after he had organized the Alabama Veterinary Medical Association and worked in other ways to establish standards for veterinary medicine in Alabama and the South, there remained individuals here and there who offered animal health services without training. While resolved to end this practice, he realized everyone was better off if he did so in due time, not necessarily overnight.

Thanks to a steady stream of graduates of the API program beginning in 1909, there were increasing numbers of veterinary practitioners in Alabama during the early years of the twentieth century. These "graduate veterinarians," as Dr. Cary called his protégés, joined a workforce that included not only graduates of other veterinary schools, but an assortment of men who had perhaps "studied" veterinary medicine with other, established practitioners in a type of apprenticeship. Such men began practicing on their own when they felt qualified or, more likely, when demand for their services provided the opportunity. These men had no formal veterinary education and practiced mostly on horses, mules, and cattle. After API began graduating veterinarians, educational and legislative leaders likely realized—or were informed—that the profession would grow quickly and that a plan was needed for regulating the growing body of veterinary practitioners.

When the Alabama Legislature convened in 1915, members considered a bill providing for the examination, licensing, and regulation of the veterinary medical profession. This bill, the "Veterinary Practice Law of Alabama," quickly passed in both the House and Senate, and Governor Charles Henderson signed it into law on March 17, 1915. As required by the new law, Governor Henderson appointed five veterinarians from various geographical areas to serve as members of the Alabama State Board of Veterinary Medicine (ASBVM). The initial board members were appointed to staggered terms in order for one to rotate off each year during the first five years. Each subsequent appointee was assigned to a five-year term. The first board included: Dr. A. H. French of Birmingham, appointed for five years; Dr. J. M. Luke of Greenville, appointed for four years; Dr. J. S. Andrade of Huntsville, three years; Dr. O. R. Eatman of Gadsden, two years; and Dr. Cary, appointed for one year.

The ASBVM first convened on May 22, 1915, in Birmingham, at the recently constructed Moulton Hotel, a 200-room, eight-story "grand hotel" which stood on the corner of Fifth Avenue North and Twentieth Street from 1914 until it was demolished in 1979. Only Dr. Luke was unable to attend. The group elected officers, with Dr. French chosen as president, Dr. Andrade as vice president, and Dr. Cary as secretary/treasurer. At the first meeting, the board unanimously approved a set of rules and regulations to govern its own activity. The board also approved unanimously a resolution which allowed qualified veterinarians practicing in bordering states to work in Alabama under the license they held from their home state "upon the submission of application, evidence of graduation, licensure and fees." The board also established a license application fee of $15 and an annual license renewal fee of $1.

Finally at this first meeting, the Board of Veterinary Medicine discussed, compiled, and approved a half-dozen printed forms to be used in applicants' petitioning for permits to work in the state. These included:

1. A form for "Permit to Practice Veterinary Medicine and Surgery" for non-graduate practitioners;

2. A form for application for a "Permit to Practice Veterinary Medicine and Surgery" for non-graduate practitioners;

3. A form for "License to Practice Veterinary Medicine and Surgery" for graduate veterinarians;

4. A form for applying for a "License to Practice Veterinary Medicine and Surgery" for graduate veterinarians;

5. A form for "Certifying to the Time of Practice for a Permit Applicant"; and

6. A form for "Certifying to the Time of Practice for a License Applicant."

The group decided to meet a few weeks later, in Auburn at the School of Veterinary Medicine during June 14-15, 1915. The agenda was planned to cover board business and for the group to examine candidates for licenses and permits. This second meeting was announced in issues of three prominent state newspapers: *The Mobile Register, The Montgomery Advertiser,* and *The Birmingham Age-Herald.*

For more than three decades, the board's regularly scheduled meetings were held twice annually. The spring meeting always was held in

Auburn with the primary goal of conducting board business and administering the graduate license examination to new graduates of API and any other qualified graduates who were prepared to sit the test. Permit applicants also were considered when necessary. The board's fall meeting always was held in Birmingham at the Moulton Hotel. At this meeting, similar to the spring meeting, appropriate business was conducted, and license and permit applicants evaluated as necessary.

Contrasted with later decades, no easy travel existed between these Alabama cities in the first half of the twentieth century, particularly for Dr. Luke coming from Greenville or Dr. Andrade coming from Huntsville. Board members likely took a train in the first several years; there may have been connection requirements and delays for connecting trips. In rainy seasons, travel from more distant cities may have required two days or been altogether impossible. ASBVM members in the early years easily could have been away from their homes, families, and veterinary practices for nearly a week in order to attend board meetings. In view of such hardship, it makes sense that they met only twice each year.

On the morning of June 15, 1915, the second meeting of the ASBVM was called to order by President French on the API campus. All members were present except again Dr. Luke. On this date, Alabama's first graduate veterinary licensing examination was administered by the board to thirteen members of the 1915 graduating class of API's School of Veterinary Medicine. All passed the exam and were granted licenses to practice veterinary medicine and surgery in Alabama. Those first licensed veterinarians included:

Dr. G. C. Bevan	Uniontown, Alabama
Dr. L. J. Bonner	Lineville, Alabama
Dr. S. G. Carter	Roanoke, Alabama
Dr. J. G. Gaunt	East Tallassee, Alabama
Dr. T. B. Giessendaner	Monroe, Georgia
Dr. T. B. Howle	Oxford, Alabama
Dr. R. M. Lambert	Perdue Hill, Alabama
Dr. I. R. Pollard	Luverne, Alabama
Dr. W. S. Siebold	Guntersville, Alabama
Dr. R. F. South	Blount Springs, Alabama
Dr. Fred Steele	Auburn, Alabama
Dr. C. Thigpen	Fort Deposit, Alabama
Dr. M. W. Williams	Center, Alabama

Additionally, three other licensed graduate veterinarians from other states were granted licenses in Alabama after giving evidence of having diplomas from established veterinary colleges and having passed the board licensing examination of their respective states. Those were Dr. J. C. Shoenlaub, a graduate of Ohio State College, who had passed State Board exams in Ohio and Tennessee; Dr. W. B. Smith of API's Class of 1914, who had passed the State Board of North Carolina; and Dr. S. D. Haynie of API's Class of 1913, who had passed the State Board of Texas.

The ASBVM issued the first reciprocity license to practice in Alabama to a licensed Georgia veterinarian, Dr. W. A. Scott of Columbus, allowing him to practice veterinary medicine and surgery in Alabama. Forty-seven graduate veterinarians were granted licenses to practice in Alabama after presenting evidence that they were graduates of legally recognized veterinary colleges and already in practice in Alabama at the time the Veterinary Practice Law of Alabama (later known as the Alabama Veterinary Practice Act) went into effect on March 17, 1915. Those granted licenses included:

Dr. J. S. Andrade	Huntsville, Alabama
Dr. C. J. Becker	Scottsboro, Alabama
Dr. L. E. Beckham	Tuscaloosa, Alabama
Dr. C. A. Cary	Auburn, Alabama
Dr. J. F. Conner	Selma, Alabama
Dr. Dan Cook	Camden, Alabama
Dr. J. S. Cook	Union Springs, Alabama
Dr. C. Daly	Mobile, Alabama
Dr. M. Dean	Alexander City, Alabama
Dr. O. R. Eatmon	Gadsden, Alabama
Dr. J. C. Edwards	Mobile, Alabama
Dr. M. S. Esslinger	Birmingham, Alabama
Dr. C. W. Ferguson	Auburn, Alabama
Dr. W. B. Fleming	Montgomery, Alabama
Dr. A. H. French	Birmingham, Alabama
Dr. A. Gibson	Birmingham, Alabama
Dr. R. V. Hazewood	Bessemer, Alabama
Dr. C. Head	Montevallo, Alabama
Dr. W. E. Hollingsworth	Lincoln, Alabama
Dr. W. L. Ingram	Florence, Alabama
Dr. M. F. Jackson	Birmingham, Alabama
Dr. A. I. Jones	Birmingham, Alabama

Dr. R. I. Kearley	Birmingham, Alabama
Dr. L. R. Kendrick	Montgomery, Alabama
Dr. G. W. Lewallen	Montgomery, Alabama
Dr. J. M. Luke	Greenville, Alabama
Dr. I. S. McAdory	Auburn, Alabama
Dr. D. J. Meador	Auburn, Alabama
Dr. M. E. Meadows	Salem, Alabama
Dr. C. C. Middleton	Eufaula, Alabama
Dr. E. D. Miley	Selma, Alabama
Dr. A. C. Misner	Decatur, Alabama
Dr. R. B. Mixon	Demopolis, Alabama
Dr. A. Moon	Marion, Alabama
Dr. L. K. Ogletree	Enterprise, Alabama
Dr. G. W. Patton	Bessemer, Alabama
Dr. O. W. Payne	Mobile, Alabama
Dr. D. A. Piatt	Birmingham, Alabama
Dr. Joseph Piatt	Mobile, Alabama
Dr. J. S. Powell	Brewton, Alabama
Dr. L. F. Pritchett	Thomasville, Alabama
Dr. C. W. M. Ressijac	Mobile, Alabama
Dr. B. E. Sawyer	Gallion, Alabama
Dr. W. D. Staples	Anniston, Alabama
Dr. J. E. Threadgill	Troy, Alabama
Dr. W. W. Webb	Auburn, Alabama
Dr. F. P. Woolf	Mobile, Alabama

One provision of the Veterinary Practice Law of Alabama held that non-graduate veterinary practitioners would have one year from the date the practice law was enacted (March 17, 1915, until March 16, 1916) to make application to the ASBVM for a non-graduate permit to practice veterinary medicine and surgery in Alabama. These non-graduate practitioners were to provide proof that they had practiced for at least three years prior to the practice law's enactment date, as well as evidence of good moral character. While not ideal, this approach was, in the view of board members—and possibly in the eyes of legislators—a fair way of dealing with men who were making a living the best they could and who represented the last of an era. During this meeting, eight non-graduate applicants for such permits were considered. Seven of those non-graduate applicants were granted permits to practice under the established conditions. Those included:

C. A. Calhoun	Lockhart, Alabama	three years in practice
John Evans	Birmingham, Alabama	twelve years in practice
W. A. Harris	Tuscaloosa, Alabama	seven years in practice
R. D. Johnson	Elba, Alabama	ten years in practice
William Palmer	Jasper, Alabama	three years in practice
C. H. Priester	Fort Deposit, Alabama	twenty-five years in practice
W. E. Torbert	Greensboro, Alabama	twenty-five years in practice

The board decided to meet during August 20-21, 1915, at the Moulton Hotel and instructed Secretary Cary to place notices in the designated newspapers' August 15 editions.

Meetings of the board for the next several decades followed and adhered to Robert's Rules of Order and saw the board typically acting to prohibit non-permit-holding, non-graduates from practicing veterinary medicine and surgery in Alabama. Other issues included ordering non-graduate men, who had been granted permits to practice in the state, to cease their use of professional titles, such as "Veterinary Surgeon," "Doctor of Veterinary Surgery," "Doctor of Veterinary Medicine," "Medical Doctor of Veterinary," and the like. These folks also were to cease issuing health certificates, and they were not to take out "illuminated advertisements" in any publication that would give the impression they were on par with graduate veterinarians.

A special notice was published to gain the attention of all blacksmiths and farriers, alerting them that it was illegal for them to operate on the feet or any other part of animals, or to attempt to treat diseases, injuries, or other ailments of domestic animals.

The board met in Auburn during June 9-10, 1916, and denied several applications for permits to practice veterinary medicine and surgery. Their reasoning was that the one-year time period, delineated in the Veterinary Practice Law of Alabama, had expired, and some applicants had not met the March 16, 1916, deadline. This decision and subsequent decisions to enforce strictly the law's provisions caused considerable anger among non-permit-holding, non-graduate veterinary practitioners.

During the 1919 regular session of the Alabama Legislature, legislation known as the McDowell Amendment to the Veterinary Practice Law of Alabama was passed and subsequently signed into law by Governor Thomas Kilby. This amendment allowed non-graduate permit applicants an additional six months—from February 17, 1919, until

August 17, 1919—to make application to the ASBVM for a permit to practice in Alabama. A special, called meeting of the ASBVM was held at the Moulton Hotel on April 25, 1919, for board members to review the methods through which applicants should apply for permits. They decided, and a notice was published, that

> All applicants for a permit to practice veterinary medicine and surgery under the McDowell Amendment of 1919 shall present to the Secretary of the ASBVM sworn statements, giving the length of time of practice, evidence from five (5) writers, stating that the applicant had practiced in Alabama from 1912 to 1919 inclusive, evidence of good moral character and the $15.00 license fee. All of these requirements shall be as near as possible the same as were required of applicants for permits when the original law was passed.

At the next regularly scheduled meeting of the ASBVM in Auburn on June 5, 1919, nine non-graduate applicants were granted permits to practice veterinary medicine and surgery under the provisions of the McDowell Amendment. Later that year, at a meeting in Birmingham on December 11, 1919, seven additional applicants—who had filed applications prior to the August 17, 1919, deadline—were granted permits under provisions of the McDowell Amendment.

After the six-month period provided in the McDowell Amendment for issuing permits to non-graduates to practice had expired, other applicants petitioned the ASBVM for permits and were denied. Some of these applicants were particularly vocal and persistent, and their petitions reached some state legislators. This situation simmered for years, the result that, on July 22, 1931, Governor Benjamin M. Miller signed into law a special act of the Alabama Legislature which allowed non-graduate practitioners an additional period of thirty days to apply to the board for a permit to practice veterinary medicine and surgery in Alabama. At a special meeting of the board, on August 22, 1931, James Monroe Abney of Lafayette was granted a permit to practice in Alabama. He was the last non-graduate veterinarian to be issued a permit to practice under "grandfather clauses" of state law.

Always concerned about public health, at the November 14, 1921, meeting in Birmingham, the board unanimously had passed a motion stating that

Milk and meat inspection are specific kinds of work or practice of graduate veterinarians who have been granted a state license from the ASBVM, according to the law approved March 17, 1915.

At the May 23, 1929, meeting, this position was reaffirmed when the board passed the following statement:

Both milk and meat inspections are functions of graduate veterinary practitioners. All meat and milk inspectors and all directors or supervisors of inspectors must be graduate veterinarians who have obtained a license to practice veterinary medicine and surgery in Alabama from the ASBVM.

The board's November 2, 1933, meeting at the Moulton Hotel produced an even stronger unanimous statement:

Hereafter, it will be the policy of the ASBVM to revoke the license of the veterinarian who endorses or recommends a layman, a quack, a permit man or a non-graduate veterinarian for a position as a meat or milk inspector in Alabama.

Over the years, there have been several unique decisions made by the board. In 1917, the board authorized Dr. Cary to purchase a $1,000 Liberty Bond in support of the war effort. In 1919, the board voted unanimously not to collect annual license renewal fees from veterinarians who were licensed to practice in Alabama but who were not actually practicing in Alabama. In June 1920, licenses issued to graduate veterinarians were numbered for the first time. Licenses that year began with number 150, that particular license issued to Dr. W. A. Fuqua of Clayton, Alabama, a member of the API Class of 1920. In 1924, the board authorized the purchase of a $1,000 Alabama Road Bond. In 1928, Board Secretary Dr. Cary was directed to write the Birmingham Humane Society and suggest that this organization employ a graduate veterinarian to provide veterinary care at its shelter.

During the first sixteen years of board activity, applications of several graduate veterinarians for licenses and the applications of numerous non-graduate applicants for permits were denied for a variety of reasons. During the board's November 1930 meeting, it became the unhappy duty of all five members present to revoke a veterinarian's license because of malpractice.

In an extraordinary act of generosity, the board voted at its November 14, 1935, meeting to donate the sum of $800 to the API School of Veterinary Medicine for the purchase of an x-ray machine to be used in the school's clinics. As Dr. Cary had died seven months earlier, the group likely made this contribution as a memorial tribute to its first secretary/treasurer and the founding father of veterinary medicine in the South.

Another problem the early veterinary examining boards faced—an issue that has persisted into modern times—was in collecting payment of license and permit renewal fees. Though the license and permit renewal fee was only $1, many holders regularly failed to pay. The board suspended payment of license and permit renewal fees beginning in January 1918 until the end of World War I and the return of soldier veterinarians, but some were in arrears through 1917 and continued in arrears for years following the war. Some practitioners owed as many as seven years' worth of fees before the ASBVM threatened to take action against them, action that was allowed in the Veterinary Practice Law of Alabama. Finally, after dealing patiently with delinquent men for years, the board voted at its November 14, 1928, meeting in Birmingham to remove from the rolls and revoke the permits of four permit-holding men and one graduate veterinarian. Board members hoped this decisive action would end the problem with delinquent license and permit renewal fees.

Governor Charles Henderson had announced on May 5, 1916, that he had re-appointed Dr. Cary to the ASBVM for another five-year term. As the years passed, Dr. Cary's importance and value to the board was appreciated by several other governors, and he was appointed to additional five-year terms in 1921 by Governor Thomas Kilby, in 1926 by Governor William W. Brandon, and in 1931 by Governor Benjamin M. Miller.

Sometime early in 1934, Dr. Cary, having reached or about to observe his seventy-second birthday, gave notice that he would not seek or accept a further appointment to the board following completion of his present term, which was to run into 1936. The governor and the other board members accepted his plan, realizing they soon would have to carry on without the imposing figure who had been with them—and with all aspects of veterinary medicine in Alabama—from the beginning. But one can assume they were counting on his counsel for a few more years.

Still, the time seemed right to them to pay tribute to Dr. Cary in recognition of his years of leadership and service in the many areas of veterinary medicine, veterinary education, in the livestock industry, and in public health in Alabama. During the May 31-June 1, 1934, meeting in Auburn, the board passed the following resolution:

Whereas: The Alabama Veterinary Medical Association, the citizens of the town of Auburn, interested and leading citizens of the State of Alabama and the Alumni of the School of Veterinary Medicine have decided to erect a tablet memorializing the great work done by Dr. Charles Allen Cary in Veterinary Medicine and in the promotion of the livestock industry of the south, and;

Whereas: It is considered right and proper by this Board that such a life given so freely and effectively for the public welfare should thus be recognized;

Therefore, Be it Resolved: That the Alabama State Board of Veterinary Medicine joins with others in commending this great man, his high sense of honor, his life of service to all, and;

Be it Further Resolved: That the Secretary-Treasurer shall, upon the request of The Chairman of this Board, pay from any funds now on hand, the amount not otherwise subscribed to accomplish the erection of this memorial, including the painting of the subject's picture to be presented to the State of Alabama; and the Chairman of the Board shall cooperate with the committee from the Alabama Veterinary Medical Association to the end that the work may be completed by February 10, 1935. The funds herein are to be made available at once upon the call of the Chairman of the Board. All members of the Alabama State Board of Veterinary Medicine voted for this resolution, except for the Secretary-Treasurer.

Dr. Cary did not live out his final term with the board. His twenty years of service as a member of the Alabama State Board of Veterinary Medicine ended with his death sometime after going to bed on Tuesday night, April 23, 1935. Wife Emma Cary sent a concise but stunning telegram through The Western Union Telegraph Company on April 24 to fifteen important colleagues across the nation—the roster of which has been lost—which read, "Doctor Cary found dead in bed this morning." The telegram was signed, "Mrs. C. A. Cary."

Dr. Cary was succeeded not only as dean of the School of Veterinary Medicine at API by Dr. Isaac Sadler McAdory, but Dr. McAdory subsequently was appointed to Dr. Cary's seat on the ASBVM by Governor Bibb Graves. Dr. McAdory's first meeting came on May 29, 1935—

a little more than a month after Dr. Cary's death—and he was elected to the secretary-treasurer post Dr. Cary had held for years. [*End of Dr. Hayes' excerpt*]

CHAPTER FOURTEEN

TEXAS TICK FEVER

Given the emergence and spread of various maladies common to farm and food animals both before and during Dr. Cary's lifetime, it makes sense that he learned from an early age the devastation caused by tick fever, brucellosis, cholera, tuberculosis, and other deadly or economy-damaging diseases. His training in veterinary school at Iowa State likely included instruction on the nature and potential cures of these diseases. In fact, one can assume Professors Stalker and Fairchild spent considerable time in class, the laboratory, and clinic discussing what they knew or suspected about these diseases.

When Dr. Cary arrived in Auburn, he found an economy that had been dependent on cotton farming, but which was headed for disaster because of the crop-killing boll weevil. He and many others recognized the need for expanded and re-constructed cattle and hog industries, but they faced long odds in accomplishing this turnaround.

In the decade following the Civil War, Alabama's horse and mule population dwindled by a third. Hog totals were halved, and the number of cattle declined from around 750,000 to fewer than half a million. The war's toll can be blamed for much of this loss, with younger men leaving farms to serve in the armed forces, many never to return. The results reduced the work force as well as took a toll on Southern infrastructure, such as it was. Some of the reduced farm animal numbers also can be attributed to theft by soldiers on both sides. Diseases such as those mentioned took others.[1]

A few generations would pass before the cattle industry in Alabama reached its peak, but a foundation for the booming years following World War II was laid in the first couple of decades of the twentieth century. Dr. Cary led many of the efforts that brought success.

Dr. Cary was aided, of course, with some changes and improvements that had taken place before his arrival in 1892. The establishment of the land-grant college at Auburn in 1872 and the federal government's campaign for eradicating the fever tick about the time of Dr. Cary's arrival were key. Increasingly, state and federal officials collaborated with private citizens to apply advances in science and technology to problems of the day. In time, the introduction of purebred British breeds aided the cattle industry, as did the move toward enclosed and improved pastures, winter forage feeding, professional veterinary care, and improved care for animals. With these enhancements, many Alabama farms bade farewell to the days of open-range drovers and landless stock raisers.

The Texas fever or cattle tick arrived on Spanish cattle brought by sixteenth-century explorers and spread through much of the country, particularly on trail drives from Texas into the Midwest. The cattle tick can bring with it the parasite *Babesia bigemina* which can cause the deadly fever. Northern winter temperatures typically killed the ticks that migrated there, but the ticks thrived in the milder, more humid South. This parasite destroys red corpuscles in the cow's bloodstream that are required to break up waste material. Within a week to ten days, infected cattle can show signs of high fever, loss of appetite, coughing, weakness, loss of flesh, accelerated breathing, and other symptoms of ill health. Early methods of eradication included cleaning cattle with oils, dipping them in arsenical or coal/tar solutions, or simply removing the ticks by hand. Dr. Cary, his team of assistant state veterinarians, and the many individuals on duty through the Bureau of Animal Industry spent years promoting and conducting the dipping method in every county of Alabama, which eventually worked to systematically de-tick the state.[2]

Federal attention to tick fever began, in a sense, with the government enlisting a British veterinarian named John Gamgee in 1868 to investigate several animal diseases around the country. He helped, at least in regard to some of the diseases and to veterinary medicine in general, but he didn't solve the tick fever problem.[3] In 1879, Dr. Daniel E. Salmon, the first recipient of a US-awarded DVM degree, was appointed to a position in the United States Department of Agriculture to bring a heavier hand to solving animal diseases. Dr. Salmon, in 1884, was named the first director when the USDA created the Bureau of Animal Industry.

In working on the tick fever problem, Dr. Salmon studied the geography of the disease and established a quarantine line that, in essence, kept cattle from being transported out of the South, at least until some protocols for regulating and inspecting cattle were put into place. The quarantine line, which would be adjusted a few times during the next several years, put Southern cattlemen at a disadvantage. An estimated fifteen million-plus cattle were kept within the quarantined area, with a little more than 20 percent of those east of the Mississippi River. Many cattle owners undoubtedly entered the business with the idea of shipping their animals off for sale. Tick fever cost ranchers collectively many millions of dollars every year. The disease was no bargain for the cattle victims, either, with estimates of 400,000 cattle dying of tick fever annually during this era.

US Forest Service Archaeologist Robert G. Pasquill, Jr., described in a highly detailed, online book-length document, *Arsenic and Old Bovine Lace—History of the Cattle Tick Eradication Program in the South*, the quarantine line as "the northern line along the thirty-seventh parallel, excepting along the eastern slope of the country where it extended halfway between the thirty-eighth and thirty-ninth parallels of latitude."[4] The thirty-seventh parallel is that line roughly along the northern borders of, from the east, North Carolina, Tennessee, Arkansas, Oklahoma, the Texas panhandle, New Mexico, Arizona, and on through the middle of California.

Between 1899 and 1906, state and federal authorities collaborated to free a dozen counties in North Carolina from federal quarantine. In 1906, Congress approved $82,500 for the USDA's plan to battle the disease by sharing costs and resources with the Southern states plus California.[5] This "Cattle Fever Tick Eradication Program" empowered the secretary of agriculture, James Wilson (1835-1920)—a former professor of agriculture at Iowa State University where in the 1890s he taught George Washington Carver—to initiate a plan for far greater state and federal cooperation on the problem, with the USDA supplying trained supervisors or tick inspectors in participating counties in a number of Southern states. Of course, the work expanded as the years went on, and federal costs rose. As success was confirmed, counties were released from the quarantine. Ideally, release was to happen in a north-to-south direction, with the government gradually moving the quarantine line south until ticks were eradicated.

Dr. Cary had been fighting tick fever for some time when, in December 1906, he attended a conference in Nashville dedicated to tick eradication. He told that gathering that the work he had done in this regard in 1906 had been difficult, with the Bureau of Animal Industry alone providing funding. Someone in Alabama's state government apparently had promised to match the BAI's financial commitment, but whichever state office was supposed to pay up did not come through. Thus, the work was performed in only two Alabama counties. With no state sanitation law in place yet to demand such work, his efforts largely focused on educating the population through Farmers' Institutes and other meetings.[6]

On March 12, 1907, the Alabama Legislature approved the state's first livestock sanitary law—authored and championed by Dr. Cary— which authorized cooperation with the BAI and which launched tick eradication programs in Madison and Limestone Counties in North Alabama. The early work also was supposed to start in Baldwin County, but farmers there met and made clear they did not wish to have cattle tick eradication efforts performed on their farms. These farmers got their way, at least for a while. Five months after passing the livestock sanitary law, state legislators—under threat of being voted out of office by the farmers back home—declared through an August 6, 1907, amendment their original livestock sanitary law inoperative in counties with more than half their lands in open-range districts. State Veterinarian Cary advised veterinary officials to carry on the project in those counties subject to stock laws, namely in the Black Belt and in the Tennessee Valley.[7] (See Chapter 12 within the *1907 Annual Report from the State Veterinarian* for more on the legislative amendment.)

Clearly, more public education was needed. Ahead of the amendment, and to boost the chances of success for himself and for the wave of state and Bureau of Animal Industry veterinary inspectors who had begun traveling the state to stamp out the tick, Dr. Cary authored Agricultural Experiment Station *Bulletin Number 141* in July 1907. This publication offered the public—including legislators—an extensive overview of the tick fever problem and served as an introduction in many corners to this tick and the disease it carried.

Dr. Cary's eighty-page tract provided a detailed scientific history of the disease and of veterinary science's pursuit of it, plus a life history of the tick itself. Several illustrations and descriptions identified the ticks known for carrying the disease. Dr. Cary described what happened to an animal contracting the ailment and how veterinarians diagnosed tick fever. *Bulletin 141* rehashed some state testing records. The author presented the clear and presumably obvious economic reasons for the state's need to eradicate these ticks and explained exactly how veterinarians proposed to wipe them out. Dr. Cary included hand-drawn proposals on how a farmer should structure his fields and pastures for crop rotation to minimize the presence of ticks. His (or somebody's) drawings showed how the constructed dipping vat should look, and included specific instructions on how to build the vat. He also suggested appropriate grasses for pastures. The exhaustive booklet concluded with a reprint of the Legislature's act which created the Live Stock Sanitary Board in Alabama and the office of state veterinarian, reminding readers that Dr. Cary now had the legal authority to direct all tick eradication in Alabama.[8]

Before the widespread use of cattle dipping vats, veterinarians and farmers tried a number of methods for killing or evading the ticks: pasture rotation to remove the host and starve the tick, time-consuming application by hand or by spray of various types of oils that would have either poisoned or stymied the tick. The most commonly used substances were various combinations of lard, kerosene, and cotton-seed oil. The most effective substance up to this time had been crude petroleum. They also tried removing the ticks by hand—Dr. Cary and others suggested feeding them to chickens before the ticks could lay eggs—and finally the dipping vat.[9] Eventually, the dipping vat proved the most effective method, with an arsenic-based mixture, though questions then arose about who would pay for the components and construction costs. Also, how were authorities to convince rural farmers that dipping their personal livestock in poison was a good idea?

One wonders what went through Dr. Cary's mind as he and his fellow tick eradicators met, at practically every turn, people opposed to their efforts. Farmers, spurred by agricultural leaders, often refused to cooperate with the dipping mandate. Some turned violent.

After substantial initial resistance, Dr. Cary continued to lobby for a statewide mandatory tick eradication law, but that legislation would not pass until 1919. In the meantime, as secretary of the State Live Stock Sanitary Board and as state veterinarian, he directed the program in stock law counties.

Dr. Cary made his thoughts plain enough in remarks to the Alabama Live Stock Association's annual convention, held January 13-14, 1911, in Montgomery, when he told those gathered:

The dairy business in Alabama awaits development. It is an inviting and open field and it requires expert intelligence and regular and careful work to make it a success. The beef cattle industry is adapted to almost every farm in Alabama and it should be nurtured, encouraged and developed.

The chief obstacle to the dairy and beef cattle industry in the South is the cattle tick. But the government, the state and the county authorities are awakening to the necessity of eradicating the cattle tick and all of its train of damages to our cattle industry. The verdict has gone forth that the cattle tick must be eradicated and it must and will be done. How soon will depend upon the interest and activities of the farmers—the parties directly interested.[10]

Not everyone was impressed or shared his will to fight this tick. A headline in the *Montgomery Advertiser* in June 1911 read, "Tick Eradication in Alabama Fails." That failure may be laid at the feet of the Legislature—neither the first nor last time that would happen—in part, for its amendment of the 1907 livestock sanitary law. But the work went on, one step at a time.

Later, as plans were made for continuing the federal funding for 1913, the US House of Representatives' Committee on Agriculture called for a group of leading Southern veterinarians and agricultural leaders to appear in Washington, DC, to report on tick eradication progress and to help the representatives understand what could be accomplished with more federal dollars. This congressional hearing on Monday, December 9, 1912, brought to the US Capitol a "Who's Who" of the early days of Southern veterinary medicine and many of Dr. Cary's closest professional associates: Dr. W. H. Dalrymple, state veterinarian of Louisiana; Dr. George R. White of Nashville; Dr. Peter Bahnsen, state veterinarian of Georgia; Alabama Commissioner of Agriculture Reuben F. Kolb; Archibald Smith of the State Agricultural College of Mississippi; Dr. C. F. Dawson, state veterinarian of Florida; Dr. W. G. Christman, state veterinarian of North Carolina; Dr. J. F. Stamford, state veterinarian of Arkansas; and Dr. Cary. The Auburn leader was the day's final speaker, and he reminded the congressmen that, while progress had been attained, the work was far from complete. He called for year-round work, not the summer-only attention the ticks were getting. Dr. Cary told them that in six years of quarantine work, about one-third of the infested areas had been cleared of ticks, and that continued work was critical to finish the job.[11]

Whether before or after this December hearing is unclear, but Dr. Cary was asked to chair a federally appointed committee on tick eradication, and he, Commissioner Kolb, and others from the committee (predominantly those who had traveled to Washington, DC, as listed above) were asked to return to Washington the first week of January 1913 for continued talks. Committee members met with a US Senate Committee on Agriculture and Forestry on Saturday, January 4, 1913, and requested an increase in federal tick eradication funding from $250,000 to $750,000 annually. Dr. Cary urged senators to support public education. "You have to educate the people in an appreciation of these things, because the people did not know why the tick injured the cattle," he told them.[12]

Dr. Cary authored a portion of Alabama Agricultural Experiment Station *Bulletin Number 171* on "Dipping Vats and Dips," which came out in February 1913. He based information on his experiences in the fields and pastures, having tried various options before he and others fighting this battle determined the best approach. In his one-paragraph preamble to *Bulletin 171*, Dr. Cary explained the multi-year nature of the investigation:

> At my request the Bureau of Animal Industry, Zoological Division, under Dr. B. H. Ransom, decided to undertake the investigation of the biology of the Texas fever tick in co-operation with the Veterinary Department of the Alabama Polytechnic Institute at Auburn, Ala. This work was carried on during 1907 and 1908. Mr. H. W. Graybill had direct charge of the work and was assisted by Mr. W. M. Lewallen, both of whom were paid by the Bureau of Animal Industry. The Veterinary Department furnished the place and the material for the work. The agreement between the Bureau and the Veterinary Department of The Alabama Polytechnic Institute was that this co-operative work could be published by both the Bureau of Animal Industry and the Experiment Station of the College. I, therefore, publish this part of the report that will be of value to Alabama farmers in the eradication of the cattle tick. In addition to this report will be found specifications and plans for dipping vats, the arsenical dip and the oil emulsion that is also used in killing ticks. It is anticipated that this bulletin, as a whole, will be of great value to the farmers of Alabama in the work of tick eradication.[13]

BAI investigators H. W. Graybill and M. W. Lewallen wrote on the biology of this tick and reminded their audience of the nature of the disease the tick caused, the damage done, and the steps the federal government had taken for many years by this time to control its harm to the various states' cattle industries. Dr. Cary followed in *Bulletin 171* with his extensive description of dipping vats and arsenic dips, including precise directions on building the vats and mixing the dip. The bulletin was made available to cattle farmers throughout Alabama to teach the lay audience the science behind the plan of attack. Dr. Cary spelled out the various lumber and cement components needed for construction of an adequate-sized vat and adjoining chute. While Dr. Cary's best intentions would not have flown with modern environmental concerns—

old dip can be run or poured into a large run or brook or creek when the latter is full of running water that will quickly dilute the solution. The sediment in the bottom of the tank should be carefully placed in some hole in the ground away from wells or drinking water. It would be safe to throw it into a creek that has a good flow of water

—his instructions for building the vats, mixing the poison, and applying it to the cattle worked when followed by the state and BAI investigating veterinarians and their farmer clients.[14] Alas, replication of the formula was not always assured, especially in the early days.

Lee County historian Alexander Nunn, in a 1968 book called *Yesterdays in Loachapoka*, described the cattle dipping process:

To see a cow leap wildly into the vat with tail high in the air and then to be forced to push and shove the next animal off the slope into the liquid dip was an experience never to be forgotten.[15]

Toward and into the 1920s, as federal and state veterinary inspectors put hundreds and thousands of miles on their buggies or new cars, Alabama counties would be released from the federal quarantine, and occasionally put back in it. During this time, Alabama's rural landscape featured thousands of these dipping vats, and millions of cattle were being dipped regularly, with the protocol calling for a cow or bull to be dipped every two weeks. (Chapter 12, related to Dr. Cary's annual reports as state veterinarian, details many yearly totals.) This work, of course, was going on in every Southern state. As an example of the progress that had been made, all sixty-seven Alabama counties were infected with ticks when the BAI program launched in 1906. By the end of 1918, twenty-four Alabama counties remained "ticky," to use Dr. Cary's expression. Forty-three of Alabama's counties by this time had been released from the economically oppressive quarantine. This feat may be considered especially meaningful when one remembers the First World War was taking place at this time, occupying America's attention and requiring many of its personal and financial resources.

Dr. Cary's situation in Alabama was aided in 1914 by the election of a progressive governor named Charles Henderson (1860-1937), who had previously served twenty years as mayor of Troy. Henderson, like Dr. Cary, was a proponent of agricultural diversification.[16]

In January 1915, less than four years after that fateful *Montgomery Advertiser* headline appeared, a combined meeting of the Montgomery Cattlemen's Club, the Southern Cattlemen's Association, the Alabama Live Stock Association, and the Blackbelt Live Stock Association resulted in the launch of a "State Campaign for the Eradication of the Cattle Tick." Dr. Cary headed the new committee and drafted a bill that the Legislature would approve.

Ten representatives from that meeting later visited with Governor Henderson at his home in Troy and told him the quarantined sections of the South were losing 20 percent of the value of their cattle annually because of the pest. (Two years earlier, cattlemen in non-quarantine counties had reported a market increase of $7.70 per cow.) Another significant step—though it was, in essence, passing the buck—took place on March 15, 1915, when the Alabama Legislature approved a bill that allowed elections in each county to determine whether tick eradication work performed under direction of the Alabama Live Stock Sanitary Board would be welcomed. A later clarification explained that elections were not always necessary, and that voluntary cattle dipping could certainly take place. Ten days after the Legislature approved that election option, the body approved $25,000 annually for the next four years for the Live Stock Sanitary Board's work in eradicating the cattle tick.[17]

Governor Henderson, the progressive, declared the week beginning April 26, 1915, as "Tick Eradication Week" in Alabama.[18] Positive stories on tick eradication efforts began appearing in the state's newspapers with more regularity. The beleaguered state veterinarian may have gotten caught up in the euphoria, as he was quoted in the *Tuscaloosa*

News and Times Gazette in its edition of April 13, 1915, as predicting, "No more ticks in Alabama after 1920"—a line he suggested the state adopt as a motto in this campaign.[19]

With this collective enthusiasm, and the coming of the boll weevil, the timing was right to tackle this tick once and for all in Alabama. While many farmers, and their cattle, were cooperating with the veterinarians—reportedly, 387,925 cattle were dipped in the 1,100-plus vats in nine participating Alabama counties during June 1915 alone—there remained opposition. There was a detrimental lawsuit here, an anti-dipping letter to the editor there, and access to dynamite seemingly everywhere. In July 1915, someone in Colbert County used dynamite to destroy two dipping vats, and another party dynamited three vats in Perry County. An alarming pattern emerged throughout the state, though in most cases, destroyed vats were rebuilt.[20]

The effort continued to see progress through 1916, with hundreds of dipping vats being constructed in various counties. Two years later, in 1918, the number of vats throughout Alabama totaled 6,638. Counties were being cleared of the tick and removed from the quarantine. Cattle were shipped out of state, and dipped cattle were selling for $7 more per head than they brought before dipping. Thus, some cattlemen in the right places were making money in what had been a devastated industry. The total number of cattle dipped in Alabama during May 1916 was estimated at 739,357, and that number would increase by almost 20,000 in August. Late that summer, three vats were dynamited in different locations of Jefferson County, but the good far outweighed the bad: by the end of the year, one-third of Alabama would be out of the quarantine.

Similar progress marked 1917 in the state: by this year's end, approximately 61 percent of Alabama's land—totaling thirty-nine counties—was out of the quarantine. The country's involvement in the World War at this time made production of quality beef, milk, and butter all the more important. Transportation of non-dipped cattle was not nearly as cost effective as shipping the more valuable, certifiably tick-free cattle. To this end, the Dr. Cary-led Alabama Live Stock Sanitary Board toward the end of that year "ordered transportation and railroad companies to close their stock pens and cattle chutes in all counties that had not taken up a tick eradication program." Similar regulations in surrounding states also made operations more stringent for the industry.[21]

Into 1918, more vats were constructed, and cattlemen in increasing numbers of Alabama locations shipped their cattle for sale out of state. Owners were getting good prices for their stock, record prices on occasion. Alabama's cattle industry became the fastest-growing in the country. Other Southern states also were making excellent progress, all due to success in tick eradication. Perhaps some over-confidence began to creep in as Dr. Cary's annual report as state veterinarian for 1918 revealed that only four additional counties had been released from quarantine that year. In the most critical areas, only about a quarter of the needed dipping vats had been constructed. Another substantial push was needed to finish this job.

Despite progress, the eradication workers and veterinary inspectors continued to meet with resistance, and the opposition seemed to peak in 1919. The BAI had come up with a slogan for that year: "Make 1919 the worst year for the tick." The USDA topped that with a silent animated film, "Charge of the Tick Brigade," an eight-minute movie showing millions of marauding ticks killing Mr. and Mrs. Cow. This cartoon, plus a thirty-eight-minute silent movie from 1922 ("Mollic of Pine Grove Vat"), were shown throughout the South from some type of projector carried in USDA vehicles that visited communities far and wide. One or the other of these films may have been the first "moving pictures" many Southerners ever viewed.[22]

Some people, however, took the tick's side, or so their actions made it seem. There were a number of reports of violence in 1919 on the part of rural farmers in Alabama and other Southern states, including dynamite being used to blow up newly constructed vats and physical threats made against inspectors. Robert G. Pasquill, Jr., wrote of this era's violence:

> Opposition to the tick eradication program came primarily from the yeoman farmers. They tended to raise just enough cattle for subsistence, and had very little interest in the cattle markets. They viewed the government programs as being costly and political and of very little benefit to them. This opposition ranged from political opposition, such as the Anti-Dipping Association in Oklahoma, to violent expressions such as blowing up the cattle dipping vats with dynamite. By 1919, the destruction of cattle dipping vats with dynamite had drawn the attention of the United States Department of Interior's Bureau of Mines, and was reported in their 1921 Bulletin 198, reporting of the regulations of explosives. In 1919, a large number of cattle dipping vats were destroyed, particularly in Arkansas, Alabama and Georgia. The vats were most often destroyed

with dynamite. Between April 13th and May 30th a total of 72 cattle dipping vats were dynamited in Arkansas. This was the worst period of destruction of vats, consisting of 47 days, since Arkansas had passed the law requiring the dipping of cattle. Not only were the vats destroyed, the arsenic charge had been scattered, poisoning the ground around the vat site. Farmers and law-abiding citizens had been forced to use firearms to protect the dipping vats.[23]

Calling on his political acumen and basing his argument on the proven, recent economic success of tick-free cattle, Dr. Cary and other like-minded leaders persuaded the Legislature to pass a state-wide tick eradication law the first week of February 1919. This legislation required tick eradication work in any county not already completely rid of the ticks. County commissioners or local boards of revenue were authorized to ensure construction of dipping vats and procurement of the products used in mixing the dip as required by the Sanitary Board and the BAI. Those individuals were also responsible for keeping the vats filled and the cattle streaming through. The law—which reflected the thorough nature of Dr. Cary—held that all mules, horses, and donkeys maintained in tick-infested places were to join their cattle cousins in being dipped twice a month. The 1919 law also required all railroad cars that transported cattle in or through the state be cleaned and disinfected, with the railroad companies responsible for any related costs. Cash fines were established for those found violating these terms, including the cattle owner who did not dip his cattle.[24]

In the first few months of the state law's being in effect, 1,900 more dipping vats were built in Alabama, bringing the state's total to more than 7,800. Two-thirds of Alabama counties were free from the quarantine. June 1919 saw 994,275 cattle dipped in the state.

But, in various corners, the idea of state-mandated cooperation and compliance brought out the defiant nature of some. Dynamiting dipping vats was a federal offense, but that did not matter to three Etowah County men charged with this crime in June that year. In fact, the summer of 1919 was the summer of dynamite in Alabama as 112 vats were destroyed in this manner in thirteen counties, at first primarily in the northern half of the state. However, dynamiting took place throughout the state in those days and was such a menace that, in the spring of 1920, Alabama Governor Thomas Kilby approved a reward of $400 "for the arrest and conviction of any person proven guilty of destroying any dipping vat in the state."[25]

Dynamite or not, progress continued, and at the end of 1919, all or parts of nine more Alabama counties were released from the federal quarantine, freeing their cattlemen to ship and sell cattle to lucrative out-of-state markets. Dr. Cary's 1919 report confirmed 8,438 cattle dipping vats at work in Alabama, with 6,174,817 cattle dippings accomplished by the year's end. At this time, only nine percent of the state's land was still in quarantine.

Thanks to the law, progress continued through 1920, and as that year ended, only about six percent of Alabama remained under quarantine, according to Dr. Cary's annual report. Occasional lack of compliance on the part of county officials and cattlemen and a reduced number of dipping vats from 8,438 to 8,014 (whether through destruction or their not being used) slowed progress in 1920. Adding to the problems for Alabama was the situation with its southern border, with proximity to Florida counties that did not have the same applicable laws. Cattlemen may have known where the state lines were, but their cattle did not. Nor did the ticks.

The state almost had won the battle against the ticks, but completely shutting the door was proving nearly impossible. The middle years of the 1920s saw continued back-and-forth political squabbles with various county officials claiming they were out of money—they likely were—plus state border problems, the occasional destruction of vats, some counties re-quarantined, etc. The Alabama Legislature approved another law in 1927 requiring counties to ensure the presence of dipping vats and the products necessary for the arsenic mix. This law, adding teeth to the 1919 law, and the continued vigilance by the undeterred Dr. Cary and many others, resulted in all Alabama counties being removed from the federal quarantine by the end of 1929. Alabama thus became the tenth of the original fifteen quarantined states to have worked its way out of the federal restriction.[26]

Dr. Cary's role in the eradication of the cattle tick came on multiple levels, all of them vital to the cause. He continued to learn about this tick and its accompanying disease and impact on cattle during his entire professional life, and he shared his knowledge with those studying under him or working for the cause. He served as state veterinarian and as an officer of both the national and state Live Stock Sanitary Associations. In those roles, he received reports and statistics and compiled records—both financial and health-related—on the various aspects of the tick eradication work as Alabama and other states worked cooperatively with the USDA and the Bureau of Animal Industry. Those records became the bulk of annual reports he painstakingly authored every year from 1907 until the end of his life.

He was active politically, educating and advising the Alabama Legislature and working however he could to ensure passage of laws, especially the key bills of 1907, 1919, and 1927 which assured him and other officials the needed level of authority and which demanded compliance from cattlemen and public servants. He was among those who worked out the optimum timing for dipping and the appropriateness of the twice-monthly dipping schedule. He wrote letters and notices to the state's daily and weekly newspapers in an era when these were the chief methods of public communication. He spoke of tick eradication at the Farmers' Institutes he directed. He taught veterinary students. He collaborated with, supported, and advised the many veterinarians who inspected cattle in every community in the state. He provided for the continuing education for many of these practitioners with his short courses at Auburn.

Dr. Cary traveled constantly to attend veterinary meetings, cattlemen's meetings, meetings with farmers and county agents, Congressional hearings, and meetings with county commissioners on this subject, always in demand as a speaker to share his knowledge and his opinion. He probably built a few cattle dipping vats so he would know how it was done, and then he provided the building instructions to others through his Experiment Station bulletins. Tradition holds that he had a dipping vat at his home on North College Street in Auburn.

Eradicating the cattle tick was high on the list of challenges that brought Dr. Cary to Auburn in the first place. As to his accomplishments as he undertook those challenges, indeed as he matched his wits against the massive, multifaceted agenda brought about by those of the status quo when he launched his veterinary career in the South, a successor dean at Auburn—Dr. John Thomas Vaughan, API Class of 1955—wrote:

> Our first dean, Dr. Charles A. Cary, was instrumental in organizing and implementing the Texas Fever Eradication Campaign in 1906, the largest single undertaking of its kind up to that time. Until the eradication of the fever tick was completed . . . in the 1920s, it was impossible to raise cattle profitably in the southern United States. The billion dollar industry that Alabama can boast today owes its origins to men of Dr. Cary's generation who many times risked their personal safety to carry out their assignments. Much of the same story can be told about tuber-

culosis and Bang's disease, screw worms and hog cholera, tetanus, rabies, distemper, pullorum, exotic Newcastle's disease, parasites and diseases of every description that have opposed the progress of agriculture and the animal industry and have presented age-old threats to man. Today many of the diseases which were once accepted as inevitable can be prevented or controlled—thanks to the development of vaccines, therapeutic methods, improved nutrition and management practices that represent the contributions and combined efforts of animal scientists, veterinarians and medical doctors working together for the common good.[27]

Because of his role in the eradication of the tick in Alabama, as well as his work in eradicating tuberculosis from milk and meat products, Charles Allen Cary was, without question, the most influential non-cattleman in the modern Alabama cattle industry and perhaps the single most important figure of his era in regard to the Southern livestock industry. Untold numbers of people are alive today because their grandparents or great-grandparents did not die from tuberculosis in the early and middle years of the twentieth century. Numerous Alabamians have enjoyed excellent livelihoods from the cattle industry that can credit at least a part of its launch to the work of Dr. Cary and other veterinarians years ago.

Still, after the tick eradication program had gained great success in Alabama and throughout the South, Dr. Cary never let down his guard. One example of his continued vigilance can be seen in an article published in the *Auburn Plainsman* on October 11, 1930, which reported on Dr. Cary's inspecting the animals of the Ringling Brothers Circus before the massive entourage was brought into Alabama:

Dean C.A. Cary Inspects
World's Largest Circus
The Ringling Brothers Circus will move into Mobile and Montgomery this week with their animals; cages and cars reeking with the odor of disinfectant as the result of a visit paid the circus Saturday and Sunday by Dr. C. A. Cary, state veterinarian and dean of the school of veterinary medicine here. Dr. Cary visited the circus in New Orleans to ascertain whether the animals offered any threat for the reinfestation by the cattle tick in Alabama, as the show had toured tick infested areas in Texas and Louisiana, it was reported. Following an inspection of the animals and a conference with officials of the circus, more than 500 horses were sprayed, all cages were disinfected and all of the cars were cleaned and

disinfected under supervision of Dr. Cary and federal inspectors. "I am entirely satisfied," Dr. Cary said last night upon his return from New Orleans, "and the circus will show on schedule."[28]

How valuable was Dr. Cary's leadership in the years-long battle to eliminate the fever tick in Alabama? In a newspaper article eighteen months after Dr. Cary died, then-Extension Service Director Dr. Luther Noble Duncan said, "Dr. Cary devoted a lifetime to clearing Alabama of certain livestock disease and pests, thus paving the way for a sound and wise livestock production program. It is hardly possible to estimate the untold value of the notable work he did in freeing the State of the cattle tick. Someone has said that the value of this piece of work alone is worth more to the State than the total cost of the entire institution at Auburn has been to the State since it was founded."[29]

Charles Allen Cary was one of hundreds of heroes of the cattle tick eradication effort—joined by state and federal veterinarians, cooperating cattlemen and county officials, dipping vat builders, those who kept watch over the vats to ensure their continued viability, and the legislators who approved necessary laws. In the middle of the main street in Enterprise, Alabama, sits a famous monument to the boll weevil, noting that insect's role in prompting a change to more diverse farming and food animal production in Alabama. Somewhere, a monument should exist to remember the heroes whose determination through many years eventually led to eradication of the cattle tick in Alabama. Perhaps the continued vitality of the cattle industry in Alabama and the strong organization that is today's Alabama Cattlemen's Association represent such a monument.

The USDA declared the cattle tick and its resulting *bovine babesiosis* eradicated in the United States in 1943, but some of the ticks and parasites never got the memo. The disease continues to crop up on occasion. In fact, a news report published in the online *San Antonio Express-News* on April 22, 2016, carried the ominous headline, "Cattle tick spread may be worst in 73 years."[30] The accompanying story blamed the spread on a type of antelope that had been imported from Asia for zoos and occasionally "let loose for trophy hunts on Texas ranches." Host cattle that have never been exposed or immunized are more susceptible to the disease if infected. Thus, the work of early eradication pioneers did the job, but did not necessarily close the door forever on this menace.

CHAPTER FIFTEEN

FIGHTING HOG CHOLERA

Hog cholera, in its 140-year run in the United States, killed more hogs than any other disease. Was hog cholera native to the United States? Opinions differ. The first references to this malady date to the 1830s in parts of Ohio and Indiana. The name cholera may have come from its appearance coinciding with an outbreak of Asian cholera at about the same time and proximity. By 1860—two years before the establishment of the US Department of Agriculture—the agriculture division of the US Patent Office had made the public aware of the prevalence of the disease within the nation's hog populations. Some held that hogs bred in the United States took the disease to Europe through trade and export; across the Atlantic, folks referred to this same disease as "swine fever."[1] But the Bureau of Animal Industry, formed in 1884 to meet this menace, among others, held that hog cholera may have come to the US from Europe in some of the hogs that were imported for the purpose of enhancing the domestic breeds.[2]

In the early days of hog-raising in the United States, these animals were apparently largely free from disease, at least from herd-depleting illnesses. Those "early days" began quite early, in fact. Spanish explorer Hernando de Soto and his troops brought the first hogs into what became the United States as they moved animals from Cuba to today's

Florida in the 1530s. Hog populations in the American Northeast came later, brought by British and Dutch explorers and colonists in the seventeenth century.[3]

An outbreak of what later was deemed hog cholera erupted in southern Ohio on one or more farms along the Muskingum River in 1833. This disorder was followed by a like disturbance in South Carolina in 1837, a flare-up in Georgia in 1838, then by outbreaks in 1840 in Alabama, Florida, Illinois, and Indiana. A disease with hog cholera's characteristics emerged in North Carolina in 1843 and in New York in 1844. The next year, a Kentucky community was hit. These outbreaks were contained within single counties in each of these states.[4]

The Bureau of Animal Industry, organized a half-century later, confirmed in an 1889 report only those ten outbreaks between 1833 and 1845, but acknowledged ninety-three instances of the disease on hog farms during the following ten years, from 1846 to 1855. Those outbreaks took place in North Carolina, Georgia, Illinois, Kentucky, Virginia, Indiana, Tennessee, Missouri, Ohio, and Texas. The BAI report noted that "there can be little doubt that between 1846-1855 hog cholera became scattered over the country . . . ."[5]

The Agricultural Research Service claimed that outbreaks in 1886, 1887—concurrent with Dr. Cary's enrollment in veterinary school in Iowa—and in 1896 each resulted in the loss of 13 percent of the country's hog populations.[6] Hog cholera had spread through most of the country by the late 1890s. By 1889, when Dr. Cary was practicing in Keokuk, Iowa, the BAI estimated the financial losses caused by hog cholera to be upwards of $25 million annually across the land.[7]

Dr. Cary, in an essay he authored for Alabama Commissioner of Agriculture Reuben F. Kolb in that officer's annual report of 1913, estimated that Alabama farmers had sustained almost unthinkable losses from hog cholera. He wrote, "During 1910 the farmers of Alabama lost $500,000 from ravages of hog cholera and in 1912 the loss from hog cholera in Alabama was $1,000,000. For 1913 the loss from the same hog disease will equal or exceed that of 1912."[8]

This menace would impact hog farmers and the public until the agricultural and veterinary medical authorities got things under control in the 1950s, a generation after Dr. Cary died. A few outbreaks took place through the 1960s and into the early 1970s; but, finally, on the last day of January 1978, US Secretary of Agriculture Robert Bergland declared the nation free of hog cholera.[9]

The disease itself is caused by a virus in the blood, urine, feces, and in secretions of the eyes and noses of affected hogs. It is highly contagious, and the nature of communal hog farming took the malady from animal to animal in short order. Hogs inflicted with the acute variety died quickly. A chronic version of the disease took longer to kill victims—weeks or months of increasing misery and debilitation before the animal died.

As with Texas fever and bovine tuberculosis, Dr. Cary spent a significant portion of his time and energy as dean of the college at Auburn, as state veterinarian, and as an active member of both the Alabama and American Veterinary Medical Associations working toward solving hog cholera. In fact, he had gotten involved first-hand with the state's swine producers early in his Auburn tenure. The January 25, 1899, issue of the *Orange and Blue* student newspaper published notice of the Alabama Swine Breeders Association meeting at Auburn during February 14-15 that year, and mentioned that Dr. Cary was serving as president of that organization. (The newspaper promised that "Some of the finest hogs in the state will be there.")

One of Dr. Cary's chief efforts was in bringing instruction related to hog cholera to his students and to practicing veterinarians through speakers at the short courses he and the college hosted each year. The other major step toward resolving hog cholera for Alabama and regional hog farmers was Dr. Cary's pursuit of an anti-hog cholera serum plant for the Auburn campus. He spoke consistently on this subject to anyone who would listen, particularly as the quality of vac cine and its proven effectiveness became obvious. One example may be found in Dr. Cary's speech as president of the Alabama Live Stock Association at the group's annual meeting held February 25-26, 1910, in Montgomery. His comments were reprinted in the proceedings of that association. President Cary on that occasion said:

> Hog cholera has injured the hog industry in Alabama during the past year, but not so extensively as during 1908. It is now quite certain that the serum treatment will prevent this disease and check outbreaks. The state should supply the funds for the preparation and free distribution of the serum to the farmers.[10]

Dr. Cary expanded on those thoughts at the Live Stock Association's meeting the next year:

> No country or land in the world can make pork at less cost than Ala-

bama. The government and the state must protect the industry—especially from the ravages of disease. Right here, let me say that the State Legislature should appropriate from $3,000 to $4,000 for the Live Stock Sanitary Board of Alabama to be used in maintaining a hog cholera serum plant where hog cholera serum may be made and supplied free of cost to the farmers of Alabama. This serum will prevent the ravages of hog cholera.[11]

Continuing his lobbying effort, Dr. Cary told the Alabama Live Stock Association membership at its February 1914 convention in Talladega that, in his estimate, hog cholera had cost Alabama farmers $1 million in losses in each of 1912 and 1913.[12] The time for producing anti-hog cholera serum had long since arrived.

After what must have been a frustrating wait for him—made all the more pressing as Georgia had opened a serum plant the previous year on the university campus—Dr. Cary achieved his goal of gaining legislative and gubernatorial support for state funding for such a serum-producing facility in 1915. He took part in—likely he oversaw—the design and construction of the facility himself. The serum plant was located approximately where Auburn University's Harrison School of Pharmacy building now sits, a few hundred feet west of Samford Hall, at that time the western edge of campus. Dr. Cary's interest in this facility was born from work done in Ames, Iowa, by his fellow Iowa State College veterinary alumnus, Dr. W. B. Niles, who had earned his degree two years before Dr. Cary.

Dr. Niles and a small team came up with the first practical preventive measure in battling this disease: an injection of anti-hog cholera serum they had developed and then an application of the offending virus. This method was successfully tested in 1907 at the Bureau of Animal Industry's field station near Ames, which would later be the site of several research successes in the battle against hog cholera. Dr. Niles and others found that serum from the blood of immune hogs provided a few weeks' immunity to inoculated hogs. They also found that injection of hyperimmune serum, plus injection of virus, gave lasting protection against hog cholera to most hogs. Research and findings continued for years, in Iowa and elsewhere, but this 1907 breakthrough helped the veterinary science world gain a handle on this massive disease. Time was needed, however, for the production of anti-hog cholera serum to effect a difference. Another outbreak, for example, in 1913 killed 10 percent of the nation's hogs.[13]

Auburn's Hog Cholera Serum Plant

Dr. Cary had lobbied President Thach, other agricultural leaders, and legislators for the serum plant for years. Early in 1915, a bill approved by the Legislature and by Governor Henderson appropriated $25,000 to API for this structure.

As with anything political with public funds attached, the plan to put the serum plant at Auburn was a fight to the end—not whether to build it for the benefit of Alabama hog producers, but where to locate the facility. A state representative, Dr. Stevenson from the Walker community of Jefferson County, lobbied for location in Birmingham "on the ground that the serum is good only ten days and that as Birmingham is a railroad center it is the best distributing point."[14] His effort was tabled, and the original bill was approved by a 62-1 vote. The record shows that Dr. Stevenson apparently had no hard feelings. He voted for the bill locating the plant at Auburn.

Representative Col. Sam Will John, who sponsored the bill, told reporters that conversations with agricultural leaders in other states had convinced him of the wisdom of locating the plant at the agricultural college. Students in agriculture and veterinary science—as well as farmers attending the Farmers' Summer Schools at Auburn—could learn how the serum was produced, its appropriate handling, and how it was to be injected into hogs. This knowledge, Col. John reasoned, would lead to more effective use of the serum in all parts of Alabama and beyond.

An article on the subject in the February 1915 issue of *The Auburn Alumnus* magazine lauded its promise:

> This bill is one of the most important acts of constructive, progressive legislation passed by the last Legislature, and the serum plant will be of untold benefit to the farmers of Alabama. That Auburn should be selected as the . . . location of the plant was most logical, for here operations of the plant can be under the immediate supervision and direction of Dr. C.A. Cary, Dean of the Veterinary Department at Auburn and recognized leader of his profession in the South.[15]

Governor Henderson signed the bill on March 4, 1915, and $25,000 was allocated toward construction.

President Thach's report to the Board of Trustees on June 7, 1915, further described campus delight in this coming facility:

It is a matter of great gratification that the Legislature recently established in connection with the College, a Hog Serum Laboratory under the direction of the State Veterinarian. This measure was passed well nigh unanimously by both Houses and duly received the approval of the Governor. The title of the Act is "To Establish and Maintain a Plant for Making Serum for Treatment of Hog Cholera, and to Regulate the Sale of the Serum." The fund is to be expended under the direction of the Trustees of the Alabama Polytechnic Institute. Appropriation of $25,000 is made for building and equipping the laboratory, and the sum of $3,000 appropriated annually for extending and adding thereto. The serum is to be sold to the farmers of Alabama at cost. It is felt that this is a great step forward in the control of the dread source which is estimated to destroy annually at least $1,000,000 worth of hogs in Alabama.

I respectfully recommend that the Board of Trustees accept the said appropriation, and that the Treasurer of the Alabama Polytechnic Institute be authorized to receive and disburse all sums of money due this Institution under the provisions of the Act.[16]

President Thach also noted that the US Secretary of Agriculture had formulated a policy whereby agricultural experts in each state would work in cooperation with and under direction of the Extension Service. To that end, API had brought on board in August 1914 Dr. H. C. Wilson, whose efforts mostly were expended toward educating the state's farmers about hog cholera. President Thach noted that Dr. Wilson's time was not charged to the API budget, but that Dr. Wilson was housed within the Veterinary Department as part of the plan. A dairy expert, paid by federal funds, was housed similarly within the API Department of Animal Husbandry.

"It is believed that the establishment of a hog cholera serum plant has been hastened by the services of Dr. Wilson," President Thach noted.

The formal launching of the serum plant was held on Saturday, January 15, 1916, with a 2:00 p.m. program in Langdon Hall. Veterinary students and faculty and a small number of invited guests were present. Col. Sam Will John, the Alabama legislator who drafted the bill calling for the funding appropriation, made remarks, as did the state's Commissioner of Agriculture and Industries James A. Wade, who "dwelt at length on the possibilities of Alabama as a meat-producing state."[17] President Thach told the crowd of the "excellent service Dr. Cary had rendered to the people of Alabama," and Dr. Cary spoke on the economic value of the serum plant to hog farmers in Alabama and beyond.[18] After the program in Langdon Hall, guests toured the plant and witnessed demonstrations of the serum production process.

The *Opelika Daily News,* in a report published two days after that grand opening event, noted that the plant's use "means the beginning of a new era for agriculture in Alabama."[19] At that point, the paper reported, serum was already in production and "all calls on the plant for serum have been supplied. No doubt the plant can supply the demands of the state." Dr. Cary had told the crowd at the grand opening that, almost overnight, the price of serum in Alabama had dropped by almost $.02 per unit.

The *Daily News'* reporter interviewed Dr. Cary that day, and the dean offered an overview of the plant's promise and its place in the framework of hog production:

> When it is known that this serum, if properly used, will effectually prevent hog cholera, and that Alabama is sooner or later going to be a hog-producing state, it can be readily seen that this plant will be of great value to our farmers in Alabama. It is not to be supposed that the use of hog cholera serum will take the place of sanitation and feed and care. It is true that there are other things needed: markets, slaughter houses, and the people must be educated. They must learn how to grow hogs, feed and market them free from disease. When hogs can be produced cheaper or at a less cost in Alabama . . . there is no reason why Alabama should not be a hog producing state. The federal government and the state are now furnishing the farmer . . . individual instruction, and also giving the farmer means by which he can obtain preventive materials, establish sanitation and get the most out of proper feeds and proper care. This serum plant is one of the factors that will help in the development of the hog industry in the state.[20]

During the year the plant was being built, Dr. Cary and other faculty members lectured their agriculture and veterinary medical students "in the manufacture of serum and the proper methods for inoculation." Farmers, too, were welcome to visit Auburn "to receive practical instruction, and those who attend the summer school will be given full opportunity to learn of the advantages and methods of inoculation," Dr. Cary promised.[21]

President Thach in his June 5, 1916, report to trustees, noted that the hog cholera serum facility was by this time in successful operation. A satisfactory tract of land adjoining the College property was purchased, suitable buildings have been erected, and the manufacture of serum has been entered upon. I am informed that since the erection of the plant the cost of serum has been greatly reduced throughout the State. The raising of swine throughout Alabama promises to be an industry of ever-increasing importance and remuneration, and the Serum Plant is rendering most valuable service in the protection of this industry against its greatest enemy, cholera.[22]

Also noted at this meeting, in a report authored by Extension Service Director Dr. J. F. Duggar, was the quality of work performed over the previous year by Dr. H. C. Wilson, whose "work in cooperation with the Extension Service and the Serum Laboratory . . . has been the means of saving thousands of dollars' worth of hogs" throughout Alabama.

Early serum laboratory directors, all hired by Dr. Cary, included:

Dr. H. C. Wilson worked for many years in hog cholera for the USDA in Alabama. Later in his career, in the 1930s, he was involved in hog cholera work in Indiana.

Dr. James Clifford Schoenlaub was a Marion, Ohio, native and a graduate of Ohio State University's College of Veterinary Medicine. By 1920, he lived and worked as a veterinarian in Montgomery. In the 1940s, he worked as a meat inspector in Bay City, Michigan. Dr. Schoenlaub died on May 18, 1954.

Dr. Everett S. Winters, a native of Society Hill, South Carolina, was graduated from Clemson Agriculture College in 1916 with a degree in veterinary science. He earned the DVM degree at Auburn in 1920 and apparently impressed Dean Cary, who wasted no time in naming Dr. Winters to the faculty as a professor of physiology and pharmacology. When Dean Sugg was called to active duty in the military during World War II, Dr. Winters filled in the dean's role in an acting capacity for three years, performing so ably that, years later, a graduate of the College contributed funding for a permanently endowed scholarship to assist veterinary students in Dr. Winters' memory as a tribute to his "holding the school together during the war." Dr. Winters died on Christmas Day, 1954, and is buried in Auburn's Memorial Park Cemetery.

The serum plant at Auburn was built less than a decade after the first anti-hog cholera serum had been produced. The Bureau of Animal Industry owned the patent for a widely used type of serum, the kind produced at Auburn and many other places. BAI ownership meant that hog farmers could obtain the serum at cost, injecting serum into all healthy hogs to prevent their acquiring the disease. Already-infected hogs did not always benefit from inoculation.

Serum alone provided modest protection of a few weeks. For a longer protection time, the serum was used in conjunction with hog-cholera virus. Infected hogs' fibrin—the insoluble protein that enables coagulation—was removed from the blood of infected hogs and the defibrinated blood mixed with a preservative to make whole-blood virus. This process was accomplished at Auburn in one side of the serum plant.

Given that hogs were, for most of Dr. Cary's lifetime, the predominant food animal species in the South—more numerous than horses, dairy cattle, and beef cattle—his Auburn veterinary students received plenty of instruction and experience in hog cholera: how to produce serum, how to inoculate hogs, and what to teach farmers in terms of the benefits of proactive health practices.[23]

The hog cholera serum plant Dr. Cary built in 1915 would be in use on campus in its original purpose and in other laboratory work, notably as a diagnostic laboratory. A generation after its launch, in 1948, Dean Redding Sugg provided funding to convert the plant into a lab for use in brucellosis eradication. The facility was demolished in 1975, with the diagnostic lab being relocated farther west on campus.

CHAPTER SIXTEEN

FIGHTING TUBERCULOSIS

The chilling words of the American Lung Association in the twenty-first century strike to the heart of life in the age of Charles Allen Cary:

> During the nineteenth and early twentieth centuries, tuberculosis (TB) was the leading cause of death in the United States, and one of the most feared diseases in the world. Formerly called "consumption," tuberculosis is characterized externally by fatigue, night sweats, and a general "wasting away" of the victim. Typically but not exclusively a disease of the lungs, TB is also marked by a persistent coughing-up of thick white phlegm, sometimes blood.
>
> There was no reliable treatment for tuberculosis. Some physicians prescribed bleedings and purgings, but most often, doctors simply advised their patients to rest, eat well, and exercise outdoors. Very few recovered. Those who survived their first bout with the disease were haunted by severe recurrences that destroyed any hope for an active life.
>
> It was estimated that, at the turn of the century, 450 Americans died of tuberculosis every day, most between ages 15 and 44. The disease was so common and so terrible that it was often equated with death itself.[1]

J. Arthur Myers, in his 1940 book, *Man's Greatest Victory Over Tuberculosis,* quoted that eminent veterinarian from Cornell, Dr. V. A. Moore, from 1911: "As a destroyer of man, tuberculosis has no equal; as a scourge of cattle, there is no other with which to compare it."

Myers also quoted Dr. A. F. Schalk, Bureau of Animal Industry TB inspector for North Dakota, from 1930, who said, "In the realm of medical and sanitary science there is perhaps no one condition that has been more insidious in its course, attended by more grief and sorrow and greater economic significance, and at the same time more colorful, than tuberculosis."

Dr. John R. Mohler, later chief of the Bureau of Animal Industry and one of the most successful veterinarians and public health administrators our country has ever produced, said about TB in 1908: "There is probably no disease of animals or man which is at present receiving more consideration for the practitioner, the sanitarian, and the economist than tuberculosis. Furthermore, it is one of the most prevalent diseases, and is responsible for more deaths among people and greater financial loss to stock owners than any other affliction."[2]

The Centers for Disease Control on its website attributes the cause of tuberculosis to the *Mycobacterium tuberculosis* bacteria group.[3] These bacteria commonly attack the lungs, but can attack other parts of the body, such as the kidney, spine, and brain. Not all people infected with TB bacteria take ill. As a result, two TB-related conditions exist: latent TB infection (LTBI) and TB disease. If not treated properly, TB disease can be fatal. Since the disease can be transmitted between animals and man, a zoonotic disease, TB-tainted meat and milk can pass along the harmful bacteria to people consuming these products.

Information from *Tuberculosis in America: The Forgotten Plague,* a website companion to the television production of the Public Broadcasting Service's "American Experience" series, noted a number of alarming reminders about TB. As of the early 1800s, the site claims, TB killed one of every seven people who ever lived. At that time, no known cure existed. Many victims were urged to try fresh air and time outdoors. By the middle years of the 1800s in the United States, many people began moving west (including to today's Midwest) for supposed health benefits. Within a few years, railroad travel made those frontier lands more accessible—for people *and* cattle. Into this environment Charles Allen Cary was born in 1861.

Writing in Alabama Agricultural Experiment Station *Bulletin Num-*

ber 67, Bovine Tuberculosis, published in 1895 in his fourth year at Auburn, Dr. Cary described this terrible disease with equally devastating language:

> No other disease is so widely distributed geographically; it is found in all climates and in all lands. It attacks man and nearly all domestic animals. Tuberculosis annually claims more victims than smallpox, cholera and yellow fever. An average of 14 percent (one out of every seven) of all the deaths in the human family is due to tuberculosis. In some of the largest cities and in some of the older and more densely populated countries the average percent is 25 (1 death in every 4 a result of tuberculosis). It is said that the civilizing (?) influences, as applied to the American Indian, have increased the mortality to 50 percent—one-half of all the deaths result from some form of tuberculosis. In Alabama during the years 1889-90-91-92-93, the annual average number of deaths from tuberculosis was 1,009; or 11.44 percent (1 in every 9) was due to tuberculosis. We legislate, quarantine and use all the methods known to expert medical men, when cholera, yellow fever or small-pox enters or threatens to enter, our country or State. Yet only a few States legally recognize tuberculosis as an infectious disease that annually destroys more lives than all of the three frightful diseases just mentioned.[4]

Today, a century after most of the preceding quotes, according to the American Lung Association, some 2.2 billion people—a third of the world's population—are infected with tuberculosis. Most of these have latent TB, meaning they carry tuberculosis germs, but their immune systems protect them from becoming sick. Worldwide, some 9.2 million people have active TB disease.[5]

Tuberculosis has plagued man and cattle since ancient times. Dr. Cary, in the opening line of his Experiment Station *Bulletin Number 67,* noted that Hippocrates in 400 BC wrote of people and animals suffering what later experts concluded was tuberculosis. A cooperative, federal-state-industry effort was launched in 1917 to eradicate the disease from cattle in the United States. When one considers the horrors of this disease, one wonders what took the authorities so long to act. Bovine TB was causing deadly problems for years before 1917, and Dr. Cary and other veterinarians and health professionals spent considerable time—long before and long after 1917—battling this disease at its front line.

Certainly, efforts had been made, but the disease was somewhat late in being described and defined. Also, not all experts were on the same page. For years, the disease was believed hereditary. French scientist Jean-Antoine Villemin proved in 1868 that tuberculosis was contagious—inoculating healthy rabbits with tuberculous tissue and infecting them, then watching them infect others. His findings, however, did not convince everyone. Robert Koch, the German physician and scientist, presented his discovery of *Mycobacterium tuberculosis* in 1882, revealing the direct cause of TB and verifying Villemin's finding that this disease is highly contagious. A decade later, Dr. Cary studied in Dr. Koch's Berlin laboratory.

Dr. Koch (profiled in Chapter 7), held monumental influence. He already had earned global praise in 1876 for having identified the cause of anthrax, another menacing killer of cattle. Six years later, at age thirty-eight, Dr. Koch read a paper before the Physiological Society in Berlin. That evening—March 24, 1882—he spoke of tuberculosis, this killer of one in seven people. Dr. Koch broke new ground, confirming to his audience of fellow scientists that tuberculosis was an infectious disease caused by a bacterium—the first time the cause had been proven.

Modern-day readers may find difficulty in comprehending the magnitude of this news. Koch's discovery was on par with confirmation of the earth being round, and not flat, according to one commentary. Koch's paper launched a revolution in science: *the* most dreaded of diseases was not inherited, and it didn't strike only the unlucky. It was infectious in nature, carried through the air and through bodily fluids by bacteria. The knowledge didn't make tuberculosis any less lethal, but it provided reason for the medical and science community, including the veterinary community, to begin studying ways to prevent it.[6]

In 1892, when Dr. Cary was working in Dr. Koch's laboratory, the Pennsylvania Society for the Prevention of Tuberculosis was organized, with goals of educating the public about preventing the disease and helping those with TB, especially the poor, to receive medical treatment and supplies believed beneficial in fighting the disease. This society represented the first such anti-TB organization in the country. In 1904, several physicians collaborated to establish the National Association for the Study and Prevention of Tuberculosis, later known as the American Lung Association. This effort, too, was largely a public education-oriented organization.[7]

The United States Veterinary Medical Association also acted in 1892, approving a resolution calling for the establishment of sanitary boards to oversee meat and dairy inspection. After Dr. Koch's findings began to circulate through the world press, information about bovine TB increasingly became the focus of veterinary association meetings and a key subject of veterinary medical literature.[8] In those same days, however, the non-veterinary/sometimes anti-veterinary agriculture press offered opposing views: that efforts to enforce any regulatory measures were sure to harm cattle and cattlemen, that American cattle were healthy and did not need such intrusion from the veterinary community, that the human and bovine TB diseases were unrelated, and the like. The agricultural press helped to persuade many farmers that veterinarians with their public health ideals were not exactly allies.[9] Dr. Cary and his lieutenants encountered this attitude among many property owners and farmers in the veterinary community's battles against hog cholera and Texas fever, as well.

Dr. Cary's November 1895 Alabama Agricultural Experiment Station *Bulletin* on *Bovine Tuberculosis* was, in essence, his "state of the disease" report to the governor and the legislature, as well as to those few veterinarians then at work in Alabama, and to the many citizens who owned livestock. He painted an accurate and alarming picture of what TB was doing to people and to animals, but he also provided a road map for man's best chance at escaping this menace.

In this 1895 *Bulletin*, Dr. Cary offered some general thoughts on the actual microbe to the reader. He:

Described the bacillus:

This microbe or germ is a one-celled plant, having the shape of a very delicate rod, about 1-2500 of an inch long and about 1-10 as broad as long. This rod is usually almost straight but may be slightly curved. It may appear alone, in pairs, or in irregular groups or masses. It absorbs coloring matters (stains) very slowly; but when once stained it holds the stain with great tenacity. It will hold certain stains when all or nearly all other germs become discolorized. This enables the pathologist to distinguish it amid myriads of other germs.

Described the methods for killing the bacillus:

If infected sputa be kept at a temperature of 158° Fah. for ten minutes the tubercle bacilli are destroyed. The germ in the same material is destroyed in 20 hours if 3 per cent. of carbolic acid is added; the germ perishes in five minutes in iodoform-ether; it dies in ten minutes in a mercuric chloride solution (1 to 1,000). According to Koch the tubercle bacillus perishes in a few hours in direct sunlight, and in five to seven days in diffuse daylight. An absolute heat of 158 degrees Fah. for fifteen minutes in meat and other tuberculous masses, will kill the germs. Boiling for one-half hour is always fatal to the tubercle bacilli. Common salt liberally applied to meats is fatal to the germ in one month; but in large masses of meat, the salt may not permeate the mass evenly and many bacilli may thus escape the destructive action of the salt.

Described the environments in which the bacillus survives:

This germ may remain virulent in ordinary living rooms from two to ten months, varying with the light, heat and the frequency of disinfection or cleansing of the room. In springs, wells and all forms of surface water, at ordinary temperature, the tubercle bacilli may maintain their virulency indefinitely. Non-sterilized water from rivers and surface wells may be contaminated; likewise public drinking troughs. Freezing will not destroy the tubercle bacillus. Fermentation and decomposition of organic materials, in which tubercle bacilli are present, will not always destroy them.

Warned about these bacilli in common environments:

poorly ventilated and dark living rooms, public halls, school rooms and churches are places where the infected sputa may be slowly dried, thus preserving its infective power indefinitely. Hence, the dust from such rooms may carry the virulent germs into the air passages, and into the alimentary canal with the food. In fact the greatest number of cases of tuberculosis in the human family are contracted by breathing tuberculous dust in living rooms, churches, school rooms and public places. The next greatest number of cases of tuberculosis are contracted by eating tuberculous food.

In this *Bulletin,* Dr. Cary instructed the veterinarian and the animal owner in practical steps to minimize the potential for development of the disease, teaching them of the importance of developing and maintaining vigor in the animal: "weakness of body, whether of tuberculosis origin or not, predisposes the offspring to tuberculosis."

To that end, he suggested that seeing a cow as a "milk-producing machine" may have contributed to the animal having

a constitutional weakness . . . close, warm, continual confinement is occasionally preached and practiced by dairymen and sometimes it is taught by instructors in agricultural colleges. Dairy cows as well as beef cattle should have exercise in open air. Exercise and fresh air will not prevent all cases of tuberculosis, but they certainly help to prevent the contraction or spreading of tuberculosis.

He argued for proper ventilation and light in those areas where cows were kept. "Light is one of nature's best disinfectants," he wrote, suggesting that moving air could take with it "foul gases" and that best practices would have avoided moist and variable climates that favored development and transmission of tuberculosis.

Dr. Cary shared some findings from European surveys of the incidence of tuberculosis in animals in recent years and offered a conclusion as to why cows were the chief animal among many which contracted TB: "This is due to the fact that the cow comes in closer contact with man and has less freedom, less pure air and receives more infected food than calves or oxen."

At the time of this 1895 writing, only Massachusetts in the United States was at work on a large-scale, state-wide testing of animals for the disease, though testing was conducted nationwide in small communities in herds where the disease was suspected. Dr. Cary and the rest of the veterinary/public health community were working toward bringing across-the-board testing to the entire population.

Before he was able to persuade any of the state's municipalities to adopt and require milk and meat inspection protocols, he gathered localized data to prove the need for such ordinances. One of Dr. Cary's efforts in this area from his earliest days at Auburn was to write to health officers in a variety of Alabama cities and towns, asking about incidents of tuberculosis in local herds. In the 1895 Experiment Station *Bulletin*, he reprinted letters he had received in reply from two health officials in Mobile that summer, both of which offered insight into the predicament growing out of the lack of oversight.

One writer replied to Dr. Cary that

> tuberculosis is prevalent among cattle here. I consider the extent alarming enough although I have no idea what the per centage is. Human tuberculosis is also quite prevalent, which is not to be wondered at, since prominent dairy herds are infected.

The other writer, Physician James A. Abrahams of the Mobile Board of Health, told Dr. Cary that no officer of this board inspects the dairy herds supplying this city with milk. If tuberculosis exists among these herds, knowledge of it is not possessed by this board. No power is possessed to make the tuberculin test, to determine the presence or absence of tuberculosis. At present we could not use the tuberculin if furnished free.

Dr. Abrahams went on to say that his fellow board members favored laws requiring inspection of milk, "and if successful we may have occasion to correspond with you on the subject of tuberculosis."

Dr. Cary's instruction to health professionals in *Bulletin 67* detailed the transmissibility of the *bacillus tuberculosis* from man to animal and vice versa. He offered a first-hand example of a family he knew, "of which nearly every member died of tuberculosis. This family's herd of milk cows nearly all died of tuberculosis. The disease first appeared in the family; later in the herd of cattle." He included as well a number of tragic anecdotes of which he had read or was otherwise familiar which confirmed his points. His *Bulletin* article detailed the anatomical processes whereby bacilli entered tissues and organs and how, once inside, they devastated the host. He described what the investigator would see in the post-mortem, acknowledging that "No tissue or part of the body is exempt from the ravages of this disease." He then spared no detail in preparing one for the necropsy experience, describing the condition of tuberculous lungs, bronchial tubes, lymph glands, the chest wall, the small intestine, the liver, spleen, kidneys, uterus, udder, bones, throat, brain, spinal cord, and muscles. As usual, Dr. Cary was thorough in his offerings.

He wrote of the symptoms of tuberculosis in living cattle and offered fascinating advice for the veterinarian, animal owner, or other health official giving a physical examination:

> If the lungs and air passages are involved there may be, in the early stages, a harsh, dry, rough cough. Violent exertion, excitement, eating dry food or drinking cold water may cause the animal to cough. Sometimes the animal coughs at the beginning of exercise or upon rising after having lain down for some time. Striking the animal over the ribs a sharp rap with the knuckles may arouse the cough. Striking the chest with the knuckles may reveal regions or spots where the sound is muffled or dull instead of being resonant as in health. If the ear be applied to the chest, it may detect a weak, highly pitched whistling sound, made by the air rushing through some partially obstructed bronchial tube. Or, the ear may

hear a sound that resembles bubbles of air passing through a thick liquid; this would indicate the presence of a liquid in the bronchial tubes. These last two tests are difficult and the trained expert is often mistaken; because there is such a limited area on the sides of the chest that can be thus inspected and because, in many instances, the area of lung tissue involved may be very small and deeply seated. A physical examination of the lungs in the living animal is satisfactory only in the advanced stages of the disease where the tuberculous animal is poor and the diseased part of the lung is very large. As the disease advances the cough may become more and more aggravated; a discharge from the nose may appear; the hair becomes rough and dry, and is not shed regularly; the skin becomes scurfy and clings closely to underlying tissues. In aggravated cases the animal may become greatly emaciated; yet, in some cases, the animal will remain in good flesh when the lungs are extensively tuberculous.[10]

Dr. Cary wrote a detailed explanation on how the trained veterinarian could recognize tuberculosis, with notice given that there could be "many dangerous and badly infected cases that can not be recognized by the veterinarian if he bases his diagnosis upon physical signs alone." He then suggested options, including microscopic evaluation of any of several bodily fluids, inoculation, or use of the recently developed tuberculin test. He detailed the merits of this tuberculin test, the fine points of exactly how to use it effectively, and the veterinarian's next steps based on the results.

Dr. Cary's Extension *Bulletin* on bovine tuberculosis, not surprisingly, was thorough and helpful to the trained veterinarian and the layperson alike, and all such bulletins were mailed at no charge to any Alabamian who asked for them. He concluded this paper with lengthy advice for the stock owner on "preventive measures," "how to disinfect," and a reminder of the duties of city and state officials in fighting this deadly menace. In fact, he touched on some of the policies he fought to get enacted in Alabama over his entire career, including city and state ordinances requiring twice-annual tuberculin testing for all dairy herds; and that all cities should have meat and milk inspectors on duty to perform these dairy inspections, as well as to inspect all carcasses at slaughterhouses and markets. Inspectors, of course, were to be trained and graduated veterinarians.

When Dr. Cary wrote this bulletin in 1895, the call was beginning to come (chiefly from himself and from President Broun at Auburn) for the governor and legislature to approve appointing a state veterinarian. Dr. Cary made that call again in the concluding section of his paper, outlining the duties that office would entail:

> Alabama should provide for a State Veterinarian and several local assistant State Veterinarians. Said veterinarians should investigate all contagious and infectious diseases among domestic animals; inspect or superintend the inspection of all dairy herds and all animals slaughtered for human food not inspected by city or government inspectors. The State Veterinarian could be an ex officio member of the State Board of Health, or work under the supervision of that Board. Said veterinarians should receive pay for time spent in actual service for the State.

He touched on the need for public slaughterhouses in each city, with the State of Alabama to underwrite costs, including paying "a small indemnity for animals condemned by the State." Dr. Cary proposed "levying a small special tax upon all the domestic animals of the State" to pay compensation to those whose animals were condemned.

Dr. Cary closed his paper by offering nineteen suggestions that had been made across the country by various "City and State Boards of Health for the prevention and eradication of tuberculosis in the human family." These tips included common-sense measures such as sterilizing all milk and thoroughly cooking meats and drinking water. But the suggestions also included a number of hardline actions that would have been controversial then and now: limiting career options for those who carry tuberculosis and prohibiting them from teaching school or marrying.

In fact, many of the suggestions Dr. Cary listed—and it's not certain he approved of every one, though one may assume he did—would have kept the tuberculous patient from many aspects of life. He acknowledged in the final two paragraphs of his paper that the "preventive suggestions may seem to be extreme, but some of them are enforced in some of the largest cities in the United States." With Dr. Cary, who understood the dangers at hand with tuberculosis and other zoonotic, deadly diseases, what was best for society in the long run outweighed the rights and quality of life of a few individuals.

"For the people in general," he would write in another Experiment Station bulletin in 1898, ". . . the question of a pure milk supply is one of the foremost sanitary problems." The idea that consumers could contract tuberculosis and a host of other dreadful, deadly diseases from drinking tainted milk "makes it of vital importance to the public that such a valuable food should be officially inspected, and every possible means should be used to keep dairy milk clean, pure and free from disease-producing germs."[11]

Dr. Cary's ongoing call for science-based dairy and milk inspection, begun almost as soon as he stepped off the train in Auburn in 1892, made a difference, actually sooner rather than later. The year after *Bulletin Number 67* appeared, on September 28, 1896, the City Council of Montgomery adopted his recommendations and propelled Montgomery to its status as first city in the nation to have such an inspection ordinance on the books. Those protocols appeared two years later in Dr. Cary's Alabama Experiment Station *Bulletin Number 97*—published in September 1898 and titled "Dairy and Milk Inspection."[12]

This ordinance regulated the sale of milk in Montgomery and spelled out the fine points of acceptable and now-required milk content; of getting the necessary license; the cattle testing requirement; and directives for treatment, handling, and feeding of cattle. Dr. Cary included in the ordinance his call for "free movement in the open air of at least six hours every day" for dairy cows as well as sufficient levels of ventilation, light, and sanitation. The fine for violating the ordinance was at least $1 and up to $100 "for each and every offense."[13]

As the nineteenth century turned into the twentieth, tuberculosis continued to rank as the leading cause of death in the United States. More than a quarter of all deaths in the country were blamed on airborne diseases, tuberculosis chief among them. One-tenth of all human tuberculosis cases were likely the result of exposure to tuberculous cattle or cattle products, and a quarter of tuberculosis cases in children were caused by the bovine TB bacterium, chiefly from their drinking tainted milk from uninspected, untested cows. In several of his annual reports as state veterinarian, Dr. Cary pointed out that TB occurred most often in dairy herds, which by their nature were kept in close confinement as opposed to other animals that were left to open pastures. Bovine TB naturally showed up more commonly in herds in or near cities, where fewer acres were available for pasture. With this in mind, Dr. Cary repeated in countless talks to farmers and veterinary students, as in Extension *Bulletin Number 67*, that all dairy cows be given several hours in the open air each day.[14]

Fortunately, Alabamians increasingly came to understand what was at stake and they approved of the public health measures directed by the state veterinarian and others. Alabama's first anti-TB society was formed in Montgomery in 1908, and a similar group was up and running in Birmingham in 1910. In 1914, the Alabama TB League formed, later to be renamed the TB Association in 1922.

In 1924, Alabama became the first state to require all milk products to be stamped with a grade, signaling their having been inspected.

The road to a healthier world may have been paved earlier and more smoothly, but front-line scientists took a long time to reach consensus. At the Sixth International Veterinary Congress, held in Switzerland in 1895, resolutions on TB and the use of tuberculin for control of the disease were debated, and while the Congress eventually supported tuberculin as a diagnostic agent, it voted no on compulsory testing.[15]

As late as 1900, experts, including Dr. Theobald Smith of Harvard, debated whether bovine TB was transmissible to humans. Dr. Smith, in 1898, had published results of his research into the relation of human and bovine tubercle bacteria, finding "well-marked morphological, cultural and pathogenic differences between them." In 1901, Dr. Koch made news again by presenting his findings (opinions?) in a famous paper in which he asserted there was "no relation existing between human and bovine tubercle bacteria." That announcement, by so eminent a scientist, brought about a flurry of global investigations into the nature of TB, collectively one of the most thorough and widespread investigations of any disease at that time. During the next several years, numerous scientists of note investigated TB from any number of angles. Their results in the early years of the twentieth century confirmed two distinct varieties of tubercle bacteria: one thriving in man, the other at home in cattle. But the results also showed the sad truth that people—especially children—were susceptible to infection from the bovine TB bacteria.[16]

One writer of the turn of that century noted that "not until recent years has so much attention been paid to this disease in cattle," suggesting that previous to all this scientific notoriety, when a farmer discovered a drooping cow, the animal "was either slaughtered or allowed to die, and nothing more was thought of it."[17]

One key issue—beyond TB having been misunderstood for millennia and governments not having funds to allot toward studying it—was summarized in a 1900 report to the New York Assembly. The report described the attitudes of farmers and stock producers, not alone in New York. "While the honest farmer does not desire to sell diseased meat and milk to the consumer, he does feel that it should be well established that his herd is responsible for infection of men before his property should be destroyed and his business ruined."[18]

Bovine TB was widespread, occurring almost everywhere cattle were held, particularly dairy cattle. The Bureau of Animal Industry estimated early in the twentieth century that 10 percent of dairy cattle in the US were infected, a percentage that may well have been higher in the South.[19] Worse in Europe, infection reached upwards of half the cattle there, according to J. Arthur Myers' 1940 book on the subject. From these European cattle, nineteenth- and twentieth-century American cows came, as cattle were imported during Colonial times to increase breeding stock in the colonies and early states. Myers noted that, around 1875, the seriousness of bovine TB among cattle was first recognized publicly in the United States. Charles Allen Cary was a teenager on his family's farm at that time. By 1916, bovine TB was causing more losses than all other infectious diseases of farm animals in the US.[20]

For years, despite the theory holding that any infectious disease *could* be contained and perhaps even eradicated, many people thought TB the exception, that it was too enormous and far-reaching a disease to be solved.[21] But some people, even if they doubted, prepared for the fight. In 1906—a full decade after the City of Montgomery adopted its Cary-driven inspection protocols—the Bureau of Animal Industry inaugurated a system of federal meat inspection to protect the public against meat deemed dangerous for human consumption, whether from tuberculosis or some other contaminant.[22] Not long afterward, in 1909, the American Veterinary Medical Association appointed a commission to investigate and report on a method for the control of bovine TB. This action resulted in a series of resolutions and a general plan of procedures for cattle owners. The AVMA would work hand-in-hand with the BAI in this war on tuberculosis.

The efforts may have had some success, but they didn't solve all TB-related problems immediately. In addition to the tragic deaths of people and cattle, economic losses were mounting year after year. Some estimates—including a report produced by the US Secretary of Agriculture—held that US farmers and producers lost collectively $25 million per year between 1914 and 1916 due to bovine TB. This amount dwarfed the estimated $9 million annual loss due to foot-and-mouth disease during that same time.[23] By 1921, US farmer and producer economic losses connected to bovine TB were topping $30 million annually.[24] This problem was spiraling out of control, not that it had been under control.

The BAI's effort, joined by state veterinarians like Dr. Cary and others from the veterinary colleges around the country, trained men for animal inspection duty. As an example, in 1915, some fifty-eight million animals—mostly cattle and hogs—were inspected by federal agents around the country. Manpower was short, however; at least another forty million animals were sold, slaughtered, and processed for meat without inspection, at least by the trained federal staff. Some of those forty million were undoubtedly inspected on the local level; but the reality was that those inspectors often were untrained or minimally trained, with some appointed to their jobs as political favors. How reassuring those inspections would have been to the mom and dad providing a beef or pork roast and a glass of milk to their children at Sunday lunch would not be difficult to guess.[25]

One of the massive problems early veterinarians and other health professionals faced was that animals infected with TB may not have shown signs of the disease for years. But those same infected animals, while appearing healthy, were capable of transmitting infection to others in their herds or to people through their milk and meat. That risk was multiplied greatly a century ago before veterinarian-designed inspection protocols were put into practice. The disease also had been, for decades of course, an economic concern for farmers and dairy operators. Bovine TB wrecked animal health and reduced production in those cattle affected. The presence of the disease led to trade restrictions, as TB in a cattle herd would cause concern about the infection spreading to other, free-ranging mammals.[26]

Dr. Cary's role in this huge enterprise was both educational and political in nature. Before landing the position of state veterinarian in 1907, he lobbied for that platform, desiring to be heard among the state's farmers and politicians and to get his preferred policies enacted. As always, he was hands-on in this fight against TB. As state veterinarian, he worked closely with the federal agents assigned to Alabama to ensure that all testing was accomplished. If the testing was not done to his satisfaction, he worked to see that it was done right. But he was only one man. He depended on lawful cooperation of farmers, not always a given because of attitudes already described. He labored every day to educate and train his Auburn students and the graduate veterinarians who attended the annual short courses in Auburn. He brought to Auburn a host of speakers during several years for talks related to bovine TB and the testing procedures then being introduced.

To the great and pleasant surprise of many people, TB problems began to turn around in the early 1920s. TB-infected cows and hogs were removed from the nation's herd populations constantly, resulting in fewer numbers of beef and dairy cows and perhaps hogs; but the healthier cows meant better breeding and more meat and milk production. The work of the federal agents and men like Dr. Cary led to far more cattle being tested, to the destruction of those animals that reacted positively to the TB tests, and to the selling of healthy milk and meat products. The result by the 1920s was a phenomenal increase in both production and consumer confidence in the meat and milk products available in stores. In 1921, for example, milk production in the US totaled ninety-nine billion pounds—a stark gain over the previous year. In 1921 alone, the number of cows in the US increased by 341,000 compared to the previous year's total. Healthy cows make healthy calves and healthy milk and beef. The resulting economic boom helped to stabilize the US dairy industry and improved the health of millions of citizens.

In 1917, the national herd consisted of almost twenty-three million cows, but tuberculosis was rampant among them. By 1929, with far more testing taking place, there were 1,074,000 fewer cows across America. But in 1929, dairy products were provided to eighteen million *more* people than were enjoying them in 1917. Also, milk consumption was up 30 percent. The eradication of TB, at least to a point, had increased the sales prices of dairy and beef cattle, returning profits to many farmers and producers.

By 1930, the average American cow was producing 5,000 pounds of milk with 200 pounds of fat each year. A few years earlier, the average American cow produced less than 4,000 pounds of milk, and that milk contained on average 140 pounds of fat, suggesting less healthy cows at that time. Some cows in more highly monitored programs in 1930 averaged producing 7,500 pounds of milk per year, with 290 pounds of fat. At that rate, if all cows had been in those programs, a national herd of fourteen million cows could have provided the dairy products needed and wanted by Americans when, previously, twenty-one million cows would have been needed to reach that level of production. The bovine TB eradication program was on the right track.[27]

Merillat and Campbell, in their marvelous two-volume *Veterinary Military History,* described the importance of those years of cooperation between veterinary medicine and other parties in fighting TB and other diseases:

The first third of the twentieth century must be credited also with establishing a closer relation between operations of the veterinary pro-

fession and public health, brought about largely through the campaign of
the United States Department of Agriculture against bovine tuberculosis
which is generally conceded to have greatly reduced the incidence of
bone, glandular and intestinal tuberculosis in children . . . .[28]

Auburn Veterinary Medicine Dean Emeritus John Thomas Vaughan,
writing a history of Auburn's College of Veterinary Medicine for the
Alabama VMA's centennial in 2007, noted that

> An immediate benefit of Cary's firsthand acquaintance with the work
> of Pasteur and Koch was that Alabama was one of the first states in the
> nation to institute the use of tuberculin for detection of tuberculosis in
> cattle and the application of public meat and milk inspection and the
> pasteurization process. This was the finest example of the practice of one
> medicine.

Dean Emeritus Vaughan also suggested that Dr. Cary's work with
tuberculosis may well have been the most important of his career.
Interviewed in the College of Veterinary Medicine's *Auburn Veterinarian* magazine in 2013, Dr. Vaughan described Dean Cary as

> . . . passionate about public health. If Charles Allen Cary . . . got his just
> desserts, he would be remembered not so much for having eradicated the
> cattle tick, but for his principal contribution of bringing under control
> tuberculosis. If the tombs could speak, when you go through Pine Hill
> Cemetery and see the number of young people buried there, a few of
> them died of scarlet fever, malaria or yellow fever, but the biggest killer
> far and away was tuberculosis.
> [Dr. Cary] went to Germany and studied under Koch. Before that, he
> had studied in Missouri under one of Dr. Pasteur's protégés. All that
> time he was learning about tuberculosis. About the time Cary landed in
> Antwerp, on his way to Germany, Bernard Bang, a Danish physician, dis-
> covered that the tuberculin that Koch had produced could be, by inject-
> ing it into cattle, a valuable screen to identify cattle infected with tuber-
> culosis. So when Cary came back to the U.S., he came back with this
> almost "insider trading" information on tuberculosis. He was one of the
> first in the U.S. to start using tuberculin to identify brucellosis infected
> cattle, and was one of the first to introduce Pasteurization of milk. The
> irony of it was, Koch, who had identified the tuberculin bacillus, wasn't
> convinced that bovine tuberculosis was transmissible to humans. He

thought all the human TB was human-to-human. He didn't realize humans were getting it from un-Pasteurized milk, from raw milk, or from inadequately inspected carcasses through the meat. It was the turn of the century before [Koch] was convinced that cattle were the chief source of infection. Eight years before that, Cary was already introducing people in Alabama to Pasteurization and was testing cattle, producing tuberculin in his own laboratory and giving it to veterinarians free. And the newspapers in New York City were bragging on Alabama's meat and milk inspection programs, their advanced level of detection of tuberculosis. This was all Dr. Cary. He was working single-handedly.[29]

CHAPTER SEVENTEEN

IN MEMORIAM

No one will be found who can combine so admirably the varied accomplish-ments of Charles Allen Cary. His Department will go on with conquest after conquest. His graduates will take up the torch which he has born with such signal courage, and scale new heights. All honor to this hero.

—Lyman Ward

L. A. Merillat and D. M. Campbell, those chroniclers of the early years of veterinary medicine in America, offered a tribute to the nation's first practitioners and their achievements that would have included—and certainly described—Dr. Cary:

The truth is the United States did not have veterinary schools that were not tainted with outstanding imperfections from 1776 until 1920, or during its first 144 years. That brilliant men, men of achievement, and a workable veterinary service for the federal government and states, could have grown out of them under the circumstances, is one of the marvels of veterinary history—another American paradox. Necessity—a vast animal industry—was more of a factor in the making of capable vet-erinarians than were the schools. Great problems develop great men to solve them in all branches of human effort.[1]

When a man reaches seventy-three years, he has lived more than 26,600 days: separately delivered, incremental gifts of twenty-four hours in which to learn, work, play, laugh, love, exalt, gripe, explore, build, run, rest, interact, reason, detach, escape.

Tuesday, April 23, 1935, was like so many before in the life of Charles Allen Cary: he rose early, had breakfast with his wife, tended to business related to his Auburn farm. Perhaps he walked from his home to the train depot for transportation to Montgomery for his state veterinarian duties, returned in the evening, and consulted with his secretary about that day's achievements and the following day's agenda for the students and faculty of the veterinary school he had built. Arriving home, he would have checked in with Emma, his Dearest, and gotten the local update, had a bite of dinner, perhaps read a bit or took care of some other business in the ground-floor study of his home, and then would have gone to bed, his mind already thinking through what he would do on April 24 to improve the lives of his fellow citizens.

The seventy-three-year-old was tired, and he apparently was afflicted by what family must have considered a spring cold, perhaps a mild influenza. He was not one to be slowed by such. The non-stop schedule Charles Allen Cary had kept during the past half-century would have worn out anyone. A few hours of sleep and he would be ready to carry on the fight.

Sometime in the hours after the lights were out in his upstairs bedroom at 360 North College Street, Charles Allen Cary's lifetime of service ended. He died of heart failure, undoubtedly related to that case of influenza that perhaps was not as mild as thought. His son, Elwyn, forty-three at the time, discovered his father's body early on Wednesday morning. Town and API Physician Dr. Benjamin F. Thomas was summoned, but there was nothing to be done. The great man was gone.

Ever the pragmatic Midwesterner, Emma Cary arranged for a telegram first thing that morning, sent from the train depot's Western Union setup to "15 important colleagues across the nation." It read simply, "Doctor Cary found dead in bed this morning, Mrs. C. A. Cary."[2]

His death was reported across the land, as befitted one of his stature. All the obituaries referred to him being seventy-four, but as his birth occurred around Thanksgiving of 1861, he was seven months shy of turning seventy-four.

The Auburn Plainsman published its Wednesday, April 24, 1935, edition with news of Dr. Cary's death at the top of the front page. That first news report of Dean Cary's death, with some errors likely related to the quick turnaround time for college journalists, read:

DR. C.A. CARY SUCCUMBS TO HEART ATTACK LATE TUESDAY

Passing Of Famous Dean of Veterinary Medicine School Is Mourned By Entire Campus; Has Made Notable Discoveries in Veterinary Research Work As Professor At Auburn

Dr. Charles Allen Cary, 74, dean of the veterinary Medicine school here, and state veterinarian, died suddenly in bed at his home here late Tuesday night. Returning to Auburn from a business trip Tuesday evening he retired as usual. Not until his son discovered his lifeless body was his illness known. Heart trouble was named as cause of his death.

A pall of gloom was spread over the entire campus this morning when word that Dean C. A. Cary had died was given out. Several faculty members who have been associated with Dr. Cary for a number of years expressed sorrow at his passing. All classes in the veterinary medicine school were dismissed this morning when word of Dean Cary's death was released. Classes in all schools will be excused during the funeral, plans for which will be announced later.

President L. N. Duncan said that "the death of Dr. Cary removes from Auburn a distinguished, able, and efficient professor and dean; and from Alabama an outstanding and invaluable citizen and official."

"I have known Dr. Cary for over 40 years," said Dean George Petrie, "and am able to speak from my personal knowledge about his many fine qualities. He was absolutely honest, he was thoroughly courageous, he was extremely industrious, and his friends knew that they could depend upon him. He was frank and outspoken, but behind a manner which may sometimes have seemed abrupt was a warm heart which was best known to his old and close friends. His friends, the college, and the State have sustained in his death a loss that would be hard to over-estimate."

"He was a man of dynamic personality, of rugged honesty, of tremendous industry, of powerful intellect, and of great administrative ability," Dean John J. Wilmore stated. "His outstanding work in his field in the nation as well as the State will stand as a monument to his memory."

As the only man to serve as dean of school of veterinary medicine and Alabama state veterinarian, Dr. Cary had been conspicuous and effective in livestock development work since 1892 when he came to Auburn as professor of veterinary medicine. His teaching developed into a department, and later a school of which he became dean. In 1907 the Alabama Legislature created the office of state veterinarian, and Dr. Cary was immediately appointed to this office in addition to his other duties.

While training veterinarians at Auburn, Dr. Cary was also the leader in the eradication of cattle ticks in Alabama, thereby paving the way to profitable livestock production. In recent times, he initiated meat and milk inspection in Montgomery, Mobile, Birmingham, and smaller towns in Alabama, his plan of inspection spreading to other states.

Recently he has devoted much time to the eradication of tuberculosis from Alabama livestock. Hog cholera control is another of his achievements. This, too, has been done in conjunction with other livestock development work. He is well known by farmers, county officials and business men throughout Alabama.

He is known nationally also in livestock circles, as an ex-president of the American Veterinary Association and otherwise. He has served on many national boards and state boards. For many years he was director of farmers' institutes at Auburn and local institutes over the state.

Dr. Cary came to Auburn in 1892 from Iowa. He graduated at Iowa State College in 1885 and in 1887. For three years he was a professor at the South Dakota State College.

He leaves a widow, Mrs. [Emma Heck] Cary; two daughters, Mrs. Herman [(Phoebe)] Shoemaker, Abbeville, Alabama; Mrs. [Lewis] (Alice) Pick, Fort Leavenworth, Kansas; and one son, Elwyn, Auburn; two brothers, [Wilford] Cary, Kansas City, Missouri; and Dr. Walter Cary, Los Angeles, California.

He was a member of Presbyterian Church, a Mason and Shriner.

Funeral arrangements will be announced later.[3]

That same issue of the *Plainsman* offered this brief but heart-felt editorial on page two:

Auburn's Loss

As the years succeed each other with relentless exactitude those men whom we have come to know as a part of Auburn are taken with equal inevitability. It is now our melancholy task to write a word in memory of Dean C. A. Cary, who died late last night.

Since 1892 Dr. Cary has devoted most of his life to work in veterinary medicine. His untiring efforts in veterinary research have brought remarkable discoveries which have made for notable advances in this field. The entire nation has recognized him for his outstanding ability.

His unselfish consideration for others, love of his fellow man, and his singular kind-heartedness made him greatly loved in Auburn. Dean Cary will live long in the memory of those who knew him as a great leader, teacher, and true Auburn man.

The Montgomery Advertiser also carried an editorial memorializing the dean:

Dr. C. A. Cary, State veterinarian, was one of the most useful Alabamians of his time. He loved animals, he understood their miseries, he understood their economic significance. He was as much interested in developing a livestock economy as he was in protecting the health of domestic animals.

Dr. Cary was modest, plain-spoken, honest and full of common sense. He was unpretentious and shy, but he was an authentic scientist who knew what he was talking about most of the time, and he knew he knew it.

Dr. Cary's long years at Alabama Polytechnic Institute were fruitful for the people of this State, and he will be missed.[4]

Another newspaper clipping of that week, found in the Cary family papers, perhaps clipped from *The Birmingham News*, offered this remembrance:

The sudden death of Dr. Charles Allen Cary, of Auburn, at the age of 74, comes as a shock to Alabamians, and particularly to the many thousands of farmers, dairymen and stock raisers to whose welfare and progress he had contributed so greatly during his long period of service as dean of the school of veterinary medicine at the Alabama Polytechnic Institute and as state veterinarian.

Dr. Cary had been at Auburn since 1892, more than 40 years. He was one of the outstanding group of Auburn faculty members who, by their exceptional ability and their long and faithful service, have so largely made Auburn the great institution that it is. The value of his services as professor and dean of the school of veterinary medicine, as state veterinarian ever since that office was created by the Legislature in 1907, as a leader in movements to eradicate the cattle tick, to improve milk and meat inspection in the cities and to raise the quality of livestock in Alabama by improvement of strains and by introduction of better methods, has been incalculable. Dr. Cary was nationally recognized as one of the foremost American veterinarians, as his selection at one time as president of the American Veterinary Medical Association and his service on various national and state boards attested.

Countless numbers of farmers, dairymen and stock raisers in Alabama swore by Dr. Cary. In instances they have named their children after him, and their prize specimens of livestock, in either case honoring the man who had served their interests so well.[5]

The *Opelika Daily News* included these comments in an editorial the day of the funeral:

To say that the passing of Dr. Charles Allen Cary at Auburn occasions deep sorrow would be putting it very mildly. His death will be as keenly felt all over Alabama, yea, all over the entire South as most any death could be. Dr. Cary was not only a respected citizen and a beloved educator; he was a living institution for the protection and propagation of animal life. His place can hardly hope to be filled.

Dr. Cary was loved best by those who knew him best. Among these fortunate ones were the students who came in direct contact with his superior influence. In the class rooms, in the cow and hog lots, on the farms, around the county fairs, at farmers meetings, or just on the College campus. Dr. Cary was always just Dr. Cary. His students sometimes in playful jest mimiced [sic] him, yet, they dearly loved and respected him. They had faith in his wealth of knowledge and experience; they liked his candor, and methods.

The Daily News joins with the thousands of others over the state in paying sincere fealty to the memory of this great worker and leader. He wrought long and well, and was surely outstanding.[6]

Dr. Cary's funeral was held in Langdon Hall on Saturday, April 27, 1935. Langdon represented the largest indoor seating capacity venue on campus. News reports of the day showed that API suspended its classes during the time of the funeral—they had Saturday classes in that era—and many local businesses also closed for the afternoon as many of the owners likely attended the memorial service. *The Plainsman,* which was publishing twice each week at this time, covered the memorial service on April 27 with a front-page story:

CARY FUNERAL IS
HELD HERE TODAY

Hundreds Attend Last Rites
For Noted Veterinarian And
Auburn Dean This Afternoon

A pall of deep sadness hung over Auburn this afternoon.

Faculty members of the college, students, townspeople, alumni from all parts of the state, and many friends gathered in Langdon Hall at 2 p.m. to pay final tribute to Dr. Charles Allen Cary, 74, veterinary medical school dean—one of Auburn's builders who had given his life to Auburn since 1892.

Dr. Cary died here suddenly at his home late Tuesday evening from heart attack. Following the funeral ceremony, burial was made in the Auburn cemetery.

In addition to his multitude of duties as dean of Auburn's school of veterinary medicine, Dr. Cary had served since 1907 as Alabama State Veterinarian. In this position he had been outstanding in the nation because of his pioneer work in livestock-disease control work in the South.

As veterinary school dean, he developed the Auburn school into one which ranks among the first throughout the nation.

Prominent in the assemblage was the 124 veterinary students who attended in a body.

Officiating at the funeral were Auburn's four ministers who read scriptural passages dear to Dr. Cary. They were the Rev. Sam B. Hay, Dr. James R. Edwards, Rev. William Byrd Lee, Jr., and Dr. R.B. McGehee. Music was arranged by Mrs. I.S. McAdory, Mrs. Mary Drake Askew, and Prof. Charles Floyd.

Pallbearers were Dr. I.S. McAdory, Dr. Fred Patterson, Dr. E.S. Winters, Dr. J.W. Isbell, Dr. H.S. Sawyer, Dr. Houston Odom, Dr. E.H. Walker, and Dr. C.B. Line—the entire faculty of the veterinary school.

Honorary pallbearers were Dr. L.N. Duncan, president of the Alabama Polytechnic Institute; Hon. R.J. Goode, commissioner of agriculture and Industries; William F. Feagin, Birmingham; Dr. B.H. Crenshaw, S.L. Toomer, and college deans—Prof. F.C. Biggin, Prof. M.J. Funchess, Prof. C.L. Hare, Prof. Zebulon Judd, Dr. George Petrie, Dr. John J. Wilmore, and Dr. John W. Scott. Maj. G.H. Franke served as marshal and was assisted by officers of the school of military sciences and tactics.

Dr. Cary is survived by his widow, Mrs. Emma Heck Cary; two daughters, Mrs. Herman (Phoebe) Shoemaker, Abbeville; Mrs. Lewis (Alice) Pick, Fort Leavenworth, Kansas; and one son, Elwyn, of Auburn; two brothers, Wilford Cary, Kansas City, Mo.; and Dr. Walter Cary, Los Angeles, Cal.[7]

After the memorial service, Dr. Cary was laid to rest in Auburn's Pine Hill Cemetery, where he would be joined in 1954 by his widow, Emma, and in 1963 by his son, Elwyn, in a family plot. The Carys' youngest daughter, Alice Cary Pick Gibson, also would be buried in Pine Hill Cemetery, but she rests in another plot, perhaps one hundred feet north of her parents and her brother. The Carys' other daughter, Phoebe Cary Shoemaker, died in 1975 and is buried in the Memorial Cemetery in Abbeville, Alabama. The Cary family plot sits in the middle of a slope running from Pine Hill's southeast corner, and from the rise above where Dr. Cary was buried, trees part in the distance to offer the cemetery's best view of the clock tower of Samford Hall on campus. That view looks to the northwest, in the direction of Ames, Iowa, where his formal education took place.

If they exist, some forgotten scribbled notes might convey for a modern audience the words said in tribute to Dr. Cary in Langdon Hall or graveside at Pine Hill Cemetery that April Saturday in 1935. Whatever was said by Dr. Cary's peers, friends, and colleagues at his memorial service, surely the finest tribute the departed dean would receive was in the form of a letter to the editor of the *Auburn Plainsman* written the day he died by veterinary student Morris David Schneider.

That letter follows in its entirety:

April 24, 1935
Neil O. Davis,
Editor, The Plainsman.

Dear Sir,

I wish to be very brief in this introduction. Really, I am at a loss as to the manner of introducing myself. However, I am a student at Auburn, the Veterinary School, and I wish to submit to The Plainsman,
My Tribute To a Most Beloved Man—Dr. Charles Allen Cary, Dean of the School of Veterinary Medicine;
The day was beaming with the laughing splendor of spring; the sun

beat down upon me from its regal place in the sky with a pervading warmth. I have not seen a jollier day in weeks. Even the tiny blades of grass rejoiced as I trod over them. And as I continued with this promenade the mild breeze tenderly kissed each blade of grass; each one, as if overcome with rapture, swayed lightly backward; then straightened again. But with all this shining happiness about me I walked, sad and dejected toward the Hill.

On the way I met students descending the Hill. We greeted each other in the same polite Southern manner, "Hi," but the voices trembled a bit. They, too, walked with dragging feet. Behind me others followed slowly, hesitatingly. Funny how speech had suddenly become paralyzed.

My feet were heavy when I at last reached the top of the Hill. I glanced about me, and my emotional being at once felt a stimulus. My inner-self battled furiously against my stern repression of feeling, and when I satisfied my brain with a second picture I knew I could never belong to the school of the Stoics.

The usual stir and bustle on "Vet Hill" had suddenly undergone a marked change. A solemn stillness filled the air, a silence of profound worshipful reverence. I deliberated for a moment, and thought to myself how unmistakably contrasted this day was to yesterday and other days before.

I turn back the pages of my youthful life, and I can't find a single individual for whom my admiration and ingenious respect has matured so rapidly. I have known him so short a period; I grieve I had not known him longer. His presence was absolutely magnetic, dynamic, hypnotizing. What was it about individuality that made me stretch my head forward each morning, and strain my brain to drink in his soothing, precious words? And can I explain why, when he had spoken, I relaxed completely in my seat and incessantly turned over in my mind those same spoken words? How could such an eccentric little man exert such a powerful influence upon me?

His lectures made my tongue cleave to the roof of my mouth; I was so fascinated. During afternoon clinics I gazed spellbound, in thorough amazement, as he brilliantly diagnosed case after case; his diagnostic ability baffled me in words beyond description.

He was rightfully named the "King," for he was truly sovereign, reigning supreme in the dominion of his dreams. "Vet Hill" was his heart and soul, his life, and even though his body has departed from the present life, yet will his heart, his soul, his life continue to reign over his precious "'Vet Hill'; the spirit of the "King" will remain forever on "Vet Hill."

Beloved old man, you are gone from sight, but those who think of you have your picture indelibly painted in their hearts.

That is why I feel dejected today; why so many others walk about speechless and mournful. A noble man has passed away, an irreparable loss among good men.

Sincerely yours,
Morris David Schneider[8]

A monthly newspaper published up the road from Auburn in Camp Hill, *The Industrial Student*, a publication of the Southern Industrial Institute, in its May 1935 issue offered these remembrances, authored by institute founder and Editor Lyman Ward:

Dr. Charles Allen Cary

Alabama has no greater son than him whose name I have just indited. Some of our friends we endow with immortality. I have never thought that I should live in Alabama when Dr. Cary was not. The lofty buildings at the Alabama Polytechnic Institute, his own spacious and beautiful home at Auburn, were to me no more permanent than the figure of Charles Allen Cary. Dr. Cary preceded me by some five or six years in residence in this state. He came to Auburn about 1893 . . . His life from that day constitutes a romantic chapter, not only in the history of Auburn but in the history of the state. One might say in simple truth that the whole program of Veterinary Science in Alabama is co-extensive with the life of Dr. Cary in Alabama.

Soon after my arrival in Camp Hill in 1898, Dr. Cary came to Camp Hill to make an address and he spent the night at my house. From that day we have been friends. I have met him here and there and yonder. He has always been to me the same simple, unaffected, gentleman. He has built up at Auburn one of the largest schools of Veterinary Science in the South. He has been Auburn's first and only dean in that Department.

Space forbids even the cataloguing in this article of the many activities of Dr. Cary. I frequently met him in Montgomery. I last saw him at his favorite hotel there. One of my pleasantest memories is a ride with him on the train one summer's night from Montgomery to Auburn. We talked of course about his favorite work. He related to me this incident: There had been for many years all sorts of laws enacted by various legislatures of the state [related] to Veterinary Science. It occurred to Dr.

Cary some years ago that it would be a great convenience not only to him but to others if these laws were codified. Someone suggested that he see the Attorney General about the matter. Dr. Cary found the Attorney General perfectly agreeable and he promised to attend to the matter soon. Dr. Cary called on this official from time to time for several months but found that no progress was being made. Finally the Attorney General, good naturedly said to Dr. Cary, "Why don't you codify these laws yourself?" Dr. Cary immediately replied that he should be very glad to do so if it could be understood that he was not intruding upon the prerogatives of the Attorney General. With this understanding, Dr. Cary codified the laws of Veterinary Science for Alabama and took his work to the Attorney General. This official simply attested what Dr. Cary had done and the result was a volume of codified laws of Veterinary Science.

No one will be found who can combine so admirably the varied accomplishments of Charles Allen Cary. His Department will go on with conquest after conquest. His graduates will take up the torch which he has born with such signal courage, and scale new heights. All honor to this hero.[9]

The API Board of Trustees' next meeting after Dr. Cary's death was not until February 12, 1936, so it was with some delay that the Board approved a brief and somewhat understated resolution lauding Dr. Cary:

WHEREAS, death on April 24, 1935, removed Doctor Charles Allen Cary from the faculty of the Alabama Polytechnic Institute after forty-three years of service, being dean of the School of Veterinary Medicine since 1907, and

WHEREAS, Doctor Cary distinguished himself at the Alabama Polytechnic Institute by the outstanding work he did as an instructor, professor, dean, and leader, rendering lasting and invaluable service to the people of Alabama and the nation,

THEREFORE, be it resolved, that we recognize the great loss to this institution caused by Doctor Cary's death and express to Mrs. Cary and other members of his family our high appreciation of Doctor Cary and our sympathy with them because of their bereavement and loss.

Weeks after Dr. Cary's death, Emma Cary generously gave much of her late husband's veterinary and science book collection to the School of Veterinary Medicine he had founded. Those books, when joined with existing volumes Dean Cary had personally ordered for the program and housed in the college library, launched the Cary Veterinary Library. The collection remains a vital resource for the College and is one of two Auburn University collections housed at its school rather than in the Ralph Brown Draughon Library (The School of Architecture's collection is the other housed on-site at the main architecture building, Dudley Hall.) The veterinary collection is housed in the College of Veterinary Medicine's Greene Hall—named after the school's fourth dean, James E. Greene—and remains known as the Cary Veterinary Library.

Ten months after Dr. Cary's death, on Friday, February 21, 1936, the Alabama Veterinary Medical Association held its next scheduled meeting at Auburn, and the association and the school's faculty and students took that opportunity to pause in their work, gather in Langdon Hall, and remember their fallen leader. After what the *Plainsman* described as "a solemn musical prelude and a touching invocation by the Rev. S. B. Hay, of Auburn," Dr. I. S. McAdory paid tribute to his mentor:

> It is fitting that, in the turmoil and stress of life, we pause and pay tribute to those who have gone before. As we travel along life's highway, we are brought face to face with the fact that life is brief and that, ere long, we too, shall fall asleep.
>
> We are assembled here to pay tribute to one of Alabama's great men, Dr. Charles Allen Cary. Dr. Cary was a scholar, a teacher, a leader and a molder of men. To the north, south, east, and west, and in many foreign countries, his students have entered fields of successful service.
>
> For thirty years I sat at the feet of this great instructor and gained knowledge from his teaching and inspiration from his example. On the morning of April [24], 1935, when a phone call came from his home, I rushed over, and upon entering his room, found that death had preceded me . . . my friend, my leader, my teacher was gone. There is an emptiness in my life that cannot be filled.

There came to the podium a succession of officials paying tribute:

Alabama Commissioner of Agriculture R. J. Goode, whose association with Dr. Cary included collaboration on state administrative and legislative activities.

Dr. R. E. Jackson of the Bureau of Animal Industry's Alabama branch, who in 1906 worked with Dr. Cary to begin the monumental, quarter-century-long program on tick eradication efforts in the state. The two would work on several other agricultural, veterinary, and public health issues and would become close friends in the process.

Dr. J. C. Flynn of Kansas City, president of the American Veterinary Medical Association.

Dr. J. S. Andrade of Huntsville, president of the Alabama Veterinary Medical Examining Board.

Dr. T. M. Dennis of Clanton, president of the Alabama Veterinary Medical Association. On behalf of the association, Dr. Dennis presented to the school a life-sized oil portrait of Dr. Cary, painted by local artist Mrs. Clyde J. Moore. That painting hangs as first in the line of dean portraits in the entrance lobby of the College of Veterinary Medicine's administrative building, James E. Greene Hall.

On that February day in 1936, the Alabama Veterinary Medical Association and the State Examining Board presented to the school another memorial recognizing Dr. Cary's service and achievement in the form of a bronze plaque, which eventually was displayed in Cary Hall. Today, the plaque decorates the main entrance hallway of Greene Hall, outside the dean's office, where all visitors can see it. That plaque reads:

CHARLES ALLEN CARY, B.S., D.V.M.
1861-1935
PROFESSOR OF VETERINARY MEDICINE AND FIRST
DEAN OF THE SCHOOL OF VETERINARY MEDICINE,
ALABAMA POLYTECHNIC INSTITUTE 1892-1935
ALABAMA STATE VETERINARIAN 1907-1935
PRESIDENT OF THE AMERICAN VETERINARY
MEDICAL ASSOCIATION 1919
PRESENTED BY THE
ALABAMA STATE VETERINARY MEDICAL
ASSOCIATION AND THE EXAMINING BOARD

Both the oil portrait and the bronze plaque were draped at the ceremony, with Phoebe Cary Shoemaker unveiling those items memorializing her father. Accepting the portrait and plaque was API President Luther Duncan.

API may have offered another tribute, albeit temporary in nature, to its late dean in the form of a street name. A ticket stub from the 1954 home football game with Chattanooga, owned by Dr. and Mrs. Cary's granddaughter-in-law, Fran Dillard, has, printed on its back side, a simple campus map showing the ticket holder how to approach then-Cliff Hare Stadium. The street north of the football field is Thach Avenue, known in its early days as Faculty Avenue. South of the field, the ticket stub shows "Cary Street." Today, that street has been re-routed and renamed as Donahue Drive, in memory of long-ago Auburn Coach Mike Donahue. The location of that era's Cary Street was near to veterinary activities in the 1940s, suggesting the likelihood that the institution designated that road in memory of Dr. Cary, at least for a few years.

A more permanent campus memorial was soon in place, more fitting than a street name. Cary Hall was dedicated to Dr. Cary's memory late on the afternoon of Wednesday, February 27, 1946—during the school's annual short course for veterinarians. Dr. W. W. Staples, president of the Alabama Veterinary Medical Association that year, presided at the dedication ceremony, attended by "large numbers of veterinarians from all sections of the country."[10] API President Duncan formally dedicated the building. Dean Cary's good friend and fellow dean, Dr. George Petrie, spoke on "The Life and Contributions of Dean Charles A. Cary." A portion of what Dr. Petrie said of Dr. Cary on that occasion:

> He had accomplished far more in a lifetime than most men do. These accomplishments were due in part to his vigor of mind and body and to his untiring industry, but also to his thorough preparation for his work.
>
> His energy, his enthusiasm, and his fine training soon bore abundant fruit. He organized the course in Veterinary Medicine, which was a pioneer in such work in the South; and, as Dean since 1907, steadily improved it until at the time of his death it was probably the foremost in all this region and recognized as such by the leading organizations in the United States. Beginning in a small wooden building about where Ramsay Hall now stands, it has grown, largely during his lifetime, until the buildings now cover "Vet Hill" and have culminated in this fine home for his beloved "Vet Science" which we are today dedicating to his memory.
>
> But his work was not confined to Auburn, he served all of Alabama, as well as the South and the nation. He organized farmers' institutes and summer courses, and held Saturday clinics for all who could come. He founded the Alabama Veterinary Medical Association and was President of the Alabama Live Stock Association. He was father of the Alabama

Meat and Milk Inspection Laws and was the grand-daddy of the fight for Tick Eradication in the South. And when I say "fight," I mean it. And he gave his strong personal support to the movement for the eradication of tuberculosis in domestic animals. In his spare moments (and I do not know how he ever found any) he wrote numerous articles for scientific journals and a well-known book on "Southern Diseases of Animals." Is it any wonder that he was made President of the American Veterinary Medical Association?

This was a great career, one of which all Auburn is proud and which I take pleasure in summarizing. But behind all these was the living man whom I knew for over forty years, and I cannot close these brief remarks without saying something about him personally.[11]

Dean Petrie then repeated the comments he had given the *Plainsman* reporter when Dr. Cary died.

Almost eleven years after Dr. Cary's death—and a little over two years after Dr. Petrie had written "The Auburn Creed"—the eighty-year-old, frail, and by-then-retired historian stood on the steps of Cary Hall, speaking of the fellow dean he had known and admired since Dr. Cary had arrived in 1892. Dean Petrie did not recite his creed on this day. But "The Auburn Creed"—which has come to symbolize the essence of the ideal Auburn experience, a world view that generations of Auburn men and women have read and against which they are asked to measure themselves—represents the ideals, characteristics, and integrity by which Dean Petrie had lived, and which he also had found in a number of Auburn leaders he had known in his time on campus and in town.[12] The creed's extolling of hard work, education, honesty, and service certainly describe the character of Charles Allen Cary.

On the final Friday of October, 2007, those who remained of Dr. Cary's family, and many of his professional descendants in the College of Veterinary Medicine family, gathered on the front lawn of Cary Hall for the dedication of a historic marker noting Dr. Cary's achievements at Auburn and the building itself. This marker unveiling was organized by then-Assistant Dean Dr. Gary Beard, a 1959 graduate of the College. The event featured remarks by one of Dr. Cary's successors, then-Veterinary Medicine Dean and future Provost Timothy Boosinger, as well as Dr. Cary's great-grandson, Charles Pick of Auburn. The occasion was jointly sponsored by the Auburn Heritage Association and the Historic Chattahoochee Commission. The historic marker was paid for by contributions from the veterinary college's Centennial Club and the Alabama VMA, both of which have ties to Dean Cary. The Centennial Club is a fundraising group of veterinary college graduates whose group name comes from its having been established in 1992, the centennial anniversary year of Dr. Cary's coming to Auburn to launch the veterinary science program. The Alabama VMA, of course, Dr. Cary resurrected, calling its re-organizational meeting in 1907 and serving as its secretary/treasurer from then until he died.

Cary Hall remains the primary named memorial to the man on the Auburn campus, the veterinary library being the other. Cary Hall was built during 1938-39 as the headquarters for the veterinary program and officially opened in 1940, during the campus presidency of Dr. Duncan, as a New Deal Works Project Administration facility, one of fourteen such campus projects completed under this program. The three-story, 26,500-square-foot building cost $200,000 to construct. Dr. Cary's original right-hand man, Dr. McAdory, oversaw some aspects of the construction as dean. After Veterinary Medicine's administrative and basic science offices and labs moved to the Wire Road location in 1970, Cary Hall was used for a time by the Department of Industrial Engineering. Later, the College of Sciences and Mathematics' Department of Biology made its home there.

Dr. Beard and faculty member Dr. Charles Hendrix, a member of the Auburn Heritage Association, collaborated on the text for the original marker which, of necessity, was replaced during 2018-2019. The text for the replacement sign reads, on one side:

CARY HALL
Built 1940
A Memorial to Dr. Charles Allen Cary (1861-1935)

Dr. Charles Allen Cary, a native of Iowa and graduate of Iowa State in 1887, came to Auburn in 1892 and taught the first class of veterinary science at the Agricultural and Mechanical College of Alabama (now Auburn University). He has been called the Father of Veterinary Medicine in the South. In 1896, he helped to establish the first meat and milk inspection system in the United States. Named the first Alabama State Veterinarian in 1907, Dr. Cary became dean of the newly formed College of Veterinary Medicine, the first in the South, in 1907. Innovative campaigns to eradicate bovine tuberculosis, Texas tick fever, and hog cholera were just a few of Dr. Cary's accomplishments, as well as work with brucellosis. He was President of the American Veterinary Medical Association, Executive Secretary of the Alabama Veterinary Medical Association, and President of the Alabama Livestock and United States Livestock Sanitary Associations.

Erected by Auburn Heritage Association and
Historic Chattahoochee Commission
2019
Funded by the College of Veterinary Medicine Centennial Club and the
Alabama Veterinary Medical Association

And from the other side:

Dr. Cary's practical teaching methods included performing animal surgery under a campus shade oak to instruct his students. His Saturday clinics and summer institutes taught farmers about the prevention and treatment of animal diseases. When he was nominated to the Alabama Hall of Fame in 1957, it was stated Dr. Cary did more for Alabama livestock production and for the protection of the purity of food products than any other man of his time.

Reflecting on the life and work of Charles Allen Cary, Dr. Calvin Schwabe, Auburn '54, said during a November 1992 centennial remembrance of Dr. Cary's arrival in Auburn that the great dean had a place of prominence among those first-generation American veterinarians who looked to their maturing science to solve problems and create for their fellow man a brighter future.

He was one of a scant handful or so of idealistic and hardworking men who—under the most difficult circumstances, including widespread public derision—saw clearly from the onset that veterinary science's total impact upon society could make it a powerful economic and human health force for public betterment. That was an accurate vision of veterinary medicine that went far beyond the readily obvious good that could be accomplished by a comparatively small cadre of persons trained to heal individual animals and to offer practical grassroots-level aid to farmer-owners within an agricultural system then highly dependent upon animal-power. Especially in beginning here at Auburn the creation of an educated profession of veterinary medicine within the southeastern United States, Cary demonstrated a remarkably broad understanding of what that could—and ultimately would—mean for mostly poor farming populations of this region. And then, through an amazing display of energy, he ultimately extended his own influence and Auburn's considerably beyond the borders of this state. I can think of no other veterinarian who more profoundly influenced through his professional lifetime the health and well-being of a whole region of his country than did Charles Allen Cary.[13]

During that same 1992 Cary centennial event, another of Auburn's distinguished veterinary graduates, Dr. Wilford S. Bailey '42, suggested that Dr. Cary's personal attributes—the ones that likely had the most influence on his accomplishments—included absolute honesty and sincerity; a motivation to bring help to others; an idealism that paired with a vision for what was possible; courage; dependability; energy and an enthusiastic spirit of industry; excellent training and devotion to being prepared for his work; and his having read broadly. There were other attributes that drove Dr. Cary and which benefited him in his pursuits, of course, but to Dr. Bailey's thinking, those were the most significant.

"Fortunately, by virtue of his genetic makeup, environment (much of which must be attributed to his parents), and his training, Charles Allen Cary had the combination of these attributes," Dr. Bailey said. "And of equal importance, he took advantage of them to achieve what few in any age are able to accomplish. Those of us privileged to follow in the house which he built can take great pride in his accomplishments and what they have made possible for us."[14]

CHAPTER EIGHTEEN

DR. CARY'S LEGACY

Visitors descending to the crypt of London's massive St. Paul's Cathedral can find the tomb of the building's architect, Sir Christopher Wren. Unlike some of Wren's permanent neighbors, who rest within elaborately constructed graves—Admiral Nelson and the Duke of Wellington among them—Wren is buried beneath a simple slab of dark marble. An understated inscription identifies him as "the builder of this cathedral." On the wall above his tomb, however, a plaque offers a more fitting tribute. Written in Latin, it translates, "Reader, if you seek his monument, look around you."

Similarly, one can visit Dr. Cary out in Pine Hill Cemetery. He's buried next to Emma, who died in 1954, and Elwyn in a family plot near the middle of the grounds. But one wishing to see his true monument need only consider the advances in man's fight against tick fever, hog cholera, and tuberculosis. Look at the work of the state veterinarian in modern times as well as the membership of the Alabama Veterinary Medical Association. And, most importantly, consider Auburn University's College of Veterinary Medicine and all that its faculty and its graduates have accomplished during and after Dr. Cary's lifetime.

When he was authorized to take his veterinary science program to the level of a degree-granting school in 1907, Dr. Cary taught a handful of students who were on track to earn the DVM in a three-year curriculum. Today, the College enrolls 120 students in each of its four classes: forty-one Alabamians, thirty-eight from Kentucky through the Southern Regional Education Board agreement (a program devised and championed by Dr. Cary's protégé and successor, Dean Redding Sugg), and forty-one at-large students from across the nation. More than 900 applicants compete for the 120 seats in each first-year class.

With this publication, Auburn has graduated more than 6,500 veterinarians since the first few crossed the commencement stage of Langdon Hall in 1909. The College also has awarded more than 500 master's and PhD degrees in that time, with most of those in the past couple of generations.

The three branches of the land-grant mission are evident in the College's offerings: teaching, research, and outreach.

As in the days of Dr. Cary, the primary work of the College comes in preparing students for careers in veterinary practice. To that end, faculty of the Department of Anatomy, Physiology, and Pharmacology and the Department of Pathobiology teach much of the content in the students' basic sciences curriculum through lectures and laboratories as they build the foundation for further, more intense, hands-on learning. The curriculum includes instruction by faculty affiliated with the College's Scott-Ritchey Research Center.

Faculty in the Department of Clinical Sciences oversee veterinary students' work in the large and small animal clinics, particularly in the senior student rotations, which take fourth-year students through an intensive, case-based "real world" education as they wind down their studies in a fashion similar to Dr. Cary's early "Saturday Clinics." They conclude their time as veterinary students away from Auburn in an eight-week preceptorship, working under the guidance of a veterinarian in his or her clinic, laboratory, zoo, or other setting.

The College also maintains an active, growing research program involving almost all its faculty. Discoveries by Auburn veterinary researchers have led to advancements in such widely varying areas as large animal reproduction, small animal neurology, parasite control, cancer, GM1 gangliosidosis, diabetes type II, avian flu, and canine performance.

In terms of service or outreach, the College operates around-the-clock clinical services for routine and wellness visits, emergency and critical care, and referral large and small animal patients. Students are assigned cases through these clinics as a significant part of their educational experience, but the clinicians represent the best in board-certified specialists and see many thousands of cases every year. Auburn faculty also can be found lecturing or demonstrating at professional gatherings throughout the country and often internationally.

As this book neared completion, the College opened a satellite, referral-only practice in Baldwin County, to extend the College's mission in that part of the state as well as to provide an additional setting for Auburn faculty to offer their services and for students to gain experience in specialty practice.

Auburn graduates have practiced in every US state over the years and they have excelled in every area of veterinary medicine, from clinical work to corporate and academic research to military veterinary service to public health. Since Dr. Cary's time, four Auburn graduates have been elected president of the American Veterinary Medical Association: Dr. Walter L. "Oogie" Martin, Jr. '53 in 1988-89; Dr. Shelton Pinkerton '54 in 1990-91; Dr. Henry E. Childers '54 in 2005-06; and Dr. James O. Cook '76 in 2008-09. Additionally, Dr. Bennett T. Simms '11—one of Dr. Cary's prized early students—served as chief of the Bureau of Animal Industry, and Dr. Lester Crawford '63 served briefly as head of the Food and Drug Administration under President George W. Bush in 2005. Several graduates have served as deans of veterinary schools . . . not only at Auburn (Redding Sugg, James E. Greene, John Thomas Vaughan, and Calvin Johnson), but at several institutions: Oregon State (B. T. Simms and Robert C. Wilson); Tennessee (G. Michael Shires); Kansas State (Tammy Beckham); Texas A&M (Eleanor Green); Missouri (Carolyn Henry); Virginia-Maryland (Greg Daniel); and Lincoln Memorial (Jason Johnson). Innumerable others have held positions of leadership and authority at all levels of veterinary medicine in academic, corporate, government, and military settings.

From its humble beginnings in a nine-room veterinary building on the northern edge of campus in Dr. Cary's early days, the College now boasts some of the finest educational and clinical facilities in all of veterinary medicine. Those include a Veterinary Education Center, with three highly advanced, 150-seat classrooms; the 92,000-square-foot John Thomas Vaughan Large Animal Teaching Hospital complex, completed in 2003; and the Wilford and Kate Bailey Small Animal Teaching Hospital, a 208,000-square-foot facility which opened in 2014.

The Cary family legacy with veterinary medicine came full circle in 2015 when Dr. and Mrs. Cary's great-great-granddaughter, Cary Frances Clark, received her DVM at Auburn's spring commencement.

Dr. Clark received her bachelor's in zoology at Auburn in 2011 and earned admission to the College of Veterinary Medicine as an at-large student from Hampton, Virginia. She was elected president of her class at the College; and, in the spring of 2014, when the new Wilford and Kate Bailey Small Animal Teaching Hospital was dedicated, then-third-year-student Cary Frances Clark was among the speakers at the ribbon-cutting ceremony. Her great-great-grandparents would have been proud, particularly the equality-minded Emma and Dr. Cary, whose life's work focused on advancing society through veterinary medicine and practical education.

ACKNOWLEDGMENTS

There are many folks I wish to thank:

Mary Ellen, for her patience and encouragement and for her sterling and level-headed advice on a regular and ongoing basis. Also, for her unsurpassed editing and proofreading skills.

Four veterinarian friends, in particular, helped in this project with a critical reading of the manuscript: Dean Emeritus Tom Vaughan and Drs. Gary Beard, Dwight Wolfe, and Henry Baker. They tried to help me avoid making major mistakes, and I appreciate their time, valuable advice, and genuine love for their college.

Dr. Beard made possible my front-row seat at the College of Veterinary Medicine for many years by bringing me on board as an editor of the quarterly magazine in 1995. That experience introduced me to the work and the history of the college. Gary's enthusiasm for veterinary medical history and Auburn history helped seal my appreciation for the college, its heritage, its people, and the importance of the work that has gone on—and continues—in its fields, pastures, laboratories, clinics, and classrooms.

For many years, I've counted as a friend Dr. Leah Atkins, one of our state's preeminent historians. Back in the day, I worked with her late husband, George, and got to know Leah through that experience. Leah generously read my manuscript, offered appropriate advice to a novice biographer, and in general pointed me, and the document, in the right direction. Her counsel made a tremendous difference in the quality of the manuscript.

I am grateful to Sid James Nakhjavan and other representatives of our College of Human Sciences, including Dean June Henton, for their interest in this book, in the Cary family, and in the Cary House. In fact, this book was Sid's idea, and I appreciate her confidence in my compiling it.

Three deans of the CVM under whom I worked, three tremendous leaders who in their own ways have been wonderful successors to the founding Dean Dr. Cary: the aforementioned Dean Vaughan, former Auburn Provost Dr. Tim Boosinger, and current Dean Dr. Calvin Johnson (who championed this book to publication). Dean Vaughan, particularly, was helpful as he alerted me to the truth behind an age-old legend. He also gave the unforgettable advice: "In a biography, not *everything* has to be included."

Cary family members, particularly Dr. and Mrs. Cary's grand-daughter-in-law, Fran Dillard. Fran generously allowed me to borrow a number of precious items of their family's heritage for my research, and I appreciate her trust in me. I should also mention the late Alice Cary Pick Gibson, whom I never met but who I remember seeing around Auburn late in her life. She preserved in boxes in the Cary House attic many important family documents, photos, papers, and mementos which were made available to me.

I would also like to thank as an institution the Auburn University Libraries, including the staff of the Cary Veterinary Library, where I accomplished a fair amount of the early research. Also the staff of the Draughon Library and its dean during this project, the now-retired Dr. Bonnie MacEwan. I am particularly grateful to my friends in the Department of Archives and Special Collections: Assistant Dean Aaron Trehub, Archivist Tommy Brown, Librarian Greg Schmidt, Library Tech Specialist Jennifer Wiggins, Library Assistant John Varner, and AU Archives' now-retired director, Dwayne Cox, who was on duty when I began. They—the folks at AU Archives—have been, time and again, tremendously helpful to me in this work and patient with my making the Archives my second home.

My years at the College of Veterinary Medicine brought me into contact with a large number of faculty, staff, alumni and their spouses, and many special people who support the college financially either because they have had animals treated at Auburn or they simply believe in the importance of good training for future veterinarians.

It's not practical to name all those folks, but all inspired me, and I hope each realizes their part in this story.

Finally, I depended on and made heavy use of a number of books that capture various aspects of Auburn's history, both city and university. I would like to acknowledge my debt to the great work the authors of those books have done, which helped me toward better understanding of the time and place and people about whom I have written in this book.

Those authors would include, but are not limited to:

Drs. Ralph Brown Draughon, Jr., Delos Hughes and Ann Pearson, authors of *Lost Auburn: A Village Remembered in Period Photographs*; Mollie Hollifield, long-ago author of a history, *Auburn: Loveliest Village of the Plain*; Mike Jernigan, author of *Auburn Man: The Life and Times of George Petrie*; Mickey Logue and Jack Simms, authors of *Auburn: A Pictorial History of the Loveliest Village*, now in its third edition; Mary Pruett Norman and Daniel Webster Hollis, III, members of the Auburn Heritage Association, for their book, *Auburn Sweet Auburn: History, Stories and Epitaphs of Pine Hill Cemetery, 1836-2010*; and Drs. Joe Yeager and Gene Stevenson, authors of *Inside Ag Hill*.

APPENDIX A

DR. CARY'S PRESIDENTIAL ADDRESS AT THE AVMA CONVENTION, COLUMBUS, OHIO, AUGUST 1919

Published in Volume 57 of the *Journal of the American Veterinary Medical Association*, April-September 1920, Pages 630-637.

NOVELTY and newness (new things, unexpected and unknown things) attract attention, excite interest and are quickly carried to the world public. The public wants exciting, thrilling news, and the daily papers supply the demand. The medical man is not unlike the average man. He has a keen outlook for new things, discoveries, and too many times he is not sufficiently conversant with the well-established facts that would make him more efficient in his profession. It is not my purpose to say that our Association shall be so conservative that it can not grow, or shall be so progressive and radical that it may grow rapidly and then rapidly decay. Unhealthy growth spells decay. Too much conservatism prevents growth.

Limitations of the Presidency

Some of our members seem to think that the President of the AVMA had unlimited powers. His official time is short, and his preparation, experience, and knowledge of the workings of the Association are very limited. Sometimes he can not get definite and positive facts about questioned subjects before his term in office expires. His powers are largely suggestive and appointive rather than constructive. And I suspect that the limited executive powers of the President are for the good of the Association. As a rule hasty changes, revolutionary or radical in effect, should not be made. Hence the value of suggestive, constructive changes, which give time for the members of the Association to measure and consider before adopting them. In suggesting I do not wish to assume the place of a prophet, or to be too arbitrary, or overreach the conditions and facts. I have at heart the good of the profession and the welfare of this great Association.

Observe and consider here that it would be a great help to the President and all officials of the Association if a copy of the business proceedings of each meeting were printed and placed in the hands of each officer and member very soon after the meeting. I have been unable to act promptly and have made some errors because I did not have such a copy.

We have five Vice-Presidents, and they have no definite work to do. It seems to be unjust to them to give them honor without work. I do not think they love mere ornamentation. Why not make these officers mean something? If possible make them into a committee or require them to give five- or ten-minute written annual reports on their respective districts, and elect these men to represent their districts.

Representation in Other Bodies

Our relation to the decennial convention that revises the United States Pharmacopoeia is one that should be considered and some action taken at this meeting. As suggested by Dr. Mohler, a Special Committee on Pharmacopeia should at once be created. This committee should at once prepare a list of drugs to be recommended to the Committee on Revision for induction into the Pharmacopoeia. Arrangement also should be made by this special committee for the admission of the American Veterinary Medical Association to membership in the decennial convention on the revision of the United States Pharmacopoeia.

No funds were available for a membership or a delegate to the National Research Council of the National Academy of Science. The affiliation can be secured if funds are made available to pay the expenses of a representative of this Association to that convention.

The New Army Veterinary Law

A few words about the new Army veterinarian may not be out of place. There are defects and good things in the new veterinary law. According to Officer John H. Gould, the most valuable feature of the new law on the Veterinary Corps is the acquisition of rank up to and including colonel. There may be many other good things come out of this new law that time and its application will bring out. While we have a very efficient and capable chief in Colonel Morse, who is now acting head of the Veterinary Corps, we can not and should not forget that our interest would be handled to our greater satisfaction, and I trust, with equal and possible better efficiency, with a veterinarian at the head of the Corps. It may take time to make the new Veterinary Corps function at its best under the new law, and by the time the new machinery gets to running we can secure another or many other advances that make for better efficiency, and then the standard may be raised. It is not my purpose to enumerate and discuss the defects in the new law. They will come out as it is put into action. And the Army veterinarians should keep our Committee on Legislation informed so that we can secure legislative improvements. I do not think it would be all that wise for personal bickerings or fights about petty or big promotions to become the foundation of our work for better and improved legislation. Such things have held us back and down in times past. Sink personal prejudices and selfishness and see the good that may come to the future Army veterinarian and the profession in a higher standard, a more equitable or favorable (as to time and service) system for promotions, more officers (active and reserve), and all other things commensurate with the requirements of a modern and growing army.

The Educational Problem

Lest I be found wanting, let me touch the great question of veterinary education. Someone has said that human medicine is made up of "facts, statistics, theories, speculations, probabilities and even possibilities," and that the student at best can take only a very small, carefully prepared, digestible, or even a predigested, portion of this great mass of knowledge and theory. Would it not be wise and simplify our teaching if the best qualified men in our profession were to sift and select the facts and the best theories in veterinary medicine and then to advise our teachers and institutions to teach and demonstrate to the student that which we know, and not waste too much time on hypotheses, speculations, probabilities and even possibilities that never

‿f baked but become factors in confusion in the minds of the ‿nt? What a field for work! Why should book writers compile ‿rks on medicine when so little of the contents are known from the experience of the writer and he possesses no means of verifying them?

The United States Civil Service Commission has recently ruled that the entrance requirements of all accredited veterinary colleges shall not be less than fourteen high-school units and the course shall cover four years in length. Hereafter all recognized colleges must equal that standard or their graduates can not stand civil-service examinations for Federal appointments. There does not appear any reason for decreasing or going backward in entrance requirements. If anyone should be so unwise as to advocate easier requirements, let him recall where the veterinary graduate stood when the tests were made of professional men in the United States Army.

A selected committee of highly qualified, disinterested men can visit every veterinary college on this western hemisphere and find a few good and efficient teachers in each and every school. However, there are inefficient teachers and instructors. Some teachers may know facts but can not lead or get the student to grasp them, or develop mental ability, activity or skill or art. Some teachers waste time in trying to make students learn and believe possibilities. For example, some teachers stuff the student with too many unimportant, useless facts. Too much of a student's time is wasted in trying to make him memorize unimportant details in anatomy. I hope to see the time when anatomy will be taught only in the dissecting room and be confined, for the undergraduate, to gross anatomy, and let the detail anatomy be given to students and post-graduates who study special anatomy for specialty practice. Quit wasting the time and mental energy of the student on the long-drawn-out anatomy of the solipeds, and give more general dissecting-room anatomy of the ox, sheep, hog, dog, cat and poultry.

Again, there are too many teachers who are in colleges because of lack of money on the part of the college to get better teachers. In some instances very good teachers for some subjects are not available. Can this be changed? Not now. When the colleges get more money and the teachers stop wasting the time of the students on the excess of nonessentials and confine their instructing and laboratory demonstrations to the fundamental and plain facts, will there be developed teachers, students and veterinarians who may grow into any specialty by study, practice and post-graduate work.

Let the laboratory teachers stop trying to empty all the questionable things into a student's head and expect him to analyze and retain and use them. Take modern bacteriology. The student is required to remember a multitude of details about a great number of germs, some of which are so uncertain and vague that the expert bacteriologists fight and disagree about their cultural and biological characters. Why not confine the teaching of such a subject to the best-known pathogenic bacteria, and leave all the rest for the man who can and will get it if he becomes a specialist? To be brief, too many teachers (didactic and laboratory teachers) believe that the whole knowledge of medicine is confined to his special subject, and then proceed to cram it all into the student, without ever stopping to consider that the general medical student must acquire some knowledge of other subjects.

Want of properly conducted clinics is a defect in some veterinary colleges. Too many of the teachers have had no field experience, and they develop a peculiar, narrow method of college or highly scientific clinics and are so exact that the student never meets the same conditions in actual practice of any kind when he leaves the college walls.

If there be one phase or feature of the domestic animal life that the veterinarian should know in its fullness, it is animal husbandry. How few veterinary schools give a reasonably full course in animal husbandry! The veterinarian must know how to judge feed and breed and to handle all kinds of farm animals. To do this he must have practice in handling and judging and feeding. He must know much about the dairy industry, sheep husbandry, swine and poultry breeding, and feeding and marketing.

In order to maintain and advance the standard of veterinary medical education in America the college must have:

(1) High entrance requirements, based not only on general educational credits, but also on credits founded on practical experience, educational and other work.

(2) Better teachers must be obtained, more all-time teachers who know by instruction and experience and can do real teaching.

(3) The laboratory work in the college must be more definite and confined to what are the facts and not waste so much time on theory and speculation.

(4) The college should be located where ample space for buildings, yards and fields may be obtained and where sufficient cattle, horses, mules, sheep, swine, poultry, dogs and cats for clinical dissection and other laboratory uses may be obtained.

(5) Buildings should be constructed and arranged upon the unit system, so that the chief departments will have separate buildings, yards, etc. Each building (with very few exceptions) should have only one story. One or two sky-scrapers with all departments crowded into them should be avoided.

(6) The undergraduate course of study should be arranged for average men who have necessary entrance requirements, and not for post-graduates or specialists.

(7) Post-graduate courses may be given to produce specialists in surgery, physiology, pathology, bacteriology, hygiene, parasitology, special animal practice, research work, specialists in municipal, State and Federal sanitary science and police, in meat and milk inspection, in animal husbandry, in dairy practice and in teaching.

(8) In no case should the undergraduate instruction or course attempt to make specialists of all kinds, as has been done in the past. The chief aim should be to give general fundamental medicine to produce or develop practitioners and men who are ready to take up a specialty.

(9) Better field and hospital work should be supplied in all colleges, and, if possible, vacation periods should be spent in hospitals or practice.

(10) It is possible that the entire year should be occupied in some line of educational work. What is now given over (three or four months) to rest and vacation could be spent in practice, in hospitals or in actual college work at some college where summer work is given.

(11) Less time should be wasted on football, other games, holidays and numerous idle periods. If exercise and development are required, let them be in the form of constructive work in gymnasiums, military drill, etc.

Reaching the Practitioners

This Association has a membership of nearly 5,000 veterinarians. The members are largely in the United States and Canada. The greater number are practitioners, yet I judge that not more than 25 per cent of the practitioners are members of our Association. Why this condition? It appears to be due to many factors and conditions. What concerns us is, Wherein is the Association wanting? Is the Association reaching the man in practice? In a great measure it is developing and benefiting many men in practice. But is there not some way by which this Association could get into closer touch with men in practice? The

Association must realize that less than 50 per cent of its members can attend its annual meetings; and, up to date, rarely do 25 per cent of its members attend annual meetings. No organization can hold and influence and benefit or build up its membership of practitioners without giving these field men something to do, some power or influence in the organization. This is not a new idea; it is as old as civilization. Governments are harking back toward pure and simple democracy in which every individual may have some power in government. Our Republic is now about to take on universal suffrage. Kings and emperors are giving way to the rule of the people.

Our Constitution and By-Laws should be amended in some way so that every member in good standing may vote on all important subjects and in the election of all important officers. This matter was considered by the Committee on Revision of the Constitution and By-Laws, and the present adopted Constitution and By-Laws provide that home members may vote to elect members of the Executive Board and on certain referendum subjects. But this does not reach the point of attraction or interest. The Secretary's records will show that too many members are sliding back and out for lack of interest and or non-payment of dues. Obviously there are factors that account for this backsliding or cutting loose from the Association. Would it not be well to have a special committee appointed to make a survey and see if some remedy or changes in our Constitution and By-Laws can be made to meet the wants of the home veterinarians who need our help?

Secretary, Editor and Headquarters

The Secretary is the main working man of this Association. He does more, controls more actions and functions than the President, and justly and rightly so. He comes close to being the heart of the Association. In order to know he must have experience and common sense, executive, clerical and emergency ability. That he may best work and best function, he should have a long term of office and be selected for his good natural sense, executive ability and honesty. To have a good Association it is self-evident that an efficient Secretary must be had. We are not doing what we could because our present arrangements do not call for an all-time Secretary. Now in order to do that it may be necessary to do the next best thing. As Dr. Mayo suggested at Philadelphia, combine the editorship of the official Journal with the secretaryship, and give him sufficient help and let him do both. The duties of Secretary and Editor are closely associated, and the same type of man is essential for both lines of work. If funds permit, it would be still better to have an all-time Secretary and an all-time Editor, and, when possible, departmental editors.

That is not all that may be done to make the Secretary and Editor more helpful and efficient. In addition to an all-time Secretary and Editor, we need an all-time home for this double head and heart of the organization. This home need not be in a big city or at a college. It should be in a small town or city centrally (geographically) located. Why there? Because it would cost less to buy a suitable, commodious, healthy place, house or houses and grounds, and would be away from untoward local influences. In it there should be educational rooms, filing and other rooms for the Secretary and his clerks, and, if necessary, space and rooms for a printing plant. We are ready for the all-time Editor and Secretary and the all-time home. Let us get together and get them, lest we forget our duty and waste more time with an inefficient system that permits us to drift. Look at the good work of the American Medical Association.

Our frequent and sudden changes in Secretary and Editor have given us no stability or definiteness of purpose, and such changes have been financially expensive. For the good of the Association we are sadly in need of a fixed, permanent home. Let us make one and keep it and develop it.

APPENDIX B

DR. CARY'S ADDRESS AS PRESIDENT OF THE UNITED STATES LIVE STOCK SANITARY ASSOCIATION

(As reprinted in the Journal of the American Veterinary Medical Association, *Volume LXXIV, December 1928 June 1929, pages 113 123)*

By C.A. Cary, Auburn, Ala.

Members of the Association and Guests:

Let me review some of the diseases a little. I am not going to try to review them all in the brief time I have, but I want to review some of the diseases which we are trying to handle under our dominion, the live stock sanitary work of these United States.

One of the first things we have to know and must know, if we are going to control, prevent or eradicate a disease, is the cause of that disease. That seems very simple in a good many of them, but when you come to analyze each one of these diseases and to look at them squarely and fairly and be honest about your opinion and the other fellow's opinion as to what we know, you find we don't know a lot about some of them, and yet we are trying to handle them. I will take up some of these individually to show you what I mean.

Tick Eradication

I shall take up the one with which I am most familiar and with which we have done most of our work in the South, that is tick eradication. What do we know about it? We know its cause; we know the hosts of this cause and the carriers of it, and as far as we know all there is to know about it is the animals it is in and whatever else is found. That knowledge gave us this position: We found out where to fight it at its vulnerable point. Knowing that this parasite had different hosts, we decided to attack it in the host that we could destroy. In other words, we wanted to stamp it out by the stamping-out method. And we are doing it over great areas and it is not returning unless we return some of these factors that carry the infection. I don't know of any disease that I have ever worked with in which we have accomplished so accurately and completely the process of eradication. Of course this means the control and prevention of the disease, but in the end it is eradication. I want you to get that point.

I want to project this problem to you. We are never going to get rid of any disease without eradication. I could give you the details of this and you would have it and get it in print, but I am not going to stop to worry you with the details. I want to take up the next disease that is most considered or has most attention and is referred to by Dr. Kegel as the great disease of man and animals, and that is tuberculosis.

Just a moment about that: We handle it, yes; we control it, yes; we prevent a lot of it, yes; and we eradicate it up to a certain point. We have gotten along that far. As we go along with it we annihilate the source of the trouble. What is the end? Eradication. That is successful. The only trouble is that when we think we have got everything we go back and find something that we have left behind once in a while. We find that in tick eradication. We have left behind some infestation of ticks and we have to go back and get it. Right now I gather from the talk given yesterday at the research meeting over at the Sherman House that some places they are leaving infected soil. We don't know all about that yet. There are some points there that we haven't got. We have to go back and get them. It isn't a question of how much we talk about methods and everything else, it is getting all infection before we get rid of it, before we eradicate it. The end is eradication there just as in tick fever, and that is the only salvation if we are going to get anywhere with it and annihilate it. Every once in a while somebody says that can't be done. I know when we started out we didn't know what we could do with tick eradication. The fact of the matter is I met with the first men that started in tick eradication; about four out of six of the men that met in Atlanta to start the movement, statewide and country-wide, were opposed to it and said it could not be done. A lot of men now say tuberculosis cannot be eradicated, but it can and it will be done, especially in domestic animals, if we keep up the fight. We have to do it. (Applause)

Anthrax

I am going after a different kind of disease, just a little bit different than either of these. I just want to say a few words about anthrax, because it gives a type that is entirely different from these two types. That is a more difficult germ to kill. There is going to be no difficulty about our stamping out and destroying all the cattle that have anthrax if we get after it, but there is going to be the most difficulty in destroying that germ in the soil and the infected places because it is a peculiar germ in spore formation that lives a long time, how long we don't know. I have in my laboratory some dried blood that was collected in Mississippi in 1889. We use that dried blood to secure our cultures of anthrax every year in the laboratory for just about forty years. That, of course, is blood protected in a hermetically sealed bottle, but how long does it live over on the deltas of the Mississippi? Have we ever worked on it? No. We don't know a lot about it. Oh, you say up in the laboratory it will do so-and-so. I want to tell you out in the field is different from the laboratory and you don't know a lot about this field condition. Some of you laboratory men rather make me tired once in a while when you tell me how to annihilate anthrax.

Quarantine vs. Vaccination

I have been in the laboratory and I have been in the field now for I don't want to tell you how long, but it is a long time. I had outbreaks of anthrax in my state, and I want to tell you it comes right down to this question of destruction of the cause. I had a whole township infected with anthrax from buzzards from Mississippi. It was a range country, and everybody said, "When you have that, that is the end of it with you; you are going to have it all over your state." If I had listened to some of you laboratory men and some of the veterinarians in my state who wanted to do a little commercial work down there, we would have it yet. The first thing I did was to put a quarantine on it. I wouldn't let a veterinarian go in there and give vaccines. God knows we have spread more anthrax with vaccines than we ever got rid of in this country. (Laughter) Don't get mad at me if you don't agree with me. To prove what you have got to do, I fought on the firing line, and what did I do? We haven't had an anthrax case in that territory since. I can take you there and show it to you. I wouldn't let a man go in there and vaccinate. I put range riders in there, and if a cow died, we didn't let a dog or any animal get to her until we burned her. That was seven or eight years ago and we haven't had a case of anthrax in that territory since. I don't say it is gone; I don't know. But it wouldn't have been gone if I had let them go in there and apply a palliative treatment and let them die and let the buzzards and dogs carry it over and plant it. I don't say we got rid of it, but we certainly did wipe out a lot of it or we would have had more of it show up at this time. That is what we want, sensible methods that work in the field as well as in the laboratory.

I would not talk this way to you but you know I am no spring chicken any more and maybe this is the last time I will get to shoot at you and I am going to hit you good and hard. (Applause) And mark you, I don't say that we are not doing anything to control anthrax in the South. The states are working very well with the conditions, and I am going to tell you a little, as the Doctor said this morning, about political influences. I have a little on infectious abortion, but I will leave that and print it with some other points. The time is rather short and I am not going to bother you with that because it is a live wire right here and we hardly know about some of it, enough for me to discuss it. I will leave these experts to tell you more about it than I can.

Just a word about poultry diseases. We have just taken up this poultry question, and when we took it up, I went over the field pretty well on literature and the pathology of poultry, and the first thing I said to myself was, "If I am going to do anything in live stock sanitary work in the way of controlling, preventing and eradicating poultry disease I have got to know more about it." That is the first thing I said. Now why? Because nearly all of the pathology and a lot of the etiology of poultry diseases have been worked up and have been written up by men who didn't know pathology. Yesterday in the research work, men read pathological work that had never been put out before on some things that we thought we knew. I said to myself when I took this thing up, "In the state of Alabama we have got to know more," and it is coming out just as I anticipated. The research veterinarians have got to work over the pathology of poultry diseases, the causes of poultry diseases, and where these poultry germs and other things live, before we can eradicate poultry diseases.

No Avian Tuberculosis in Alabama

We made a good start in bacillary white diarrhea. We made a good start in tuberculosis of poultry. Let me say just a word about tuberculosis. It is a funny thing to me that when I want to give a demonstration at our short course for veterinarians in Alabama, I have to send to Illinois or somewhere else to get birds to give demonstrations. As far as I know, I haven't seen a tuberculous chicken in the State that was not imported into the State. Isn't that remarkable? What does that? I don't know, but it is true.

Now there is a problem. Some of you fellows who don't get out in the field as I do and go back and forth from laboratory to field don't see these things. Every once in a while somebody says to me, "Why, you are not doing the right thing. You are dean of a college, State Veterinarian, and too many things." I want to tell you this: I will stack my state up against any of them right now. (Laughter and applause)

I am not going to tell you the good and bad things about this white diarrhea disease and tuberculosis in chickens because we have many of them. I am not coming up here to tell you what to do. It is your problem and my problem. The first thing you know I am going to stick a quarantine on all you people up here. (Laughter) When they had foot-and-mouth disease in Texas, I stuck a state-wide quarantine on Texas and said they couldn't take anything out of the State. Everything was under embargo. Some little fellow in Texas who had cotton and oil out there wanted to know what I meant by everything. I wired him back and told him to go to the dictionary and find out. (Laughter)

Let me talk about a different kind of disease than what I have already talked about. I want to say just a few words about hog cholera. We have that and you have that. So far as I know it is about as widely distributed, probably more so, as tuberculosis, especially in hogs. I have no fight to make on what has been done. I say the anti-hog cholera serum discovery and the double treatment was one of the greatest things ever done. Let's look at it squarely in the face. Have we eradicated hog cholera?

Hog Cholera

It is a filtrable disease. We know it is in the hog. Where else do we know it lives? Has anybody found it definitely anywhere else but in the hog, in any of the other animals? Why does it come in the same old way that it came before we got hog cholera serum and virus? There is a problem. I honor the men who have gone as far as they have and I believe it is a great work, but has it brought what we ought to get and has it eradicated hog cholera? Just look over your own field. You needn't take what I say. We haven't eradicated it. It still comes in waves. It is one of these filtrable viruses.

Dr. Kegel said something about smallpox. You may not have as much of this history as I have. I am not a human physician but I know something about smallpox. If you lived in the [derogatory term deleted] country like I do, you would know something about it. (Laughter) Jenner, way over a hundred years ago, discovered cow pox vaccination of men would prevent virulent smallpox in men and they commenced to use it and they did have a lot of good just like we have done with hog cholera. They have broken up little outbreaks here and there when they have run their course and probably stopped the immediate infection in a way. Just as he said about this disease of typhoid out there, when they dropped the bars or let down the sanitary requirements, the cleanliness, the care of milk, typhoid came back. When we in the South don't look after the [individual] and he gets filthy and dirty and under bad conditions, he gets smallpox just as he always did. Have we annihilated smallpox? We haven't annihilated smallpox, we haven't eradicated it; in all these hundred years or more, the human physicians haven't eradicated it. Now why? Because they don't know enough about where this smallpox virus or cow pox virus lives. They say it lives only in the animals, but how they keep it up all the time? How does it come about when we have a looseness in sanitary requirements? In other words we don't know all about it. And I want to drop this remark: Vaccination never eradicated a disease except temporarily. Write that in the history if you want to. It never has done it. Let's go on to a few others of this kind.

Foot-and-Mouth Disease

Just take foot-and-mouth disease caused by a filtrable virus. What has Germany been doing and some of those European countries? They have been trying all kinds of sanitary treatment. Some of them projected vaccination. Have they got rid of it? Doesn't it come out there in cycles and waves? How did we get rid of it? By the stamping-out method, by getting rid of and destroying all the animals and every bit of the infection. That is the only way. We never controlled it by laws to amount to anything. The fact of the matter is, one time down in Texas one uncontrollable Texan said they wouldn't let him do it. Judges got out an injunction against getting rid of foot-and-mouth disease. They had to dissolve that in about a week and they went on and got rid of it. It took two trips to do it, but they did it. How did they do it? By the stamping-out method. They didn't do it by vaccination. We sent a commission over to Europe to discover some method of vaccination or what not, I don't know. I said, "I hope to God they never find out a method of vaccination." (Laughter) I just want to look these fairly in the face because you are live stock sanitarians. What have you got to do? Some things you can only control. Some things you can only slightly prevent. There are a lot of diseases you can destroy and eradicate. That is the end of our work, eradication. I don't say it can be done in all these things, because it cannot.

Probably you have heard enough of my individual experience and ideas of what we are going to do. How are you going to do them? I don't know, but that is one of our problems, to find out, and I am a little bit tired of laboratory men sitting up in the laboratory and telling me just how to eradicate disease in the field. (Laughter) I am not opposed to laboratory work, and they are good workers and they are the kind of men we want and we want a lot of good ones. I just tell you this: All honor to Dr. Theobald Smith for discovering the cause and the carrier of tick fever, but if we had listened to Dr. Cooper Curtice or Dr. Smith in the eradication, we would have been about where we started. They didn't know how to handle this in the field. In all my experience I have never worked in a country in any year where we did not get something new that worked better and faster than anything we had ever had before. That was taught to us by experience. You know Patrick Henry, when he made his famous speech in St. John's Church, said, "The greatest light of the world is the light of experience." We have an idea the laboratory man can furnish us everything. I have no fight with him at all, not a bit.

Let us get clearly in mind immunization is a temporary makeshift that we use when we don't know what else to do. (Laughter) You go after it when you haven't got anything else because you have got to earn your salary. (Laughter)

I have a few words of advice to this Association, and some words to live stock sanitary men. First I am going to pay my respects to the politician who interferes with live stock sanitary work. (Laughter)

Separate Sanitary Work from Politics

This is what we want: Separation of live stock sanitary work from federal, state, county and local politics. Every sanitarian who has had field experience knows that politics has made the work of control, prevention and eradication of animal diseases cost more, take more time, than any other public or private factor. I studied this statement, and I make it and am going to have it printed in the report so you can read it. I am not referring to any criticisms on this state when I give you a notice of what has occurred in tick eradication. One state in the South, since tick eradication has begun, has spent $20,000,000 and has but one or two counties clean of ticks. That has not been the fault of the workers or the government workers. No! It has been the fault of the politicians who interfered with the work, and they are about where they were when they started. Think of a state spending $20,000,000 and having got nowhere. I am not criticizing anybody. These are the conditions there. Isn't that enough to indict a political machine that obstructs good work like that?

Just a word about what the Doctor spoke of this morning, human sanitary control. We have all the advantages of them in the world. They are obliged to take palliative measures once in a while because they can't kill a man to get rid of the disease. They are obliged to take these temporary acts because they can't kill all the children when they get diphtheria. Have they annihilated the disease? The other day right down in my town the doctor had a bacteriological examination of the child's mouth and it had diphtheria. Everybody said, "You oughtn't to have that. What is the matter? Eradicate it." I said, "That is not my work, that is the physician's work." But that shows you that some of these emergency methods, palliative methods, to get by, don't get at the source of the cause. In human medicine they cannot control quarantines like we do. Human people won't stand for quarantine. You can't put them within a fence or a house and lock them up, unless they are in the penitentiary. But they get by somehow.

I am not here to knock human physicians, but I want to mention this fact to you: you hear about this great eradication of mosquitoes. If it were not for the screens, the improved houses, the drainage, and the clean-up, we would be eaten up in the South with mosquitoes. They talk about eradicating them. I don't know anything about the yellow fever. They have done a good deal of the work; I don't say they haven't. But pouring oil on the water is a mighty defective method of getting rid of the mosquitoes in our territory. I don't know about Chicago, but it doesn't work with us. It doesn't get rid of them. Putting mosquito-killing minerals in the water doesn't do much good. Drainage and cleanliness are the greatest things in the world to get rid of mosquitoes, as well as all filth diseases.

The Influence of Politics

How are you going to eliminate politics from the State Board and from the Federal Department? Somebody said they haven't got it up there. I don't know what they have in Washington if they don't have some of it. I am not saying it affects the animal industry department more than others. I have seen some times when they had some influence on the Secretary of Agriculture somehow or other. I don't know how it came about, but it was there. It permeates the make-up of politics from Washington down. That is what it does. You need not tell me that it doesn't, because it does. That is its influence. If you can get live stock sanitary men so placed that they are entirely without the sphere of the politicians you have the best results in the world if you have good men to work it.

I want to say one thing about the states that change state veterinarians every year and sometimes twice a year. (Laughter) How do you expect a state veterinarian to learn anything about his business in a year or two years? He would hardly get the A, B or C out of it in four years, and most of you change your state veterinarians every time you get a new governor. How can you eliminate that I can't tell you; that is your work, but let this Association take that problem up to see if we can't get the sanitarian outside the control of politicians so he can be honest. You know they won't hardly let him be honest if he wants to. I have seen so much of it and have had so much fight about it myself, especially all along the lower lines of the politicians in my State, I have one county which is the last county in the state that has ticks in it. I have had them in the Supreme Court four times. Every time I whip them in the Supreme Court they take an appeal. I am going to fight them if it takes all summer. (Laughter)

Now a few more suggestions. I am not giving you any panacea for political eradication. (Laughter) I am just telling you about a few things that I think we could work out. The old subject of standardization and uniform laws has been discussed and I am not going to take that up. I just suggest that we look that matter over.

Just a word about this Association. I have been this year the head of this Association, and one year I spent at the head of the American Veterinary Medical Association. I want to say a few words about the work of these associations. They are both very much alike in some things. They have some defects. The greatest defect about both organizations is they have top-heavy, overloaded deadwood in committees. What do I mean by that? You have a committee with seven, eight, ten or fifteen on it, and when they get together they talk. Most of you have never been in a faculty meeting in a college, have you? It would remind you sometimes of a lot of old women in a sewing circle. (Laughter) They talk, talk, talk, and get nowhere. Each committee with six or eight members has at least five to six that are dead timber. Three men on a committee can do all the work and do it better than a dozen. I have found this out from experience. I sit with the committees sometimes in an organization, and by George, I can't get in a word edgeways. They talk and talk and do nothing. When you push them for activity, they say, "Let's wait for some other day."

Let's correct that in this organization. Let's cut down this committee work. Then if a committee has to travel anywhere you don't have a lot of extra expense to be carrying this big committee around doing something that you get nowhere with. I believe that is a vital thing of interest. I will admit when you appoint three men on a committee you are going to be more careful about appointing them. You are going to appoint good men; if you don't, you will be responsible for them.

Just another word about this organization. I have to make some of these suggestions, but as I told you, this is the last time I am going to shoot at you. The name of this Association should be changed, just the same as the American Veterinary Medical Association. Why? It is no longer a United States association, in fact it is an American association. Why not say so? That is obvious. It needs no discussion at all. We ought to have it called "The American Live Stock Sanitary Association," just the same as the American Veterinary Medical Association changed its name several years ago from the United States Veterinary Medical Association. That is consistent.

One more, and I will have done. Some may not like what I have to say here, but nevertheless I feel it is my duty to say it. Remember, in saying this I have no fight on any class of people or anybody else, but I have come to this conclusion through years of experience in handling these products and that is this: The potency, real value and standardization of biological products should be more rigidly controlled and regulated so as to protect the houses that make them and also the public that uses them.

I thank you, gentlemen. (Applause)

APPENDIX C

AUBURN UNIVERSITY
COLLEGE OF VETERINARY MEDICINE DEANS

Dr. Charles Allen Cary, 1907-1935
Dr. Isaac Sadler McAdory, 1935-1940
Dr. Redding Stancil Sugg, 1940-1968
Dr. James E. Greene, 1958-1977
Dr. John Thomas Vaughan, 1977-1995
Dr. Timothy R. Boosinger, 1995-2013
Dr. Calvin M. Johnson, 2013-

NOTES

Chapter 1: The Man Who Found Dr. Cary

1. Michael B. Ballard, *Maroon and White: Mississippi State University, 1878-2000*, (University of Mississippi Press, 2008), 25.

2. Tait Butler to Luther Noble Duncan, May 18, 1938, Luther Noble Duncan Presidential Papers, Auburn University Archives.

3. Mike Jernigan, *Auburn Man: The Life & Times of George Petrie* (Montgomery, Alabama: The Donnell Group, 2007), 35.

4. Jack Simms and Mickey Logue, *Auburn: A Pictorial History of the Loveliest Village*, 2013, page 8.

5. Charles Coleman Thach, "Dr. William LeRoy Broun," *Studies in Southern and Alabama History*, in API Historical Papers, Montgomery 1904, 1.

6. Ibid., 8.

7. Ibid., 77.

8. Ibid., 61.

9. Ibid., 77.

10. Ibid., 41.

11. Ibid., 5.

12. Ibid., 7.

13. Ibid., 18.

14. Ibid., 48.

15. *Auburn Sweet Auburn: History, Stories and Epitaphs of Pine Hill Cemetery,* 1836-2010, Auburn Heritage Association, 113.
16. Thach, "Dr. William LeRoy Broun," 14.
17. Malcolm McMillan and Allen Jones, *Through the Years: Auburn From 1856,* 1973. Publication of Auburn University, 5.
18. McMillan and Jones, 7.
19. Thach, 36.
20. Ibid., 90.
21. McMillan and Jones, 7.
22. Simms and Logue, 57.
23. McMillan and Jones, 7.
24. Thach, 15.
25. McMillan and Jones, 9.
26. Jernigan, 29.
27. Ibid., 53.
28. *Auburn Plainsman,* May 2, 1929.
29. *American Times-Recorder,* June 13, 1893, cited in "A Look at Auburn Through Old Newspapers," edited by William L. Dennis, Auburn University Library, 46.
30. *Auburn Alumnus,* November 1915.
31. Jernigan, 61.
32. *Auburn Alumnus,* September 1914.
33. *Auburn Alumnus,* November 1915.
34. Simms and Logue, 72.
35. John M. Heisman and Mark Schlabach, *Heisman: The Man Behind the Trophy,* (New York: Howard Books, 2012), 173.
36. Joe Yeager and Gene Stevenson, *Inside Ag Hill,* Auburn University College of Agriculture, 2000, 17.
37. Ibid., 30.

Chapter 2: Midwesterners

1. Winthrop Worthington, "Pictorial Review of Noted Veterinarians: Charles Allen Cary, B.S., D.V.M.," *American Journal of Veterinary Medicine,* December 1915.
2. Much of the family history in this chapter comes from documents and various papers found in the family's collection.
3. From an unidentified newspaper found in the family's collected papers.

Chapter 3: Forebears

1. This chapter's contents based on information found in the family's copy of

Henry Grosvenor Cary's manuscript, *The Cary Family in England*, published by Rev. Seth Cooley Cary, (Boston, 1906).

Chapter 4: Dr. Cary in Ames

1. B. W. Bierer, *A Short History of Veterinary Medicine in America*, (Michigan State University Press, 1955), 22.
2. Louis A. Merillat and Delwin M. Campbell, *Veterinary Military History*, (Kansas City, Missouri, The Haver-Glover Laboratories, 1935), 176-177.
3. Source online at www.cfsph.iastate.edu/Factsheets/pdfs/bovine_babesiosis.pdf.
4. Source online at www.cfsph.iastate.edu/Factsheets/pdfs/classical_swine_fever.pdf.
5. Source online at www.cfsph.iastate.edu/Factsheets/pdfs/influenza.pdf.
6. Ibid.
7. *Report of the Secretary of the Iowa State Agricultural Society for the Year 1879*, John R. Shaffer, Secretary, Des Moines, 1880, 38.
8. Bierer, 27.
9. *Hog Cholera: Its History, Nature and Treatment*, a publication of the Bureau of Animal Industry/U.S. Department of Agriculture, Government Printing Office, Washington, DC, 1889, 63.
10. "The Veterinary Student," *Iowa State University Veterinarian*: Volume 2: Issue 1, 1939.
11. Charles H. Stange, *History of Veterinary Medicine at Iowa State College*, 1929, Ames, Iowa, 10.
12. Ibid., 6.
13. Merillat and Campbell, 409.
14. Stange, 86.
15. Ibid., 85.
16. Merillat and Campbell, 320.
17. Ibid., 394.
18. Stange, 39.
19. Merillat and Campbell, 394.
20. Stange, 9.
21. Ibid.
22. Ibid, 12.
23. Ibid.
24. Source online at add.lib.iastate.edu/spcl/exhibits/150/template/timeline-1875.html.
25. Stange, 70.
26. Ibid.

27. *Journal of AVMA*, Chicago, Illinois. May 1935, Volume 86, Number 5.

28. Merillat and Campbell, 397.

29. Source online at kcvma.com/about.html.

30. Stange, 77.

31. Source online at lib.dr.iastate.edu/iowastate_veterinarian.

32. Merillat and Campbell, 410.

33. "Millikan Stalker," *The Annals of Iowa* (1909), Volume 9, Issue 3, 239.

34. Stange, 80.

35. *Opelika Morning Post*, December 10, 1897.

36. Martia Graham Goodson, editor, *Chronicles of Faith: The Autobiography of Frederick D. Patterson,* (Tuscaloosa: University of Alabama Press, 1991), 12.

37. Ibid.

Chapter 5: Dr. Cary and the AVMA

1. D. S. Fairchild, "Medical Education in Iowa," *Journal of the Iowa State Medical Society*, 1927, online at iagenweb.org/history/Medicine/PartThird.htm.

2. *American Veterinary Review*, Volume 15, January 1891, 538.

3. *Journal of the American Veterinary Medical Association*, Summer 1935, 705-708.

4. J. F. Smithcors, *The American Veterinary Profession, Its Background and Development*, (Ames: Iowa State University Press, 1963), 481.

5. *American Veterinary Review*, Volume 14, October 1890, 384.

6. Ibid., 387.

7. Smithcors, 482.

8. Ibid., 487.

9. Ibid., 488.

10. Ibid., 517.

11. Ibid., 491.

12. Ibid., 493.

13. Ibid.

14. Ibid., 494.

15. *American Veterinary Review*, Volume 22, 1899, 498.

16. Smithcors, 494.

17. *American Veterinary Review*, Volume 23, 1899, 505.

18. Ibid., 504.

19. Smithcors, 501.

20. *American Veterinary Review*, Volume 25, 1901, 780.

21. From "A History of U.S.A. Water Polo in the Olympic Games," published by U.S. Water Polo, 1996 publication online at waterpolointernational.org.

22. *American Veterinary Review*, Volume 28, 1904-1905, 602.

23. Smithcors, 515.

24. *American Veterinary Review,* Volume 32, 1907, 142.

25. Smithcors, 516.

26. *American Veterinary Review*, Volume 37, 1910, 23.

27. Smithcors, 518.

28. Ibid., 530.

29. Ibid., 523.

30. *Journal of the American Veterinary Medical Association*, Volume 53, 1918, 129.

31. Ibid., 1919.

32. Linda Deitch, "A Grand Hotel at Broad and High," *The Columbus Dispatch*, August 21, 2013.

33. *Journal of the American Veterinary Medical Association*, Volume 57, 1920, 238.

Chapter 6: Dr. Cary in Columbia

1. *Veterinary Medicine: University of Missouri, Columbia, 1872-1968*, Aaron H. Groth, (Columbia: University of Missouri, 1969), 3.

2. Ibid., 4.

3. *American Veterinary Review*, Volume 13, Number 1, April 1889, 53.

4. I. N. Love, MD, editor, *Medical Mirror: A Monthly Reflector of the Profession and Its Progress*, (St. Louis, Missouri, Volume 4, 1893), 535.

5. Source online at shs.umsystem.edu/manuscripts/columbia/1024.pdf.

6. *Kansas City Independent*, January 20, 1917.

7. Source online at cafnrnews.com/2014/02/fever-fighters/.

8. Ibid.

9. *Holt County Sentinel* newspaper, November 21, 1890.

Chapter 7: Auburn, Then Germany

1. William LeRoy Broun to C. A. Cary, William LeRoy Broun Presidential Papers, Auburn University Special Collections and Archives.

2. William LeRoy Broun to C. A. Cary, William LeRoy Broun Presidential Papers, Auburn University Special Collections and Archives.

3. All entries excerpted here from diary of C. A. Cary from 1892, among Cary family items.

4. Excerpts from Dr. Cary's letters to the Jennings, La., *Reporter* taken from copies found in Cary family items.

5. Source online at rki.de/EN/Home/homepage_node.html.

6. Thomas D. Brock, *Robert Koch: A Life in Medicine and Bacteriology*, (Madison, Wisconsin, Science Tech Publishers, 1988), 117.

7. Ibid., 222.

8. William LeRoy Broun to C. A. Cary, William LeRoy Broun Presidential Papers, Auburn University Special Collections and Archives.

9. C. A. Cary to William LeRoy Broun, William LeRoy Broun Presidential Papers, Auburn University Special Collections and Archives.

Chapter 8: The Auburn Dr. Cary Found

1. Allen Johnston Going, *Bourbon Democracy in Alabama 1874-1890*, (Tuscaloosa, University of Alabama Press, 1992), 99.

2. Ibid., 127.

3. Ibid., 83.

4. Sheldon Hackney, *Populism to Progressivism in Alabama*, (Princeton: Princeton University Press, 1969), 81.

5. Agricultural and Mechanical College of Alabama Board of Trustees Minutes, June 13, 1890.

6. Agricultural and Mechanical College of Alabama Board of Trustees Minutes, June 10, 1891.

7. Agricultural and Mechanical College of Alabama Board of Trustees Minutes, January 13, 1892.

8. Agricultural and Mechanical College of Alabama Board of Trustees Minutes, June 13, 1892.

9. Merillat and Campbell, 139.

10. Ibid., 316

11. Ibid., 409-422.

12. Agricultural and Mechanical College of Alabama Board of Trustees Minutes, June 13, 1892.

13. Agricultural and Mechanical College of Alabama Board of Trustees Minutes, June 12, 1893.

14. Ibid.

15. Agricultural and Mechanical College of Alabama Board of Trustees Minutes, September 7, 1893.

16. *Glomerata*, 1897, 29.

17. Yeager and Stevenson, 9.

18. Agricultural and Mechanical College of Alabama Board of Trustees Minutes, June 15, 1894.

19. Ibid.

20. Draughon, Hughes and Pearson, 14.

21. *Auburn Alumnus*, June/July 1936, 12.

22. T. R. Gray, "Opening of New Auburn Construction Era Recalls Pioneer Main Hall," *Auburn Alumnus*, December 1929, 7.

23. *College Index*, January 1893, Volume 1, Number 3, 27.

24. *College Index*, June 1893, Volume 1, Number 8, 29.

25. Emma Cary, "History of Auburn College-Woman's Club Closely Linked," *Lee County Bulletin*, March 9, 1944.

26. Malcolm McMillan, *Auburn Presbyterian Church: One Hundred Years*, (Auburn, Alabama: Bulletin Publishing Company, 1950), 6-22.

Chapter 9: Starting Up a Veterinary Program

1. Yeager and Stevenson, 60.

2. Kaye Lovvorn and Jerry Roden, *A History of Veterinary Medicine*, Auburn University, 1970.

3. Redding Sugg, "Dean R.S. Sugg: A Memoir," *Auburn Veterinary Quarterly*, Summer/Fall 2004, 6.

4. Redding Sugg to H. C. Morgan, June 18, 1991. Collection of the author.

5. *Glomerata*, Agricultural and Mechanical College of Alabama, 1897, 31.

6. Oron Percy South, *Farm Organizations in Alabama From 1872-1907*, Alabama Polytechnic Institute master's thesis in history, May 1940, 70.

7. Calvin Schwabe, "Man of the New South: Charles Allen Cary, Auburn's Rural Health Pioneer," speech given at Auburn University on November 15, 1992.

8. South, 70.

9. *Journal of the American Veterinary Medical Association*, Volume 55, April 1919, 103.

10. Sam Hendrix, "Young Prince, Wise Minister," *Auburn Veterinarian*, Fall 2013, 36.

11. *American Veterinary Review*, Volume 30, June 1906, 361-362.

12. "The Polytechnic Institute Exhibit," *Orange and Blue*, November 21, 1894.

13. *Opelika Morning Post*, November 28, 1894.

14. Notebooks of C. L. Jenkins, Auburn University Special Collections and Archives.

15. *Orange and Blue*, March 31, 1909.

16. *Orange and Blue*, October 12, 1912.

17. James Clyde Adams, editor, *Tilling the Soil for Profit and Pleasure: A Compendium of Agricultural Science and Practice on Field, Orchard and Garden Crops, Spraying, Soils, The Feeding and Diseases of Farm Animals, Dairy and Poultry Raising in the Southern States*, (Atlanta: Austell Publishing Company, 1908).

18. Ibid.

19. Schwabe.

20. *Orange and Blue*, February 27, 1901.

21. *Opelika Morning Post*, October 8, 1897.

22. *Auburn Plainsman*, November 16, 1923.

23. Wilford S. Bailey, "Charles Allen Cary: The Man and His Legacy," speech given at Auburn University on November 15, 1992.

24. Papers of Franklin A. Clark, Auburn University Special Collections and Archives.

25. *Auburn Alumnus*, January 1918.

26. T. H. Ferguson to Luther Noble Duncan, June 3, 1935, Luther Noble Duncan Presidential Papers, Auburn University Special Collections and Archives.

27. *Auburn Plainsman*, May 18, 1928.

28. J. Alec Barger to James E. Greene, December 1, 1962.

29. API *Catalog*, 1901.

30. Jernigan, 185.

31. Alabama Polytechnic Institute Board of Trustees Minutes, June 3, 1907.

32. *Glomerata*, 1909.

33. *Auburn Alumni Quarterly*, Volume 1, Number 1, August 1, 1912, 9.

34. *Auburn Alumni Quarterly*, Volume 2, Number 1, August 1913, 64.

35. *Glomerata*, 1913.

36. Proceedings of the Alabama Live Stock Association, 1910, 12.

37. *The Quadrennial 1948-1952*, published by the Alabama Polytechnic Institute School of Veterinary Medicine Class of 1952, J. R. Kinsaul, president. May 1952, 100.

38. Sugg, 6.

39. Linda O. McMurry, *George Washington Carver: Scientist and Symbol*, (New York: Oxford University Press, 1981), 146-148.

40. *Auburn Plainsman*, December 10, 1932.

41. *American Veterinary Review*, Volume 23, March 1908, 211.

42. Merillat and Campbell, 339.

43. Ibid., 301.

44. *Orange and Blue*, October 1, 1910.

45. H. Preston Hopkins to Luther Noble Duncan, May 5, 1935, Luther Noble Duncan Presidential Papers, Auburn University Special Collections and Archives.

46. Alabama Polytechnic Institute Board of Trustees Minutes, February 21, 1920.

Chapter 10: Farmers' Institutes

1. Report of President William LeRoy Broun to the Board of Trustees, June 1893.

2. South, 72.

3. Report of President William LeRoy Broun to the Board of Trustees, June 13, 1898.

4. Report of President William LeRoy Broun to the Board of Trustees, June 15, 1899.

5. Report of President William LeRoy Broun to the Board of Trustees, June 10, 1901.

6. Report of Interim President O. D. Smith to the Board of Trustees, June, 1902.

7. "Farmers' Institute to be Held in Cullman," *Montgomery Daily Advertiser*, August 5, 1898.

8. South, 88.

9. Report of President Charles Coleman Thach to the Board of Trustees, June 6, 1904.

10. Report of President Charles Coleman Thach to the Board of Trustees, June, 1905.

11. Merillat and Campbell, 319.

12. Report of President Charles Coleman Thach to the Board of Trustees, June, 1905.

13. Report of President Charles Coleman Thach to the Board of Trustees, June, 1907.

14. "Farmers Here for Summer School," *Orange and Blue*, September 7, 1908.

15. *Auburn Alumnus*, May 1913, Volume 1, Number 4, 108.

16. *Auburn Alumnus*, July 1915, Volume 4, Number 1.

17. Report of President Charles Coleman Thach to the Board of Trustees, June 7, 1915.

Chapter 11: Dr. Cary and the Alabama VMA

1. Redding S. Sugg to Will Howard Smith, March 18, 1957, in Cary Family Collection.

2. *Orange and Blue*, February 25, 1899.

3. Elizabeth Diane Schafer, *Reveille For Professionalism: Alabama Veterinary Medical Association, 1907-1952*, Master's Thesis at Auburn University Libraries, 1988, 12-13.

4. *American Veterinary Review*, Volume 15, October 1891, 538.

5. *Opelika Morning Post*, October 5, 1895.

6. *Journal of the American Veterinary Medical Association*, Volume 74, June 1929, 129.

7. Schafer, 28-30.

8. *American Veterinary Review*, Volume 34, October-March, 1908-1909, 779-780.

9. *American Veterinary Review*, Volume 37, June 1910, 807-809.

10. *American Veterinary Review*, Volume 39, June 1911, 695-698.

11. *American Veterinary Review*, Volume 41, September 1912, 730-732.

12. Smithcors, 522.

13. Merillat and Campbell, 345.

14. Ibid., 386.

15. Ibid., 553.

16. Ibid., 916.

17. *Auburn Alumnus*, Volume 2, Number 7, March 1914, 139.

18. *Journal of the AVMA*, Volume 48, October-March 1915-16, 139.

19. Smithcors, 501.

20. Ibid., 509.

21. Ibid., 513.

22. *Journal of the AVMA*, Volume 51, April-September 1917, 274.

23. *Journal of the AVMA*, Volume 53, April-September 1918, 129-133.

24. *Journal of the AVMA*, Volume 55, April-September 1919, 156.

25. *Journal of the AVMA*, Volume 57, April-September 1920, 335.

26. *Journal of the AVMA*, Volume 59, April-September 1921, 254.

27. *Journal of the AVMA*, Volume 61, April-September 1922, 215-218.

28. Sugg, 6.

29. B. F. Kaupp, "The World's First Poultry Congress," *Veterinary Medicine*, Volume 27, Number 1, January 1922, 8.

30. Smithcors, 526.

31. *Journal of the AVMA*, Volume 64, October-March 1923-24, 778-780.

32. Smithcors, 552.

33. *Journal of the AVMA*, Volume 67, April-September 1925, 123-125.

34. *Journal of the AVMA*, Volume 90, April 1937, 574.

35. *Journal of the AVMA*, Volume 69, April-September 1926, 257.

36. *Journal of the AVMA*, Volume 73, May-November 1928, 118-120.

37. Notebook from Alabama VMA meetings, maintained in Auburn University Special Collections and Archives.

38. Smithcors, 579.

39. *Journal of the AVMA*, Volume 74, January-June, 1929, 956-958.

40. *Journal of the AVMA*, Volume 76, January-June, 1930, 739-741.

41. Notebook from Alabama VMA meetings, maintained in Auburn University Special Collections and Archives.

42. *Journal of the AVMA*, Volume 95, July 1939, 118.

43. *Journal of the AVMA*, Volume 78, January-June 1931, 599-600.

44. Notebook from Alabama VMA meetings, maintained in Auburn University Special Collections and Archives.

45. Smithcors, 374.

46. Ibid., 636.

47. *Journal of the AVMA*, Volume 80, January-June 1932, 665-667.

48. *Auburn Plainsman*, February 8, 1933.

49. *Journal of the AVMA*, Volume 84, January-June 1934, 684.

50. *Auburn Plainsman*, February 13, 1935.

51. *Auburn Plainsman*, March 23, 1935.

Chapter 12: Annual Reports of the State Veterinarian

1. *American Veterinary Review*, Volume 31, 1907, 113-117.

2. *Birmingham Weekly Age Herald*, "To Regulate Sale of Milk and Meat," December 20, 1898.

3. Schwabe.

4. Boone Aiken, "Dr. Cary Would Be Pleased With Growth," *The Birmingham News*, November 7, 1971, 22.

5. Annual Reports of the State Veterinarian, many of which are summarized in this chapter, may be found in the Archives of the Auburn University Libraries.

Chapter 13: State Board of Veterinary Medical Examiners

1. Information in this chapter was provided to the author by Dr. Arthur David Hayes, Auburn University Class of 1968, a former member of the Veterinary Board of Examiners and author of "A Brief History of the Alabama State Board of Veterinary Medical Examiners."

Chapter 14: Texas Tick Fever

1. Brooks Blevins, *Cattle in the Cotton Fields: A History of Cattle Raising in Alabama*, (Tuscaloosa: University of Alabama Press, 1998), 30.

2. Ibid., 58.

3. Smithcors, 437.

4. Robert G. Pasquill, Jr., "Arsenic and Old Bovine Lace—History of the Cattle Tick Eradication Program in the South," source online at fs.usda.gov/Internet/FSE_DOCUMENTS/stelprdb5396091.pdf, September 2012, 10.

5. Ibid., 11.

6. Ibid., 53.

7. Ibid.

8. Charles Allen Cary, *Texas or Tick Fever*, Agricultural Experiment Station *Bulletin Number 141*, Alabama Polytechnic Institute, July, 1907.

9. Pasquill, 14.

10. *Proceedings of the Alabama Live Stock Association*, 1911, 12.

11. Pasquill, 24.

12. Ibid., 24.

13. Charles Allen Cary, *Dipping Vats and Dips*, Agricultural Experiment Station *Bulletin Number 171*, Alabama Polytechnic Institute, February 1913.

14. Ibid.

15. Alexander Nunn, *Yesterdays in Loachapoka and Communities Nearby*, Loachapoka Homecoming Association, (Alexander City, Alabama: Outlook Publishing Company, Inc., 1968), 128.

16. Encyclopedia of Alabama, "Charles Henderson," found online at encyclopediaofalabama.org/article/h-1461.

17. Pasquill, 59.

18. Blevins, 60.

19. Pasquill, 60.

20. Ibid., 75.

21. Ibid., 77.

22. See "Charge of the Tick Brigade" online at youtube.com/watch?v=C9d9BE0znQk, or "Mollie of Pine Grove Vat" at youtube.com/watch?v=Rb76EPAXfkE, films preserved by the National Archives.

23. Pasquill, 44.

24. Ibid., 78.

25. Ibid, 81.

26. Ibid., 195.

27. J. Thomas Vaughan, "Auburn at the Crossroads," *SVM Quarterly Report*, Volume 5, No. 1, Winter 1982.

28. *Auburn Plainsman*, "Dr. C. A. Cary Inspects World's Largest Circus," October 11, 1930.

29. *Opelika Daily News*, "Ag Research, State, Slowly Dying, Lack Funds," September 9, 1936.

30. Source online at expressnews.com/business/local/article/Cattle-tick-spread-may-be-worst-in-73-years).

Chapter 15: Fighting Hog Cholera

1. Neal Black, *Animal Health: A Century of Progress*, (Richmond, Va.: United States Animal Health Association, 1996), 43.

2. *Hog Cholera: Its History, Nature and Treatment*, a publication of the Bureau of Animal Industry, 1889, 10.

3. Merillat and Campbell, 52.

4. *Hog Cholera*, 9.

5. Ibid., 10.

6. Source online at ars.usda.gov/is/timeline/cholera.htm.

7. *Hog Cholera*, 13.

8. Charles Allen Cary, "Brief Outline of the Work of the State Veterinarian Dur-

ing 1911-1912," in the Annual Report of the Alabama Department of Agriculture and Industries for the Fiscal Year 1913, (Montgomery, Alabama: Brown Printing Company), 29.

9. Black, 49.

10. *Proceedings of Alabama Live Stock Association*, 1910, 10.

11. *Proceedings of Alabama Live Stock Association*, 1911, 10.

12. *Proceedings of Alabama Live Stock Association*, 1914, 11.

13. Source online at ars.usda.gov/is/timeline/cholera.htm.

14. *Opelika Daily News*, "Hog Cholera Serum at Cost," February 8, 1915.

15. *Auburn Alumnus*, Volume 4, Number 1, February 1915, 129.

16. President Thach, Report to Alabama Polytechnic Institute Board of Trustees, June 7, 1915.

17. *Opelika Daily News*, "State Hog Cholera Serum Plant Opened," January 17, 1916.

18. *Auburn Alumnus*, Volume 4, Number 4, November 1915, 93.

19. *Opelika Daily News*, "State Hog Cholera Serum Plant Opened," January 17, 1916.

20. Ibid.

21. *Auburn Alumnus*, Volume 4, Number 9, April 1916.

22. President Thach, Report to Alabama Polytechnic Institute Board of Trustees, June 5, 1916.

23. Merillat and Campbell, 57.

Chapter 16: Fighting Tuberculosis

1. Source online at exhibits.hsl.virginia.edu/alav/tuberculosis/.

2. J. Arthur Myers, *Man's Greatest Victory Over Tuberculosis*, (Baltimore, Maryland: Charles C. Thomas publisher, 1940), 338.

3. Source online at cdc.gov/tb/topic/basics/.

4. Charles Allen Cary, *Bovine Tuberculosis*, Alabama Agricultural Experiment Station *Bulletin Number 67*, 1895, 198.

5. Source online at lung.org/lung-health-and-diseases/lung-disease-lookup/tuberculosis/learn-about-tuberculosis.html.

6. Lee B. Reichman and Janice Hopkins Tanne, *Timebomb*, (New York: McGraw-Hill, 2002,) 23.

7. Source online at pbs.org/wgbh/americanexperience/features/timeline/plague-timeline/

8. Merillat and Campbell, 303.

9. Ibid., 304.

10. Charles Allen Cary, *Bovine Tuberculosis*, Alabama Agricultural Experiment Station *Bulletin Number 67*, 1895, 215.

11. Charles Allen Cary, *Dairy and Milk Inspection*, Alabama Agricultural Experiment Station *Bulletin Number 97*, Agricultural and Mechanical College, September 1898.

12. Ibid, 255-257.

13. Ibid.

14. Mitchell V. Palmer and W. Ray Waters, *Bovine Tuberculosis and the Establishment of an Eradication Program in the United States: Role of Veterinarians*, published online at www.ncbi.nlm.nih.gov/pmc/articles/PMC3103864/ on May 17, 2011.

15. Merillat and Campbell, 305.

16. V. A. Moore, *Bovine Tuberculosis and Its Control*, (Ithaca, New York: Carpenter & Co., 1913), 17.

17. *Tuberculosis and Other Diseases of Animals*, Report of the Special Committee of the Assembly, February 1, 1900, State of New York, 8.

18. Ibid., 22.

19. Moore.

20. Myers, 13.

21. Ibid., 340.

22. Ibid., 269

23. J. F. DeVine, *Bovine Tuberculosis*, (Chicago: American Veterinary Publishing, 1917), 7.

24. Myers, 340.

25. DeVine, 9.

26. Source found online at www.cdfa.ca.gov/ahfss/animal_health/tb_info.html.

27. Myers, 341.

28. Merillat and Campbell, 314.

29. Hendrix, "Young Prince, Wise Minister," *Auburn Veterinarian*, Fall 2013, 34.

Chapter 17: In Memoriam

1. Merillat and Campbell, 316.

2. From "A Brief History of The Alabama State Board of Veterinary Medical Examiners," by Dr. Arthur David Hayes, provided to the author.

3. *Auburn Plainsman*, "Dr. Cary Succumbs to Heart Attack Late Tuesday," April 24, 1935.

4. *Montgomery Advertiser*, April 25, 1935.

5. *The Birmingham News*, April 28, 1935.

6. *Opelika Daily News*, April 27, 1935.

7. *Auburn Plainsman*, April 27, 1935.

8. Ibid., 3.

9. Lyman Ward, "Dr. Charles Allen Cary," *The Industrial Student*, May 1935, Volume 35, Number 5, Camp Hill, Alabama.

10. *Opelika Daily News*, February 27, 1946.

11. *The Auburn Alumnews*, March/April 1946.

12. One source for "The Auburn Creed" is the Auburn University website, auburn.edu/main/welcome/creed.html

13. Schwabe.

14. Wilford S. Bailey, "Charles Allen Cary: The Man and His Legacy," speech given at Auburn University, November 15, 1992.

SELECTED BIBLIOGRAPHY

Adams, James Clyde, editor. *Tilling the Soil for Profit and Pleasure: A Compendium of Agricultural Science and Practice on Field, Orchard and Garden Crops, Spraying, Soils, The Feeding and Diseases of Farm Animals, Dairy and Poultry Raising in the Southern States.* Atlanta: Austell Publishing Company, 1908.

Allen, Lee Norcross. *The Woman Suffrage Movement in Alabama.* Master's Thesis at Alabama Polytechnic Institute, 1949.

Auburn Sweet Auburn: History, Stories and Epitaphs of Pine Hill Cemetery, 1836-2010. Auburn Heritage Association, 2010.

Ballard, Michael B. *Maroon and White: Mississippi State University, 1878-2003.* University of Mississippi Press, 2008.

Bierer, B. W. *A Short History of Veterinary Medicine in America.* East Lansing: Michigan State University Press, 1955.

Black, Neal. *Animal Health: A Century of Progress.* Richmond: United States Animal Health Association, 1996.

Blevins, Brooks. *Cattle in the Cotton Fields: A History of Cattle Raising in Alabama.* Tuscaloosa: University of Alabama Press, 1998.

Brock, Thomas D. *Robert Koch: A Life in Medicine and Bacteriology.* Madison: Science Tech Publishers, 1988.

Cary, Charles Allen. "Bovine Tuberculosis." *Bulletin of the Alabama Agri-*

cultural Experiment Station. Number 67. Alabama Agricultural and Mechanical College, 1895.

Cary, Charles Allen. "Dairy and Milk Inspection." *Bulletin of the Alabama Agricultural Experiment Station.* Number 97. Alabama Agricultural and Mechanical College, 1898.

Cary, Charles Allen. "Dipping Vats and Dips." *Bulletin of the Alabama Agricultural Experiment Station.* Number 171. Alabama Polytechnic Institute, 1913.

Cary, Charles Allen. "Texas or Tick Fever." *Bulletin of the Alabama Agricultural Experiment Station.* Number 141. Alabama Polytechnic Institute, 1907.

DeVine, D. F. *Bovine Tuberculosis.* Chicago: American Veterinary Publishing, 1917.

Draughon, Ralph B.; Hughes, Delos; and Pearson, Ann. *Lost Auburn: A Village Remembered in Period Photographs.* Montgomery: NewSouth Books, 2012.

Going, Allen Johnston. *Bourbon Democracy in Alabama 1874-1890.* Tuscaloosa: University of Alabama Press, 1992.

Goodson, Martia Graham, editor. *Chronicles of Faith: The Autobiography of Frederick D. Patterson.* Tuscaloosa: University of Alabama Press, 1991.

Hackney, Sheldon. *Populism to Progressivism in Alabama.* Princeton, New Jersey: Princeton University Press, 1969.

Heisman, John M. and Schlabach, Mark. *Heisman: The Man Behind the Trophy.* New York: Howard Books, 2012.

Hog Cholera: Its History, Nature and Treatment, a publication of the Bureau of Animal Industry/U.S. Department of Agriculture. Government Printing Office, Washington, D.C., 1889.

Jernigan, Mike. *Auburn Man: The Life & Times of George Petrie.* Montgomery, Alabama: The Donnell Group, 2007.

Lovvorn, Kaye and Roden, Jerry. *A History of Veterinary Medicine.* Auburn University, 1970.

McMillan, Malcolm. *Auburn Presbyterian Church: One Hundred Years,* Auburn, Alabama: Bulletin Publishing Company, 1950.

McMillan, Malcolm and Jones, Allen. *Through the Years: Auburn From 1856,* 1973. Publication of Auburn University.

McMurry, Linda O. *George Washington Carver: Scientist and Symbol.* New York: Oxford University Press, 1981.

Merillat, Louis A. and Campbell, Delwin M. *Veterinary Military History.* Kansas City: The Haver-Glover Laboratories, 1935.

Moore, V. A. *Bovine Tuberculosis and Its Control.* Ithaca, New York: Carpenter & Co., 1913.

Myers, J. Arthur. *Man's Greatest Victory Over Tuberculosis.* Baltimore: Charles C. Thomas publisher, 1940.

Nunn, Alexander. *Yesterdays in Loachapoka and Communities Nearby.* Alexander City, Alabama, Outlook Publishing Company, Inc., 1968.

Reichman, Lee B. and Tanne, Janice Hopkins. *Timebomb.* New York: McGraw-Hill, 2002.

Schafer, Elizabeth Diane. *Reveille For Professionalism: Alabama Veterinary Medical Association, 1907-1952.* Master's Thesis at Auburn University, 1988.

Simms, Jack and Logue, Mickey. *Auburn: A Pictorial History of the Loveliest Village,* 2013.

Smithcors, J. F. *The American Veterinary Profession, Its Background and Development.* Ames: Iowa State University Press, 1963.

Smith, Jamie Elizabeth. *Woman Suffrage Movement and the 1901 Alabama Constitution Convention.* Honors College Thesis, Auburn University, May 2005.

South, Oron Percy. *Farm Organizations in Alabama From 1872-1907.* Alabama Polytechnic Institute Master's Thesis, Alabama Polytechnic Institute, May 1940.

Stange, Charles H. *History of Veterinary Medicine at Iowa State College.* 1929, Ames, Iowa.

Thach, Charles Coleman. "Dr. William LeRoy Broun," *Studies in Southern and Alabama History.* API Historical Papers, Montgomery, 1904.

Wright, John Peavy. *Glimpses into the Past From My Grandfather's Trunk.* Alexander City, Alabama: Outlook Publishing Company, Inc., 1969.

Yeager, Joe and Stevenson, Gene. *Inside Ag Hill.* Auburn University College of Agriculture, 2000.

INDEX

University of Texas, 6, 8, 9
University of Virginia, 5, 7, 11-12, 18
US Department of Agriculture, 16, 37, 40,
    152, 158, 258-259, 267, 269, 273, 280
US Live Stock Sanitary Association, 77,
    173
USVMA. *See* American Veterinary Med-
    ical Association

Vanderbilt University, 6, 8-9, 13
Vaughan, John Thomas, 122, 270, 298, 321
Vaughan (John Thomas Vaughan) Large
    Animal Teaching Hospital, 321
Veterinary Building (Auburn), 103-104,
    118, 120, 126, 140, 143, 179
Victoria University, 81
Villemin, Jean-Antoine, 286
Virginia-Maryland College of Veterinary
    Medicine, 321

Wade, James A., 278
Walker, E. H., 307
Ward, A. R., 68
Ward, Lyman, 301, 310
Warwick, Bishop Billing, 147
Washington State University, 50, 101
Wasserman, August von, 94-95
Webb, W. W., 70, 224, 226, 250
Welch, Adonijah S., 46
Welch, William, 46
Wheeler, A. S., 68
White, David S., 76
White, George R., 68, 189-190, 194, 262
Whitfield, F. B., 224, 229
Williams, M. W., 248
Williams, W. L., 59, 62, 64, 68, 123, 203
Williamson, A. H., 202
Wilmore, John Jenkins, 14, 113, 145, 303,
    307
Wilmore Laboratories, 14
Wilson, H. C., 191, 232, 278, 280
Wilson, James, 52, 259
Wilson, Robert C., 321
Wimberly, Thomas, 105, 106
Winters, Everett S., 153, 159, 280, 307
Woolf, F. P., 152, 218, 222, 225, 229, 250
Worrall, J. B., 23
Wright, J. M., 155
Wright, Orville and Wilbur, 17

Yeager, Joe, 117, 162
yellow fever, 133
Yerion, E. D., 220, 222

Other books published by The Donnell Group:
God's Receiver: The Terry Beasley Story
Only Doing My Job: Memories Of A World War II Fighter Pilot
Touchdown Auburn: Memories And Calls With Jim Fyffe
Troy: 1838-2006
Down Through The Years: Great Quotations On Auburn Football
The Church Of The Ascension: A Resurrection Story
St. John's Episcopal Church: A Brief History
Iron Butterfly: A Genealogy
Auburn Man: The Life And Times Of George Petrie
My Times With Coe: Fred Fields And Free Enterprise
A Novel: An Ancient Goddess In Old Mobile
My Way: The Norval Morey Story
Lewis Colbert: The Unlikeliest Auburn Tiger
Brother Sid: A Novel of Sidney Lanier
From Ramer To Rutgers: The Education Of Milly Cowles
The Stars Are Friendly: A Genealogy
Genius in America: The Story of C. Harry Knowles, Inventor
From The Top, A Memoir: Robbins Taylor
Momma's Love: Momma Goldberg's Deli
Deals On Wheels: Sid Smith